MW00650129

Construction Jobsite Management

Fifth Edition

William R. Mincks, Ph.D.

Hal Johnston

Cengage

Australia • Brazil • Canada • Mexico • Singapore • United Kingdom • United States

Construction Jobsite Management, 5e
William R. Mincks, Hal Johnston

SVP, Product: Cheryl Costantini

VP, Product: Thais Alencar

Portfolio Product Director: Jason Fremder

Portfolio Product Manager: Emily Olsen

Product Assistant: Janell Whitted

CL VCM Project Manager: Ramkumar Palani

Content Manager: Valarmathy Munuswamy,
Lumina Datamatics Ltd.

Digital Delivery Lead: Elizabeth Cranston

VP, Product Marketing: Jason Sakos

Director, Product Marketing: Neena Bali

Content Acquisition Analyst: Erin McCullough

Content Acquisition Project Manager: Shaarmila
Ezhumalai, Lumina Datamatics Ltd.

Production and Composition Service: Lumina
Datamatics Ltd.

Designer: Tim Biddick

Cover Image Source: Ant Clausen/Shutterstock.com

Interior image Source: CoolKengzz/Shutterstock
.com

For product information and technology assistance, contact us at
**Cengage Customer & Sales Support, 1-800-354-9706
or support.cengage.com.**

For permission to use material from this text or product, submit all
requests online at **www.copyright.com.**

Library of Congress Control Number: 2023915381

ISBN: 978-0-357-45294-3

Cengage
5191 Natorp Boulevard
Mason, OH 45040
USA

Cengage is a leading provider of customized learning solutions. Our
employees reside in nearly 40 different countries and serve digital learners
in 165 countries around the world. Find your local representative at
www.cengage.com.

To learn more about Cengage platforms and services, register or access
your online learning solution, or purchase materials for your course, visit
www.cengage.com.

Printed at CLDPC, USA, 09-24

Dedication

To our fathers,

Ralph Mincks and Harold "Bud" Johnston,

who taught us that construction

is a respectable profession.

Contents

Construction Jobsite Management introduces students in two- and four-year construction management programs to all facets of construction project management from the contractor's point of view. This text examines the duties that are handled by the project manager, construction superintendent, and construction engineer throughout the progress of a job, from the configuration of a project team through project closeout. With a dedicated focus on the activities of jobsite personnel, this book shows students a wealth of helpful techniques and procedures for effectively managing projects from start to finish.

Construction today involves much more than the physical erection of a project. The contractor must systematically plan, organize, manage, control, and document jobsite activities. No margin for error exists on the jobsite in today's construction market; therefore, good organizational skills and the ability to anticipate problems are essential tools for effective jobsite managers. An efficiently managed jobsite should result in a profitable construction project. A good documentation system increases the manager's awareness of problems that develop early on in the construction process, which saves the effort and expense normally expended for claims and litigation. The current legal climate requires a detailed documentation of construction activities and events.

Approach and Organization

The procedures and methods contained in this book focus on the contractor's operation; however, many of these procedures and methods apply to owners' representatives, architects and engineers, specialty contractors, and construction managers as well. The methods herein are applicable primarily to commercial and industrial building construction, although many can be applied to all types of construction. Each project, depending on its size and specific attributes, will have different jobsite management needs. The constructor should use the procedures that will meet the needs of the project. Small projects normally consolidate several of the functions and activities detailed herein, but they nevertheless need the proper management to maintain profitability.

The five sequential, generally recognized phases of the construction process are predesign, design, bid/award, construction, and postconstruction. This book focuses primarily on the construction phase of the process, although other phases are discussed. The construction period begins after the contract for construction is awarded and includes preconstruction meetings and activities and the actual physical construction of the facility. This book also examines closeout and completion procedures after substantial completion, usually classified in the postconstruction phase. Additionally, jobsite management activities associated with project scheduling, project safety, contract documents, and building codes are addressed; however, for a detailed look at these activities, numerous sources are available for further reference.

The project management system should meet project requirements and blend with company policy. The management system and organization should be designed to optimize efficiency at the jobsite but minimize direct overhead and labor costs. The contractor's primary goal during a construction project is to make a profit while satisfying contractual requirements. Thus, the main objective for a project management system is to facilitate the completion of a project as efficiently as possible.

This book addresses many of the methods involved in the management of construction job-sites. Each project, depending on its size, location, company policy, and contractual requirements, may use varying configurations of project management methods and structure. The contractor should evaluate each particular situation and use the proper tools accordingly. The procedures described in this book are illustrative rather than literal descriptions; however, they do not specifically apply to all situations on the jobsite.

Features of This Text

We wrote this text in clear, concise language to provide an essential introduction to the "real world" of effective management techniques. Several key features distinguish this text as a valuable resource for students and professionals:

- *Discussions* of current philosophies, procedures, and methods of management stress application over theory, making this book ready-made for use on the jobsite.

- *Hands-on experience:* The authors bring numerous years of actual construction project management experience to life so that concepts are immediately applicable to the real world.

- *Documents* used in project management are discussed, including the use of common forms such as AIA papers that can be directly applied to project situations.

- *Up-to-date information:* The chapters on safety and computerized project management are thoroughly up-to-date, keeping on pace with emerging technologies and jobsite conditions.

- *Review:* Chapter objectives and review questions reinforce concepts, and an Instructor's Manual with answers to the review questions is available on Cengage Learning's Instructor Companion Site.

New to the Fifth Edition

- Standardization of Learning Objectives throughout all chapters.

- Chapter 1 includes a discussion about the importance of leadership by Project management.

- Chapter 2 includes discussion about project communication and introduces the "single source of truth" concept.

- Chapter 3 updates the use of electronic versions of construction documents on the jobsite.

- Chapter 4 updates the importance of submittal review by the contractor. It also discusses software use in submittal review.

- Chapter 9 contains updates regarding hazard analysis/assessment, accident investigation, first aid training, tool box training meetings, and substance abuse.

- Chapter 11, Quality Management, includes a specialty contractor quality management example.

- Chapter 13 is updated to reflect current processes for LEED Certification throughout the stages of construction.

- The use of computers is discussed in the appropriate project management method. Computer use and electronic aids have been updated throughout the text.

- Chapter 15 on Building Information Modeling (BIM) discusses the use of the BIM model from the design stage through post-construction, explaining the difference between two-dimensional construction documents and three-dimensional models and illuminating the advantages of BIM for the project owner.

- Chapter 17 updates the closeout procedure with a discussion about closeout software.

- An all-new Chapter 18 on Lean Construction introduces lean construction methods to increase efficiency eliminating wasted cost and enhancing the value of the project. Lean construction uses progressive methods that will continue evolution of construction in the future.

- Example forms have been updated throughout.

Instructor Resources

Cengage Learning offers a robust suite of Instructor Resources to accompany *Construction Jobsite Management* at Cengage's Instructor Companion Site. With this unique resource, instructors can spend less time planning and more time teaching. The Instructor Companion Site includes the following:

- An *Instructor's Manual* containing instructional outlines and various resources for each chapter of the book, available in Adobe Acrobat® PDF format.

- Cengage Learning Testing Powered by Cognero. With hundreds of questions and different styles to choose from, instructors can create customized assessments for students and add unique questions and print rationales for easy class preparation.

- Customizable instructor support slide presentations in *PowerPoint*® format that focus on key points for each chapter.

- An *Image Gallery* to enhance instructor support slide presentations, insert art into test questions, or add visuals wherever you need them. These valuable images, which are pulled from the accompanying textbook, are organized by chapter.

Acknowledgments

We, the authors would like to thank our wives, Rena and Joy, for their patience, inspiration, and help in this undertaking.

The authors would like to acknowledge the encouragement and mentoring of the late Professor Richard Young. He knew we could do it, but he didn't get to see the final product. We also would like to thank our department chairs, Rafi Samizay, School of Architecture, Washington State University, and Jim Rodger, Department of Construction Management, California Polytechnic State University, for their support and help. We also appreciate the encouragement of our colleagues Ken Carper, Larry Fisher, Ed Turnquist, and Jim Borland. Several individuals helped us with information for this book: Colin Matsushima, Ron Warrick, and Bill Davis. Thanks for your help.

We'd also like to thank the following firms and organizations for technical information and documents: American Institute of Architects; Concrete Reinforcing Steel Institute; International Conference of Building Officials; Associated Builders and Contractors; Primavera Systems, Inc.; ChemRex, Inc.; Meridian Project Systems; Microsoft Corporation; and the Associated General Contractors of America, Inc.

About the Authors

William R. Mincks, PhD, is a Certified Professional Constructor (AIC) as well as a member of the AACE International. He has taught construction management at Washington State University, South Dakota State University, Boise State University, and Drexel University. He is experienced in many areas of construction and consults on project management, construction quality management, and housing issues.

Hal Johnston is a past Certified Professional Estimator (ASPE) for 30 years and is a licensed general contractor for the State of California. He is a Professor Emeritus of Construction Management at California Polytechnic State University, San Luis Obispo, California, and a Visiting Professor in the Department of Construction Management and Economics, Civil Engineering, Czech Technical University in Prague (CVUT), the past four years and continues in that position.

Chapter 1

Introduction to Project Management

Objectives

This chapter introduces the theory of project management, leadership, and the attributes of construction projects that require unique management. The objectives of this discussion are to present the following:

- What are the reasons for a different type of management for project-based firms?
- Identify the attributes of construction projects requiring special management techniques
- Describe the goals and objectives of construction projects
- List the management techniques that can be used to successfully meet the goals and objectives of construction projects
- List the personnel within the contractor's organization that typically provide the leadership to accomplish the project goals

Introduction to Project Management

Management is a discipline that provides tools to direct people in pursuit of specific goals and is used to conduct efficient business organizations. The discipline of management is a large, broad-based field that encompasses all businesses and all business methods. Most management techniques can be adapted to most businesses, although in construction there are subsets of business conditions that require specialized techniques and a slightly different focus.

Project management is one such subset of the management discipline. It focuses on the management of several projects as separate entities rather than the whole business. In construction, these projects are also the profit centers for the company. Project management is also used in other types of businesses for a variety of purposes, such as the development of new products. Whatever the goals of the project, the project is managed by a key group of individuals focused on the project goals.

One of the prime characteristics of a project is its finite time frame, associated with a completion date. Under traditional business or manufacturing management, it is assumed that there is no completion date for the process. In project management, the specific techniques, management team, source of funding, and project emphasis conclude at the completion of the project. Each project usually has unique characteristics that require creative management and decision making, which end at the completion of the project.

As the characteristics of each project vary, the management approach must address each project separately and appropriately. The management team has a responsibility to achieve the project goals and to communicate with upper management. The overall management usually provides services to the projects, such as accounting, which can help tie all of the project operations together.

The primary purpose of the management team is to achieve the goals of the project. The goal of a construction project is to complete the project successfully, within the project parameters. "Successfully" usually means profitably, which is usually achieved with the appropriate quality and time frame. Construction firms are in business to make a profit that compensates the investment and ensures continuation of the business. The goal of the project, then, is to make a profit as the project is assembled.

Attributes of Construction Projects

Construction projects have some particular attributes that set construction firms apart from other businesses. These attributes require special management attention, different from management activities in other firms. The management of construction projects requires a focus on solving problems as they develop during the project.

The following is a discussion of construction project attributes that require project management techniques:

- The construction project is a unique assembly with specific parameters, such as duration, quality, budget, assembly team, location, and other factors. Even a "cookie-cutter" house is a unique project with different site conditions, weather conditions, duration, subcontractors, and jobsite labor.

- The project will be completed within a finite duration; it has a specific start date and a specific completion date. Most projects have specific completion date requirements. Even large projects, which seem to continue forever, have specific completion milestones.

- The construction projects are usually located geographically away from company or corporate management. Whether down the street or on the other side of the world, the physical project is in a separate location from company offices.

- Separate management of each project is necessary. One project manager may direct several projects, but the management organization and techniques are specific to the needs of each project.

- Since each project has its own manager, there is a single source of responsibility to upper management for each project.

- The construction project is a separate cost accounting element, just as it is separated geographically and by its unique requirements. Each project's profits gauge the effectiveness of its management. The conclusions from project-based cost accounting directly relate to personnel decisions, operations methods, and the type of project that the contractor chooses to undertake in the future.

- There are thousands of parts, systems, and equipment within a single construction project. This complex assembly is purchased from many sources and differs from those in other projects.

- Substantial purchases and custom fabrications may be required for each project.

- Substantial subcontracting is used to construct the project. Some projects are 100 percent subcontracted. Commercial building projects are 70 to 95 percent subcontracted. Even where the contractor performs a large portion of the work, some subcontracting is included in the project.

- The construction project is usually not the only project under construction by the construction company. Most construction companies have numerous projects under construction at the same time, each requiring separate management.

- There is a single owner, or customer, for each project. There may be several layers of customers or users, but usually there is a single source of payment for the project.

- Each site is controlled by the contractor, including security and safety responsibilities at each site.

These attributes of the project, correlated with the goals of the construction firm for each project, will mold the techniques used to manage the project.

Goals and Objectives of Construction Projects

Each project will have some specific goals for the project to meet. As mentioned previously, the goal for the project may be that it is successful and profitable. "Successful" can mean many things, but generally it means that the project is completed within the time frame, the quality is acceptable, the customer is pleased with the project, and there is no continued active liability, such as lawsuits. "Profitable" generally means that the project produces at least the initially expected profit. As business growth is a typical goal for the overall company operations, increased productivity and the resulting increased profit are expected to be added to the estimated profit. In other words, "profitable" really means achievement of the optimum profit available for the project. Aggressive companies will set challenging goals for their projects or profit centers.

Objectives are definable tasks that support the goals. For a successful and profitable project, the objectives would be the following:

- Completion of the project within the specified or expected time frame. This is a gauge of success by the customer. If a project extends beyond the expected time frame, there usually are extended overhead costs such as a superintendent and jobsite facilities, which will also impact the profitability of the project.

- Completion of the project within the specified level of quality. Quality has several indicators:

  - Material and equipment furnished to be of the specified parameters and to perform as expected.

  - Workmanship is of the expected level. Generally, the customer does not like to notice evidence of the installation effort.

  - Integration of all components to a complete package.

- Effective cost control to assure that project costs are under or meet the estimated costs for the project. This, of course, directly relates to the profitability of the project. Cost control is also an indicator of the productivity of the project and the effectiveness of the project management.

- Effectiveness of the jobsite safety program. Success of a project relates directly to the safety and well-being of the personnel working on the project. Accidents have a direct effect on the profitability of the project and the overall profitability of the company, both currently and in the future.

- Customer satisfaction. Customer satisfaction can be achieved by all of the previous objectives; however, it requires management attention in order to be achieved. Failure to satisfy the customer can result in delays in payment and the final completion of the project, and it also can hinder the company's ability to obtain future projects. Gaining customer satisfaction involves effective communications, salesmanship, and attention to detail, as well as completion of the physical project as expected.

- Effective management of subcontractors. Since subcontractors perform a substantial amount of the work on the jobsite, they need to be coordinated to ensure that they meet all of the previous objectives. If the subcontractors do not meet the previous objectives, the contractor will not either.

- The previous objectives are interrelated. If the project lags behind schedule, cost and quality are affected. If quality is not met with either materials or workmanship, the schedule and cost will be affected. If the safety of the project is not maintained, accidents can greatly affect the schedule, quality, and cost of the project.

Management Techniques to Achieve Project Goals and Objectives

The process of building a construction project does not necessarily ensure that the goals and the objectives of the project are met. Management is necessary to control the building of the project in order to achieve the project objectives. Professional constructors familiar with a wide variety of management techniques are necessary to bring projects within the goals and objectives in the current competitive market. The time when only a "master builder," an individual who understood how to assemble the building parts, was necessary for construction is gone. Our constructed facilities today are much too complex to be designed and built by one individual; it takes a team of design and construction professionals. Managers are necessary to build the project and to control all of the variables of the project.

The following is a brief discussion of the types of management techniques that can be used to help achieve the goals and objectives of a construction project. This book discusses these techniques in considerable detail.

Organization of the Project Delivery System

The organization of the management personnel on a project needs to be a cost-effective system in order to meet project requirements. Some projects will require more controls and more communication data, requiring more jobsite management personnel. There will be company organization policies assigning personnel to different areas of responsibilities and usually separate, flexible plans for project management.

Project management personnel can include project managers, superintendents, area or trade superintendents, field engineers, office engineers, and several other classifications. The type and quantity of jobsite personnel will vary because of many factors:

- Duration of the project (how quickly the owner needs the facility)

- Size of the project, usually indicated by the cost of the project

- Amount of self-performed work

- Personnel available, considering each individual's strengths

- Size of crews for the project

- Multiple areas of work

- Multiple contracts

- Reporting requirements to the customer

- Extent of cost control required by the company

- Amount of reporting and documentation required by the company

- Public versus private work (normally public work requires more reporting and record keeping; however, some private clients require an extraordinary amount of record keeping)

- Type of contract

- Construction market, particularly on lump-sum projects. In tight construction markets, jobsite overhead is reduced and management tasks are consolidated.

Although poor organization is not always recognizable as a cause for poor project performance, skillful organization of management personnel is essential in management practices. Therefore, the project organization needs to be carefully formulated during the planning process. Chapter 2, The Project Team, discusses organization forms commonly used in construction delivery systems.

Leadership

Most construction operations are performed remotely from company headquarters and are contained as a project. A project is a self-contained construction operation intended to fulfill certain parameters. The project rarely has parameters similar to those of other projects and can be unique in all aspects, including scope, duration of completion, cost, and quality. Each project requires leadership to reach its goals. We use diagrammatic and written depictions and specifications to communicate the attributes of the project, but we need leadership to obtain the desired results. Construction projects require direct leadership to achieve the desired results on the project.

Although some project managers and superintendents can use their leadership skills on multiple projects, leadership on each project is provided specifically for that project. Leadership is provided in part by all team members in order to successfully complete the project. Within the contractor's organization, project managers, superintendents, project engineers, and craft foremen typically provide leadership to accomplish the project goals.

The variety of construction projects we encounter require different leadership skills. Part of training for project managers, superintendents, foreman, and craftsman naturally includes leadership skills. Leadership skills are learned from experience and the continual drive for success in projects. Leadership consists primarily of "soft-skills," or skills that facilitate human contact. Contractors typically value good communication skills from all management. Fair treatment of employees is essential to effective jobsite leadership.

The project manager (construction leader) needs to develop the abilities to achieve the following goals:

- Vision to see and implement paths to success

- Providing a learning environment for the improvement of individual skills

- Building successful teams to optimize cost, duration, quality, and a safe jobsite environment.

Leadership abilities, whether an individual's or the entire project management team's, consist of the following attributes:

- Vision of the entire project and what needs to be achieved

- Plan for achieving the completed project

- Insistence that the project meet the intended financial goals with continual monitoring of costs

- Understanding of the crews and the motivation necessary to achieve the project goals

- Communication skills to facilitate progress of the work

- Maintaining a relationship with upper management to be able to control the project without interference

- Realizing that the timing of every decision is critical to the completion of the project

- Loyalty to the company and the project goals and realizing that personal achievement is accomplished through the company and project successes

Construction leaders need to nurture several skills as they develop with their communication expertise, vision for the project and company, technical understanding of construction and changes, understanding of business conditions, integrity and image shown to stakeholders, ability to make decisions, and the ability to obtain desired results.

There is a direct connection between effective construction leadership and the success of the project. Participants in the management process gain skills progressively to increase their effectiveness. Understanding of the process and use of "soft-skills" will provide a basis for successful projects.

Problem Solving

Just as project managers encounter a unique set of individuals and work requirements on each project, they also find unique problems arising during the course of each project. Each problem needs to be solved immediately and correctly. Any delay in solving problems can result in work delays. This sounds easy, but it is probably the main contributor to project delays and extra, unwarranted costs. The problems encountered in a construction project are usually complex, including several trades, subcontractors, and suppliers. Project management needs to analyze each situation and make the decision that has the least unfavorable impact to the project.

Some considerations that need to be recognized in project problem solving are the following:

• Full impact of the problem on subcontractors and suppliers, as well as on the contractor

• Cost impact of the problem, including responsibility for extra cost, minimal cost impact, and indirect costs

• Time impact of the problem, possibly resulting in a time extension and additional overhead compensation

• Best solution for project conditions, considering crew, environment, project progress, and customer needs

• Best method of resolving conflicts between project participants as quickly as possible

Problem-solving techniques are addressed throughout this book.

Reporting and Record Keeping

To jobsite personnel, reporting and record keeping may seem like a waste of time. These activities, however, are essential to project management systems. Reporting and record keeping provide the following:

• Communication between the field and home office

• Communication with the client and the client's consultants

• Systematic and regular analysis of current conditions by field personnel, providing a basis for problem solving

• Historical record for documentation of the project

Chapter 5, Documentation and Record Keeping at the Jobsite, looks at project record keeping in depth.

Planning and Scheduling

Planning and scheduling construction activities enables the project to complete on a finite date. The plan organizes the project, and the schedule is the tool for communicating the plan. The schedule communicates the plan to field personnel, home office personnel, the customer, the customer's consultants (architects and engineers), suppliers, and subcontractors. The schedule can be used as a tool for duration control of the project, managing subcontractor work, problem solving on the job, and increasing jobsite productivity, as well as a means of communication. Plans and schedules are flexible; they can be modified to changing conditions. Initial planning of the project provides a basis for the management of the project, while continual planning and scheduling are necessary throughout the project to address conditions that arise during the project. Chapter 12, Time and Cost Control, covers some uses for the schedule in managing the project.

Cost Control

Cost control involves containing construction costs within the budget established by the cost estimate. Cost control is more than accurately reporting costs and comparing them to the estimate. It involves the use of the comparison to indicate a need to change methods, techniques, or crew composition to achieve the desired profit on the project. Cost and productivity control can help achieve additional profits on the construction project.

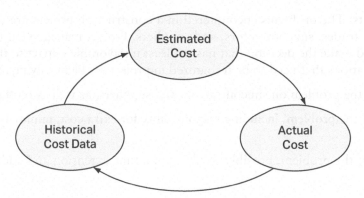

Figure 1–1   Flow of Cost Information

Collection of actual construction costs for work activities also ensures an accurate cost database for the construction contractor. The use of accurate, proven construction costs can help with the accuracy of estimates. Figure 1–1 shows the continual flow of information from estimating to actual cost to historical cost data.

Chapter 12 also examines some cost control techniques used by jobsite management.

Quality Management

Quality management has become an important part of project management's tasks. Quality has several meanings within the project context: meeting the expected level of material, maintaining the level of workmanship, and earning general customer satisfaction. As each project is unique and has many subcontracted portions, meticulous care is required to obtain proper results during the construction process. Subcontractor and trade coordination, inspection, and checklists facilitate achievement of quality in the project. Chapter 11, Project Quality Management, discusses project quality and the methods used to ensure quality in the project.

Safety Management

Most construction contractors are realizing the economic benefits of a proactive safety management program. Considerable savings can be made to workers' compensation premiums and insurance premiums by having a good safety experience rating. This is an instance where project costs often exceed the apparent immediate benefit to the project itself. The safety records for previous projects reflect on the rates paid for today's project. This is a tie between the individual project and company-wide performance. An effective project safety and accident prevention program reflects on the individual project, but it has an even greater effect on the company-wide performance record.

Safety management is characterized by the implementation of safety plans, the application of safety procedures and proper equipment in work tasks, the encouragement of jobsite safety meetings, the provision of appropriate protective equipment, and the management of potentially hazardous substances on the jobsite. The goal of safety management is to prevent all accidents at the jobsite. Chapter 8, Jobsite Labor Relations and Control, deals with safety management.

Contract Compliance

Most construction projects have numerous requirements and procedures that must be met. A wide variety of submittals needs to be made to the client during the course of construction:

- Material and permanent equipment submittals (Chapter 3, Use of Construction Documents on a Jobsite)

- Shop drawings for project-specific material fabrications (Chapter 3, Use of Construction Documents on a Jobsite)

- Project meetings (Chapter 6, Jobsite Layout and Control)

- Change control, documentation, and compensation (Chapter 18, Project Closeout)

- Progress payments (Chapter 16, Changes and Claims)

- Project closeout (Chapter 17, Progress Payments)

Computerized Record Keeping

Computerized record keeping helps the project manager to compile, organize, and analyze information about the progress of the project. Time, cost, and project data are recorded by computers on the jobsite. The timely production of quality, usable information facilitates problem solving and communication during the project. Chapter 12, Time and Cost Control, addresses current uses of computer technology in jobsite management.

Summary

Construction organizations rely on project management to manage their profit centers because the source of their profit-making activity is at temporary sites, remote from the home office. Construction projects have unique attributes that require a different emphasis in management style. The goals of a construction project are for it to be successful and profitable. Success may relate to many different factors, but usually it relates to on-time completion, achieving acceptable quality, and satisfying the customer without lingering disputes. Profitability is achieving at least the expected profit from the project. Computers are now a necessary component of project management. They quickly record, track, and distribute documents to the key people involved in the construction project.

To obtain the goals and objectives of the project, the project team needs to use a variety of techniques:

- Organization of the project delivery system

- Leadership, from the very start of the project through its completion

- Problem solving

- Computerized reporting and record keeping to facilitate the construction process

- Planning and scheduling

- Cost control

- Quality management

- Safety management

- Contract compliance

This text discusses all of these items to facilitate the successful completion of construction projects.

Review Questions

1. What are five attributes of construction projects that require project management techniques?

2. Compare a manufacturing firm, in a single location with a single product, to a construction firm with several projects. What are the primary differences between these firms? Why is a different management approach needed for each firm?

3. What are the typical goals of a construction project?

4. Discuss the purpose of five techniques used in project management. Describe how these techniques help managers achieve the goals mentioned in the previous questions.

Chapter 2

The Project Team

This chapter discusses common construction delivery systems and the roles within those systems. The objectives of this chapter are to recall the following:

- The description of the traditional delivery system (Design-Bid-Build)
- What the roles and responsibilities are of the participants (the owner, architect, and contractor) in the traditional system (Design-Bid-Build)
- Given a construction management form of the construction delivery system, what are the relationships of the roles within that system
- The advantages of the design-build delivery system

Roles, Responsibilities, and Authority of Project Participants

There are many ways to structure a construction project. The **delivery systems** provide a matrix of organization, with formal and informal contractual relationships between participants. Participants are assigned certain specific responsibilities within their contracts. Standard contractual forms are available for each delivery system, using generally uniform terminology and defining the roles and responsibilities for participants. Professional and trade associations produce and endorse contractual agreements that are widely used throughout the construction industry. The American Institute of Architects (AIA) publishes a complete set of contractual documents, including architect and contractor agreements. The Engineers Joint Contract Documents Committee has produced a set of contract documents that is primarily used in engineering construction. The Associated General Contractors of America, Inc. (AGC) also produces a set of contractual documents that includes agreements between contractors and owners and between contractors and subcontractors. The Design-Build Institute of America has developed contract documents including agreements between the owner and the design-build firm. ConsensusDocs also provides a complete set of contract documents, which are used extensively. Owners who use any of these forms can supplement and modify the standard contract with specific clauses relating to their particular needs. Public agencies such as municipalities, states, and the federal government have custom contract forms that meet the contracting regulations that are legislated specifically for them.

This chapter examines three basic project delivery systems:

- Traditional system
- Construction management
- Design-build

There are many variations and hybrid combinations of these three basic systems. Basic roles will be defined that can be used as a standard; however, these roles will change as the delivery system changes.

The Traditional Contract Project Delivery System (Owner-Architect-Contractor)

The traditional project delivery system, also frequently referred to as "design-bid-build," has been the most used project delivery system since the late 1800s. The legal separation between design professionals and construction forces was created by the Miller Act of 1935. This law required the contractor on federal construction projects in excess of $100,000 to post both a performance bond and a labor and material payment bond. Prior to the middle of the nineteenth century, the most common project delivery system was through a master builder.

The traditional system has three primary contractual parties:

- The owner
- The architect
- The contractor

The owner and the architect execute a contract for applicable studies, design, production of construction documents, and administration of the construction process at the beginning of the project process. The AIA agreement between the owner and the architect is AIA Form B-141. The owner and the contractor execute a contract for the construction of the project, according to the construction documents prepared by the architect, after the design and construction documents are completed. The architect then administers the contract as an agent of the owner. There is no direct contractual relationship between the architect and the contractor, but an indirect relationship exists because the architect is acting as the agent of the owner during the construction phase of the project.

Since neither the architect nor the contractor actually does 100 percent of the work assigned to their own forces, each party makes an agreement with the other business firms involved to accomplish specific areas of the work assigned under their contract. The architect will normally utilize the services of professional consultants, referred to as sub-consultants within the contract matrix, such as civil and environmental engineers, structural engineers, mechanical engineers, electrical engineers, and several other specialties contained within the project. These sub-consultants have an agreement (AIA Form C-141) with and provide specific services for the architect. There is no contractual relationship between the sub-consultant and the owner. The architect is responsible to the owner for the competent completion of his work, including work performed by the sub-consultant. For example, if the structural engineer made a serious error in the design of the structural members of the roof, resulting in the roof's collapse, the owner would seek relief from the architect as the responsible party because the owner and the architect have an agreement that requires competent design of the entire project. The architect would then subrogate the claim to the structural engineer, who was contracted by the architect to design the roof system.

In building construction, much of the work is accomplished by specialty contractors who have an agreement with the contractor to complete a specific portion of the work covered by the contractor's contract requirements. This subcontract agreement details specific responsibilities of the work, with requirements added by the contractor. The subcontract agreement is between the contractor and the subcontractor. A common type of this contract is AGC Form 600; however, many contractors have their own standard subcontract agreement. Like the architect and sub-consultant relationship, there is no direct contractual relationship between the subcontractor and the owner. The contractor is responsible to the owner for complete compliance to the contract documents even though portions of the work have been subcontracted. If in the previous example the roof structure was improperly installed by the subcontractor, the owner would seek relief from the contractor for repair and for relief of damages. The contractor would in turn look to the subcontractor for repair and damages appropriate to the subcontract agreement.

Figure 2–1 illustrates the relationships between parties in the traditional delivery system. Note that the heavy dark lines indicate a **direct relationship**, also known as **privity of contract**, and the light line represents an **indirect relationship**, also known as an **agency relationship**.

The traditional contract delivery system is not always the best delivery system for every situation. It is, however, the most prevalent of the delivery systems in the building construction industry and is used on every size contract by both private and public owners. Other delivery systems, such as construction management or design-build, are growing in use, but the traditional system is still used by the majority of owners for their construction projects.

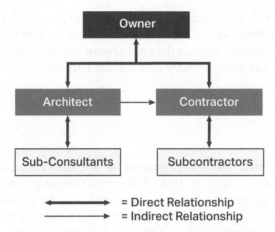

Figure 2–1   The Traditional Construction
Delivery System

There are several methods of compensating the contractor for work completed:

- Lump-sum contract: This is the most common method, where the contractor gives the owner a lump-sum price to complete the project according to the contract documents, which include the contract provisions, drawings, and technical specifications. Changes to the scope of work are accomplished through change orders, which adjust the lump-sum amount during the construction period. The contractor is normally paid on a monthly basis during the construction period for the work installed and for the materials furnished during the month.

- Cost, plus a fee: In some cases, usually when the scope of the work is difficult to define, the contractor is reimbursed for costs on the project, plus a fee that includes indirect overhead and profit. "Costs" normally refer to labor, material, equipment, subcontracts, and direct (on-site) overhead. This method of payment is often referred to as "cost plus" or "time and material."

- Cost plus, with a guaranteed maximum price: This method of compensation for the construction contract is a hybrid of the lump-sum and cost plus contracts. This method is commonly referred to as guaranteed maximum price, or GMP. In this method, the contractor quotes a maximum price for the scope of work and proceeds on a cost-plus-a-fee for the project, often with an arrangement to split the savings between the contractor and the owner.

- Unit price contract: This method lists quantities for components of the project, which are priced per unit by the contractor. The total of the product of the quantity and the unit price is then added to determine the lump-sum price for the bid. Payment is based on the completion of the quantities for each line item. Unit-price contracts are not common in the building construction industry but are quite common in civil engineering projects.

Responsibilities of the Contractual Parties

The responsibilities of the three contractual parties—the owner, the architect, and the contractor—should be well defined by the contract. A brief summary of the common responsibilities of the participants in the traditional delivery system is discussed next. (Refer to the AIA or AGC agreement forms for a complete definition of the responsibilities of each party.)

The Owner

The owner is responsible for paying for the work contracted to the architect and to the contractor. He is responsible to the contractor for providing coordination of the project, whether through an architect, an in-house representative, a project manager, or a "clerk of the works."

The owner also provides the site for the project, provides the architect with whatever one needs, and may determine the scope of the project. Additionally, the owner provides the contractor with documents that adequately describe what the project will entail.

The Architect

The architect normally provides the owner with the design of the project and the construction documents, based on the owner's needs. The architect is often engaged in providing construction administration for the project, acting as the owner's agent. The architect also provides interpretation of the contract documents.

The Contractor

The contractor is responsible for providing the labor, material, equipment, and expertise to complete the project, as indicated by the documents furnished by the owner, for compensation as stipulated. The contractor is responsible for developing the means and methods of accomplishing the work, including sequencing, labor plan, equipment usage, and schedule. The contractor also is responsible for coordinating the work, including hiring the subcontractors, and paying for all labor, material, and subcontracts contained within the work.

During the actual construction of the project, a number of participants are involved, each having several different roles in the process. The following list describes the major parties that are involved in the construction phase of a project:

Owner	Architect
Capital Projects Officer	Principal-in-Charge
Financial Officer	Project Manager
Owner's Representative	Project Architect
Owner's Inspector	Contract Administrator
Testing Agency	Sub-Consultants
	Specialty Coordinators
	—Project Coordinator
	—Mechanical Coordinator
	—Electrical Coordinator
Contractor	**Other**
Officer-in-Charge	Building Inspector
Project Manager	Plumbing Inspector
Superintendent	Electrical Inspector
Project Engineer	Fire Marshal
Field Engineer	Elevator Inspector
Foremen	Safety Inspector
Craftspeople	
Subcontractors	
—Foremen	
—Craftspeople	

The Owner's Roles During the Construction Phase

The structure of the construction project in the owner's organization will vary greatly, depending upon the size of the project and the level of involvement in managing the project. The portion of an owner's organization chart that deals with capital projects may be like the one shown in Figure 2–2, which illustrates some of the roles in the owner's organization that are involved in the construction process.

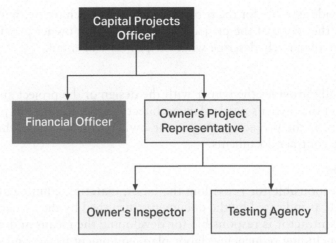

Figure 2–2   The Owner's Organization for the
Construction Project

Capital Projects Officer

The capital projects officer is the individual responsible to the owners and/or stockholders of the company for the project. This position may be filled by the owner of the company, the chief executive officer (CEO), the president, the vice president in charge of capital projects, the facility manager, or several other responsible people. This person normally is involved at the inception of the project but may not intimately participate in day-to-day construction activities. He authorizes major changes and oversees the construction phase on a periodic basis.

Financial Officer

The financial officer for the owner is concerned primarily with the disbursement of funds for the project. As monies for payment of construction activities usually come from sources other than operating funds, the financial officer must anticipate and plan for the financial needs of the project, or what is commonly referred to as project cash flow management. The contractor provides the financial officer with a cash flow projection, which relates the project's schedule of values to the construction schedule.

Owner's Representative

The owner's representative, sometimes referred to as the owner's project manager, is the owner's daily representative during the construction project. This individual may perform other responsibilities for the owner but is the owner's prime contact for the architect and the contractor. The owner's representative conducts business with the project managers for the architect and the contractor and will be the conduit of information between the architect and the owner's ultimate decision maker, the capital projects officer, and should be knowledgeable about construction practices. For owners who do not have continuous construction programs, the owner's representative is often a trained construction professional who may be hired solely for the project's duration.

Owner's Inspector

The owner's inspector, sometimes referred to as the clerk of the works, is an individual who reports to the owner's representative. This person observes the construction process and documents the progress and the problems encountered and is normally concerned with the quality of the construction work as it is installed and with transmitting information on any deviations to the architect and to the owner's representative. The inspector has no authority to direct craftspeople, subcontractors, or the contractor to stop work. Such direction will come from the owner's or architect's representative. Depending upon the conditions of the project, the owner's inspector may be on the jobsite full-time or part-time. Or the owner may decide not to have an inspector on the project at all, relying instead on an inspection by the architect.

Testing Agency

An outside testing agency is often contracted by the owner to perform certain quality control tests to verify that the materials are installed to the specified standards. Some of these tests might include soil compaction tests, concrete strength tests, reinforcing steel placement inspections, weld inspections, and bolt torque inspections. The testing agency is contracted by the owner, and its reports are directed to the owner, with copies normally sent to the architect and contractor. The owner can transfer the responsibility for testing to the contractor in the contract documents.

The Architect's Roles During the Construction Phase

The complexity of the architect's organization is dependent upon the size of the architectural firm and the size of the construction process. Some architectural firms will combine the roles of project manager, project architect, and contract administrator, relying on one individual to perform all of these roles during the process. Figure 2–3 depicts an organizational strategy for an architectural firm.

Principal-in-Charge

The principal-in-charge is an upper-management-level individual who is the ultimate decision maker for the firm on the project. The individual could be the owner of the firm, the CEO, the president, or one of the principals. The principal-in-charge usually has been involved in obtaining the contract for the architectural firm. A business relationship exists between the principal-in-charge and the capital projects officer in the owner's organization. Like the capital projects officer, the principal-in-charge is not involved in the project during the construction phase on a daily basis and limits his participation to major issues only. The principal-in-charge, however, maintains high-level communication between the architect and the owner.

Project Manager

The project manager oversees the project from beginning to end. This person may be working concurrently on other projects but is still fully responsible for each one. The project manager is the architect's primary contact with the owner's representative. The project manager provides direction to the architect's other employees and to the sub-consultants who are working on the project. The architect's project manager is also the direct liaison with the contractor's project manager and is concerned with the project budget and with the costs incurred by the architectural firm. The project manager is responsible for the architect's team composition and its ability to fulfill its contractual obligations. This person will be involved in all the decisions concerning changes in the construction contract and in evaluating the validity of those changes to the project.

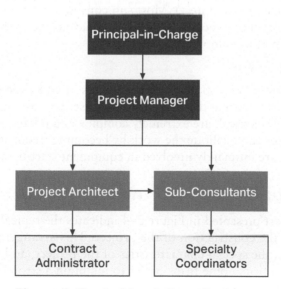

Figure 2–3 Architect's Organization

Project Architect

The project architect is involved primarily in the design of the project and construction documents. This person coordinates the designers, architects, engineers, draftspeople, specification writers, and sub-consultants in the process that ultimately produces the construction documents. By being involved in this process from the project's inception, the project architect is considered the expert regarding the intent and interpretation of the contract documents for the architectural firm but does not participate daily in the construction process. The project architect is probably the best source for the review of shop drawings for the project, if time allows. This person can also serve as a reference if other parties are to review the shop drawings. Some architectural firms do not have a contract administrator in their organization but instead utilize the project architect as the liaison during the construction phase. In that case, the contract administrator's duties, explained next, would be the responsibility of the project architect.

Contract Administrator

Many architectural firms employ a contract or construction administrator who is a specialist in projects that are under construction. The contract administrator processes shop drawings, progress payments, requests for information, change orders, and correspondence relating to the project. This person also conducts meetings with the contractor and issues minutes of the meetings. The contract administrator is the primary day-to-day contact for the contractor's project manager and superintendent and observes construction and relates information about the project to the project manager. The contract administrator may also be responsible for making certain decisions on the project, depending upon the level of involvement of the architect's project manager during the construction phase.

Some architectural firms always have an inspector on the jobsite. This inspector is a clerk of the works who fulfills the duties of the owner's inspector, described earlier. On projects that require a full-time inspector, this person is employed by either the architectural firm or the owner but usually not by both.

Sub-Consultants

The sub-consultants provide design services and portions of the construction documents that are not provided by the architect's in-house staff. Typical sub-consultants used on a building project include civil and environmental engineering, structural engineering, mechanical engineering, electrical engineering, and interior design firms. Other specialty sub-consultants, such as acoustical, kitchen, detention, and industrial engineering services, also may be used, depending on the specifics of the project. During the construction phase, the sub-consultant reviews shop drawings and provides input relevant to one's portion of the project to the architect and to the contractor (through the architect). Most sub-consultants retain some involvement during the project, usually relating to special installations that are needed to execute the work and approve the installation at its completion.

Specialty Coordinators

The specialty coordinators are inspectors and engineers hired by the sub-consultants who provide services on the jobsite during the construction phase. Because many of the specialty areas, such as mechanical and electrical, are extremely complex and relate to the work of many trades, the specialty coordinator can facilitate the work by becoming frequently involved in the project. These specialists often are intimately involved in equipment start-up and testing.

The Contractor's Roles During the Construction Phase

The organizational chart presented in Figure 2–4 indicates the typical hierarchy of the contractor's organization for the construction of the project. This arrangement may vary, depending upon the project's size, the special characteristics of the project, and the management philosophy of the construction firm. Some firms prefer to maintain a strong management presence on the jobsite, while others prefer to keep management to the minimum.

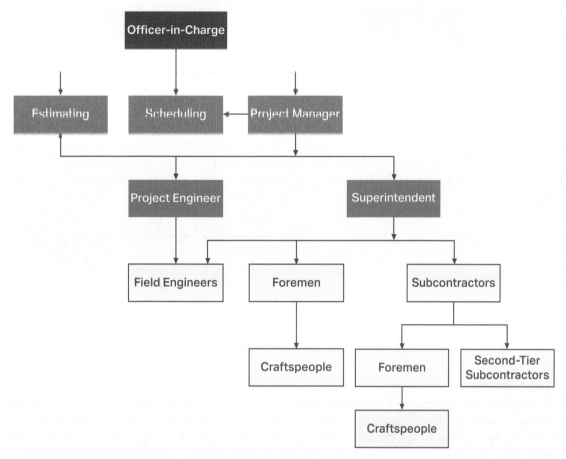

Figure 2–4   Contractor's Project Organization

Officer-in-Charge

The officer-in-charge, like the owner and the architect, is responsible for the firm's performance. This individual may be the construction company's owner, president, CEO, vice president, or district manager. This person has a business-level relationship with the owner's capital projects officer and the architect's principal-in-charge. The officer-in-charge normally is not involved with the project daily but is involved in matters that affect the success of the project.

Project Manager

The contractor's project manager organizes and manages the contractor's project team. This person's responsibility to upper management is to ensure the project's profitability. The project manager selects and maintains the appropriate team to complete the project economically and efficiently to the owner's standards, as set forth in the plans and specifications, while making a profit for the construction company. The project manager is responsible for implementing time and schedule control, cost control, and quality control during the project and conducts business with the owner's representative and the architect's project manager. In most contractor organizations, the project manager operates at a higher level than does the superintendent; however, the latter has a great deal of autonomy in managing the project's physical construction. In some organizations, the superintendent is considered an equal to the project manager. Normally, the project manager is more involved in the business and formal requirements of the contract, while the superintendent usually is associated with the activities regarding the construction of the facility. While the organizational chart in Figure 2–4 represents the lines of command where the superintendent reports to the project manager, Figure 2–5 illustrates the contractor's project organization where the superintendent and project manager are at equal, or parallel, hierarchy levels. In this case, an operations officer supervises the superintendents.

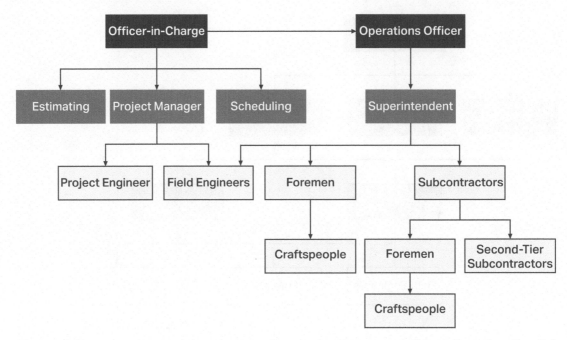

Figure 2–5   Contractor's Project Organization, Project Manager, and Superintendent Parallel

During the construction phase of the project, specific estimating and scheduling functions need to be accomplished. Estimating functions during the construction phase relate primarily to estimating changes to the contract. The schedule, of course, is a major planning tool of the construction process and provides a standard for measuring success in compliance to the time constraints on the project. Both elements fall under the project manager's domain, but for smaller projects, the project manager may actually personally perform each of these functions. Large construction organizations have estimating and scheduling departments that perform these services for the project manager. Sometimes these duties may be assigned to lower-tier management personnel such as the project or field engineer.

Superintendent

With either organizational structure presented, the superintendent is responsible for the correct, timely, and profitable construction of the project. The superintendent has the necessary skills and understanding of common construction methods and practices. This person manages a crew of craftspeople employed by the contractor and subcontractors. It is the superintendent's responsibility to coordinate labor, material, equipment, and subcontractors during project installation. The superintendent determines the labor force, equipment on site, and timing of the delivery of materials and subcontractor work and is responsible for the jobsite: its safety, efficiency, and compliance to the parameters required by the construction documents and regulatory codes. The superintendent is considered a full-time representative of the contractor at the jobsite, while the project manager may be assigned to several projects. The superintendent gives direction to the foremen and craftspeople who are employed by the contractor, coordinates subcontractors, and is the point of contact for subcontractor foremen. The superintendent normally communicates with the architect's contract administrator. If there is an on-site inspector, for either the owner or the architect, the inspector's point of contact will be the superintendent. Depending upon the management philosophy of the contractor, field management employees, such as the field engineer, may report to the superintendent or project manager. The superintendent is often the only member of the contractor's management personnel on the jobsite on small to medium-sized projects. On some small projects, the superintendent actually participates in work activities. In these instances, this person is called a "working superintendent."

Project Engineer

The project engineer usually reports directly to the project manager. This person performs paperwork activities for the project manager such as subcontract agreements, material submittals and shop drawings, payment requests, contract change orders, requests for information, correspondence with subcontractors and suppliers, and project documentation. The project engineer normally assists the project manager with any activities that are necessary to keep the project flowing and on track. This person will informally communicate with the architect's project manager, contract administrator, and inspector; however, formal conversations with these individuals usually are pursued by the project manager or superintendent.

Field Engineer

The field engineer reports to either the project manager/project engineer or the superintendent. The field engineer is involved in the layout of work and the interpretation of the construction documents. This person should be knowledgeable about the contents of the construction documents and is often responsible for documenting jobsite conditions and conversations. The field engineer is responsible for issuing requests for information to the architect about clarifications, differing field conditions, and erroneous information contained in the construction documents. The field engineer may order materials and review and/or process shop drawings and submittals and is often responsible for quality control and assurance in the project. This position is the lowest tier on the management side of the contractor's employees, but the field engineer is responsible for a wide variety of tasks in assisting the superintendent and project engineer. Some firms will divide the responsibilities of the field engineer, such as assignment of the layout and field coordination, to them. Office work, such as submittals, payments, and change orders, is assigned to the office engineer. In other firms, the assistant superintendent performs most of the tasks described for the field engineer.

Foremen

Foremen are supervisory personnel. They usually are paid hourly and receive slightly higher pay than craftspeople. Foremen are responsible for directing the labor crew in their work activities. Foremen, as hourly employees, are not considered management but, rather, labor. Foremen are usually knowledgeable about the installation techniques that are necessary to perform the work of the crew. Foremen create work assignments for craftspeople. They are normally in charge of a crew made up predominantly of their craftspeople, such as carpenters; however, a crew can include several different craftspeople, such as carpenters, laborers, operating engineers, and cement masons. Foremen are responsible for preparing time and quantity in-place reports for cost and schedule control purposes. They also are responsible for reporting work-ready or complete-for-quality inspections. Foremen are responsible for successfully completing work activities within a specific budget and time frame. Depending upon the size of the crew and the nature of the task, foremen may act in a purely supervisory role, or they may actually perform some of the labor for the task, in which case they may be referred to as working foremen.

On large construction projects, a lead craftsperson is used to supervise each crew when the foreman oversees several crews. The lead craftsperson normally performs work activities with the crew.

Craftspeople

Craftspeople are hourly employees who are trained to perform specific tasks. Each craft or trade performs its work assignment with a high level of efficiency and quality. The following is a list of some common craftspeople who could be directly employed by the contractor:

Laborer

Carpenter

Operating engineer

Teamster

Ironworker

Cement mason

Construction trades or crafts distinguish between classifications of work performed, resulting in a slight wage differential. The trained craftsperson, receiving the full wage under the work classification, is referred to as a **journeyman**. **Apprentices** are journeymen-in-training and receive a lower wage than journeymen. Some crafts use a **helper**, who aids the journeyman and is similar to a laborer but lacks the training progression and wage increase of the apprentice. Current trends show that the general contractor is employing fewer and fewer craftspeople, relying now on much of the construction labor to be furnished by subcontractors.

Subcontractors

Subcontractors are separate business entities from the contractor. They provide labor, material, equipment, and occasionally second-tier subcontracts to complete a specific portion of the construction. They have agreements with and are responsible to the contractor. All correspondence and requests for clarifications from the subcontractor go to the contractor, who determines which course of action to take. The subcontractor management usually will contact the contractor's project manager or the project engineer for clarifications and contractual discussions. The subcontractor's foreman at the jobsite communicates with the contractor's superintendent concerning work parameters, changes, and directions.

Subcontractor Foreman

The subcontractor foreman is the subcontractor's site representative. Larger subcontracts will require a superintendent for the subcontractor when there are several crews and a variety of work, for instance, with a large mechanical subcontract. The subcontractor's foreman is responsible for the quality of work accomplished by the crew or crews. The subcontractor's foreman is often a working foreman in that this person also works with the tools. The subcontractor foreman's primary task is to facilitate a profit for the subcontractor on the particular work assigned for the project and provides direction to one's crew or crews to install and complete the work assigned.

Subcontractor Craftspeople

The subcontractor directly employs craftspeople as hourly laborers on the project. Different training and classifications are assigned to craftspeople who are doing specific tasks. Figure 2–6 lists some of the trades that subcontractors utilize on the jobsite. Some subcontractors employ the same craftspeople as the contractor; however, they usually perform different types of tasks.

Other Roles in the Construction Process

Significant roles in the construction process are played by entities other than the owner, architect, and contractor. The majority of these individuals represent regulatory agencies, as required by the municipal, state, or federal governments. There are a number of inspectors from different agencies and levels of government who need access to construction sites. These inspectors examine the installations for compliance to codes that are legislated standards of compliance

Laborer	Glazier	Lather
Carpenter	Plasterer	Taper
Operating Engineer	Ceramic Tile Installer	Floor Covering Installer
Teamster	Terrazzo Mechanic	Painter
Ironworker	Elevator Mechanic	Millwright
Cement Mason	Plumber	Pipe Fitter
Bricklayer	Steamfitter	Sprinkler Fitter
Roofer	Mechanical Insulator	Temperature Control
Sheet Metal Worker	Refrigeration Mechanic	Mechanic
	Electrician	

Figure 2–6   List of Trades Employed by Subcontractors

Inspector	From	Items Inspected
Building Inspector	City, County	Concrete Footings, Concrete Reinforcing, Wood Framing, Steel Framing, Final Compliance
Plumbing Inspector	City, County	Plumbing Rough-In, Sewer Installation, Water Line Installation
Electrical Inspector	City, County, State	Electrical Roughin, Electrical Finish
Fire Marshal	City, State	Fire Alarm Systems, Fire Protection Systems
Elevator Inspector	City, State	Elevators, Conveyance Systems
Safety Inspector	State, Federal (OSHA)	Safety Compliance of Jobsite

Figure 2–7 List of Typical Inspections

necessary to protect the public. The codes apply to the design and installation of the particular systems in the project and supersede the contract documents. It is assumed that the contractor has met all the codes with the installations. State industrial safety agencies and the federal government industrial safety agency, the Occupational Safety and Health Administration (OSHA), also have the right to inspect the jobsite for safety compliance.

Figure 2–7 lists some of the inspections that are common to building construction.

Communications in the Traditional System

The previous discussion indicated that there are distinct hierarchical levels within each organization. Communications, whether they are verbal or written, are normally between individuals at the same level. Figure 2–8 illustrates a communications matrix indicating direct, or contractual, lines of communications, and indirect, or nonbinding, communications. This is one possible communications matrix, with other matrices being utilized when other contractual agreements are chosen.

During the construction phase, special care must be taken to avoid communications that transcend the contractual lines of privity. Subcontractors should not communicate directly with

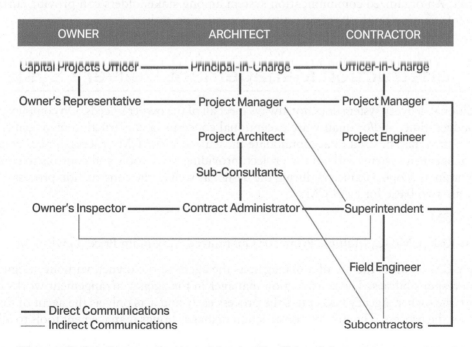

Figure 2–8 Communications Matrix, Traditional System

the architect but should approach the contractor's superintendent or project manager. Most problems on the jobsite have a larger impact than just the particular subcontractor's work, and the superintendent or project manager has the responsibility and perspective to discern the full impact of the change or concern. There is often informal communication between parties; however, throughout the construction process, considerable communication takes place between the sub-consultants and subcontractors that may be technical in nature and may be misconstrued if transferred through several parties. Informal communication is important for clarifications, but binding clarifications, changes, and directions must go through the proper contractual channel, preferably, and are often required in writing. The sub-consultant and subcontractor should be careful to transmit information that has an impact on the contracts to the architect and contractor for official and binding communication.

Construction projects contain thousands of interacting elements, requiring interpretation of installation details to be an integral part of the constructed system. Several opinions as to correct installation techniques often occur from different trades and workers. Most of the discussions concerning technical issues are eventually resolved but may not be clearly communicated to all concerned. Typically, changes should be made via the change order process and documented appropriately. Many of the technical changes are not formally transmitted to the appropriate crews. Communication and direction often do not reach those involved in the proper execution of the work.

A management trend, "single source of truth," is being used by companies employing several data sources for implementations. "Single source of truth" is a concept used to ensure that everyone in an organization bases business decisions on the same data. The management system provides relevant personnel that can discern the appropriate data.

In construction, a decision clarifies the implementation before mistakes are made and remediation required. Single-source decision making can facilitate rapid installation, eliminate repair work, and maintain the quality of the installation. Consistent decision paths help the firm acquire consistent quality assessments.

An individual or dedicated team can control the communication and implementation of decisions concerning materials and installation. The project superintendent typically is the ultimate decision maker on the project. Assistant superintendents and project engineers are often involved in material and installation information and decisions. A communication source, such as a project engineer, should be appointed to establish a single source of truth/information on the project. An organized communication system among stakeholders can provide current and accurate information on the large quantity of construction tasks.

The Construction Management Delivery System

The traditional delivery system does not always meet all of the owner's needs. On complex projects, where budget, time, and/or quality are exceptional concerns, a construction management (CM) delivery system may be used to accommodate those needs. The CM process applies contractor-based management systems early in the project, providing more tools and controls to contain the project within its scope parameters during the design as well as the construction process.

There are two basic forms of CM:

• Agency CM

• CM-at-Risk, CM/GC, Multiple Prime, or Guaranteed Maximum Price (GMP)-CM

Agency CM involves the use of a manager, as the agent of the owner, without design or construction responsibilities. The construction manager in the agency arrangement works on a fee basis with the owner. Agency CM enters the process early and acts only as the agent of the owner throughout the process. The Agency construction manager brings management tools to all phases of the work without having a vested interest in either the design or construction of the building.

Figure 2–9 illustrates the organization of the Agency CM arrangement.

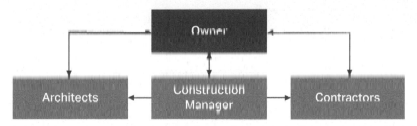

Figure 2–9   Organization of the CM Delivery System (Agency CM)

Under the Agency CM system, the contracts for the architects and contractors are written directly with the owner; however, the construction manager acts as the owner's agent and manages both the architect and the contractor. Depending upon the level of service offered by the construction manager, the contractors may be trade contractors, execution contractors, or specialty/subcontractors, without a general contractor, and may be managed by the construction manager. This type of system is usually referred to as "Multiple Primes," where there are multiple contracts directly to the owner, managed by the construction manager. Under this system, the architect's position in the construction phase of the project is reduced to an advisory role, with the construction manager providing the construction administration for the owner. Figure 2–10 illustrates a typical Multi-Prime contracting arrangement.

Although the CM system adds another layer of bureaucracy to the project, it provides a more intense and appropriately focused management of the process than does the traditional process. It is best utilized by an owner who has little or no construction expertise within one's organization, relying on the CM firm to coordinate the project. One prominent CM firm advertises its services as "Extension of Staff." The CM process provides the owner with specialized management to control problems with project duration, project budget and cost, or project quality. Although the fee for the CM firm appears to be an additional cost to the owner, the construction manager is replacing the owner's in-house construction manager, also a significant project cost. CM Agency can be utilized with virtually any project delivery system.

CM-at-Risk is similar to the GMP arrangement in the traditional system, except that the construction manager is involved in the conception and design of the project rather than entering after the completion of the contract documents. The construction manager in this arrangement provides the owner with a maximum price for the project, considering the project's initial scope. The GMP construction manager manages the construction phase much like a contractor does under the traditional system, often subcontracting out all or most of the work. The roles during the construction phase under the CM system are modified from the traditional system.

The roles involved during the construction phase for the CM system include the following.

- The owner, who still provides funding for the construction and the site for the project. The owner makes the decisions about the project but is advised in all matters by the construction manager. As the construction manager handles the entire project, from conception through completion, the owner has little day-to-day involvement.

- The construction manager, who is responsible for the administration of the construction contracts during the construction phase of the project. The construction manager maintains a liaison with the architect for advice on intent of the documents. This person schedules and manages the submittal process, while the architect reviews the submittals and shop drawings. The construction manager may provide a detailed schedule for the completion of the construction and acts as the communications conduit for the contractor or contractors on the project. The construction manager also will process progress payments and contract completion.

- The architect, who is engaged to design the project and prepare construction documents. During the construction phase, the architect serves as a reference and an adviser on the intent of the construction documents, but the construction manager is responsible for the

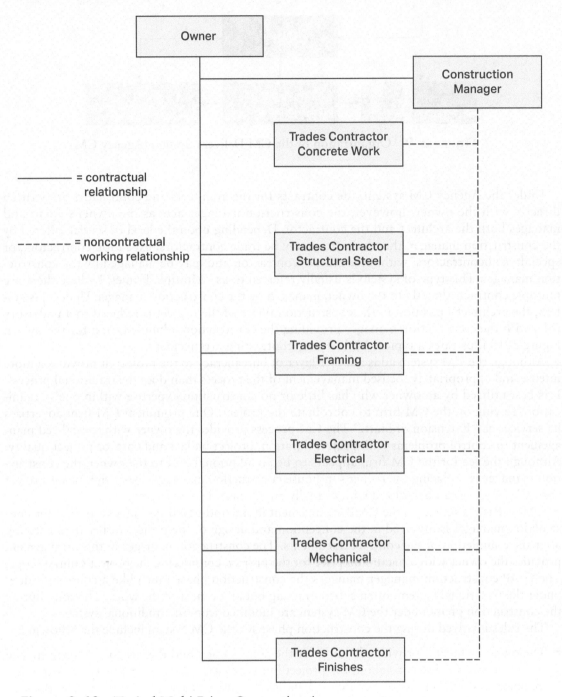

Figure 2–10   **Typical Multi-Prime Contracting Arrangement**

administration of the project. The architect is involved in reviewing submittals and shop drawings but under this system is not normally involved on a daily basis in the construction of the project.

- The contractors, who, under the CM process, play a role similar to that of the subcontractor in the traditional system. The contractor may be assigned a large element of the work, such as the foundation or building envelope, or may be awarded a small contract, such as caulking and sealants. The smaller subcontracts, which encompass work by a single trade, are usually called **trade contracts**. For larger portions of work, the contractor would employ a superintendent but would still look to the construction manager's superintendent for coordination of the work.

Roles of the CM Project Team

Figure 2–11 illustrates the roles of personnel within the CM project team. Each project and CM firm will use a variation of this basic arrangement.

The roles involved in the CM team include the following.

- The project manager, who is the party responsible to the owner for the success of the project. The project manager is in charge of all of the CM employees on the project. This person primarily oversees the construction process; however, most of the contact with the contractor during the construction phase is handled by the construction administrator.

- The design manager, who is involved with the architect during the design and construction processes. The decisions concerning contract packaging, early purchase of materials, and project strategies are made during the design phase of the project. Some CM firms have the design manager act as the construction administrator, while other firms will use different individuals who possess specific skills for their phase of the project. Liaison and communication need to continue between the design manager and the construction administrator concerning the intent of the design.

- The construction administrator, often referred to as the construction manager, who is in charge of the construction process for the CM firm. The construction administrator is the contact person for the contractors' project managers and is responsible for the entire construction process, delegating part of the field responsibilities to the construction superintendent and the field engineers.

- The construction superintendent, who coordinates the field activities. Unlike the traditional delivery system where the construction superintendent is in charge of direct labor and subcontractors, in the CM delivery system this person manages only the trade or execution contractors, as the construction manager does not use direct labor. In cases where the contractor or contractors do substantial portions of the work, such as when using Multiple Primes, providing coordination of the subcontracts within their scope, the construction manager may use a construction administrator and not a construction superintendent. It is essential, however, to have a knowledgeable construction superintendent on the site when using myriad trade contractors in order to provide some order to the process. The construction superintendent is responsible for maintaining the construction schedule, for ensuring compliance of all work to the documents,

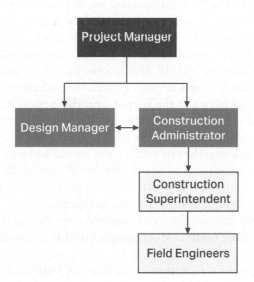

Figure 2–11 Construction Management Roles

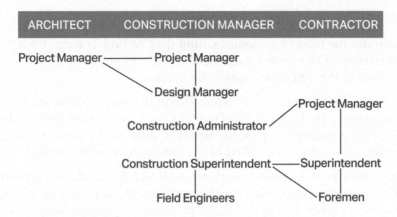

Figure 2–12   Communications in the Construction
Management System

and for coordinating all of the trade contractors. The construction superintendent may need
assistance from the field engineers, depending upon the scope of the project.

- The field engineer, who is responsible for the coordination of shop drawings, submittals,
layout, subcontractor organization, payment verification, and whatever duties are assigned
by the construction superintendent or construction administrator.

Communications in the CM Delivery System

The matrix of communications lines in a typical Agency CM project for the construction phase
is illustrated in Figure 2–12.

Since the construction manager is the controlling entity in the project, all communications
flow through this person. This system should facilitate prompt responses to communications
throughout the construction phase.

The Design-Build Delivery System

Both of the previous systems can be cumbersome for the owner who wants to avoid conflict
between the project participants during the project while still striving for a project that meets
their needs in a short period of time. The design-build delivery system is a single-source procurement for the owner. Design and construction—and even occasionally the purchase of the
site—are provided to the owner for a GMP, also known as a "cost not to exceed" price from the
design-build firm. There often is a cost-savings split clause, which will split the savings between
the GMP and the actual cost between the owner and the design-build contractor. Instead of
creating an adversarial relationship between the architects and contractors, as in the other two
delivery systems, the design-build firm acts as the facilitator for designers and constructors in
the design-build team to work together to achieve the owner's objectives.

There are four basic configurations of the design-build firm, with numerous variations. The
first is the design-build firm that exclusively does design-build work and has under its direct
control both designers and constructors, as shown in Figure 2–13.

This type of organization provides internal control over design and construction, resulting
in a high-value package for the owner. Most design-build firms with this type of organization
are large.

The second is the design-build firm that contracts out both architectural and construction
services. The design-build firm could have its origins in architecture/engineering, construction,

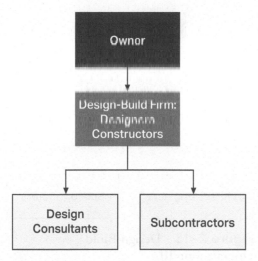

Figure 2–13   Design-Build
Organization I

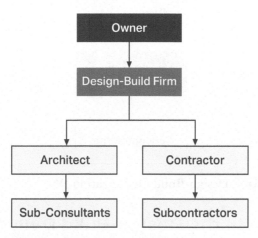

Figure 2–14   Design-Build
Organization II

or even property development. This is a popular organizational model for developers who are involved in design-build construction. Figure 2–14 illustrates this type of design-build organization.

The third is the contractor-lead venture, with the contractor being the contracting point with the owner and the designer being subcontracted to the contractor: This type of organization is frequently used when determination of the successful design-build team is based on bids. Figure 2–15 illustrates this type of organization.

The fourth is a hybrid of the previously mentioned systems, when an architectural engineering firm and a contracting firm form a joint venture or a partnership for one specific project. This type of organization pools resources and can rely on the reputations of the two firms. Figure 2–16 illustrates this type of design-build organization.

Each of these organizational types provides the design-build firm with funding, leadership, and the resources necessary for the particular type of project. These different options are available to firms that are working in the design-build area. The first organization, shown in Figure 2–13, represents a firm that would work exclusively in design-build projects. The other three organizations, shown in Figures 2–14, 2–15, and 2–16, can be composed of firms that would work in both the traditional and the CM delivery systems as well as in the design-build system.

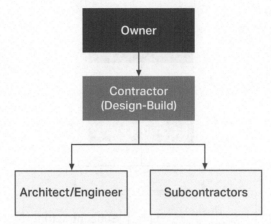

Figure 2–15   Design-Build
Organization III

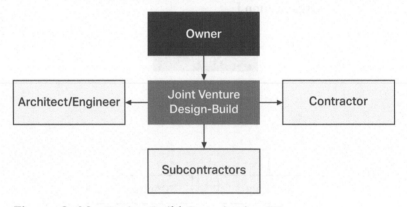

Figure 2–16   Design-Build Organization IV

Communications in the Design-Build Delivery System

Communications between the design-build firm and the owner, regardless of the configuration, are rather simple. The owner's representative communicates with the design-build firm's project manager. The design-build firm, then, needs to determine the best way to achieve its objectives, through its own communications matrix, determined by the exact relationships within the design-build firm. The design-build team acts as an in-house operation, as there should be no conflicts between entities, as in the other processes. The design-build team is focused on producing a solution to the owner's needs in a project within the scope of time, budget, and quality. Figure 2–17 illustrates the typical communications matrix for the design-build delivery system.

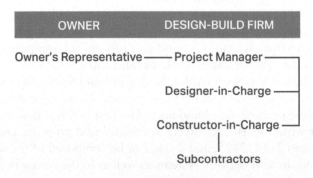

Figure 2–17   **Design-Build Communications**

Engineering-Procurement-Construction

Another type of delivery system, actually a form of design-build, is the Engineering-Procurement-Construction (E-P-C) system, commonly referred to as E-P-C. E-P-C is a common delivery system for industrial plants, power plants, refineries, and other heavy construction facilities. Under this agreement, the E-P-C firm provides engineering for the facility, procurement of all material and equipment, and construction of the facility, with its own forces or those contracted to other firms. As with the design-build system, there is a single point of contact with the owner during the entire project.

Summary

Three primary delivery systems—the traditional system (also known as design-bid-build), the CM system, and the design-build system—are used in the construction of building and industrial facilities today. Each of these systems has different roles for the contractor, architect, and owner, and each has a different communication network between the parties in the system. Understanding these systems is necessary for effective project management.

Although the traditional system is the most common delivery system currently used, the alternative systems of CM and design-build offer opportunities to provide more management in the process, controlling cost, time, and quality. Each project situation has unique parameters that need to be examined to determine the most desirable delivery system for the owner.

Each of the three delivery systems is effective in certain situations and project communications vary greatly in each. Comparison of the three communications charts in this chapter (Figures 2–8, 2–12, and 2–17) indicates the relative amount of communication complexity. The challenge then in each delivery system is to recognize where the problems might arise and to use management techniques to eliminate or minimize those problems.

Review Questions

1. In the traditional contract delivery system, what are the direct contract relationships between the three principal parties?

2. What are the responsibilities of the owner, architect, and contractor under the traditional delivery system?

3. Describe some of the duties of the following positions in the traditional delivery system: owner's representative, architect's contract administrator, and contractor's project manager.

4. What are the lines of communication for a subcontractor with a concern about the constructability of a system shown and described in the construction documents?

5. What are the primary roles of the construction manager in Agency CM?

6. What is the difference between an Agency CM and the CM-at-Risk?

7. Describe the responsibilities of a design-build firm.

8. What type of delivery system is E-P-C?

Chapter 3

The Use of Construction Documents on the Jobsite

Objectives

This chapter is an introduction to construction documents and the importance of their use during the construction project. The objectives of this chapter are to:

- Name the purpose and intent of construction documents
- Recognize the common elements of construction documents
- Relate the project manual, to its components, organization, and contents
- Discuss the Construction drawings, including a discussion of their organization and content
- Recall the uses of the construction documents at the jobsite, including familiarizing construction professionals with the project, preparing crew assignments, and problem solving

In most construction projects, the contractor does not develop the design of the project. The design is envisioned by the architect or engineer and is then transmitted to the contractor through drawings and written specifications. These construction documents describe the nature of the project, the materials desired, the level of the quality of work desired, the connection of materials, and the installation and systems necessary to achieve the project. The construction documents indicate to the contractor what will be built. The documents should be complete enough to construct the intended facility with little or no further clarification.

Construction documents, however, are *not* for the novice. The terminology used in these documents is a special language that accurately describes construction components. The plans, elevations, details, and diagrams used in construction are fairly unique to the industry, not readily understandable to the general public. The construction documents are written with the assumption that the contractor is experienced and knowledgeable and will understand them. It is also assumed that the contractor is experienced and knowledgeable in the means and methods of constructing the particular project. The documents usually do not indicate the way in which the project will be built, that is, the means and methods. The contractor furnishes one's expertise for construction of the project, just as the architect and the engineer do in the design of the project. The contractor is expected to know how to construct the different systems composing the entire project—the crafts and subcontractors to use, the quantity and type of material necessary, the type of tools to use, and the type of equipment necessary. The contractor also is expected to possess the expertise to ascertain the quality level required by the documents and implement that quality level into the project and to construct the project in a safe and legal manner.

Although codes and regulations are not formally included as construction documents, they are the governing regulations for compliance of design and construction. Codes are normally referenced in the construction documents, but the contractor is obligated to comply to codes and regulations even if they are not specified or referenced. The contractor must comply to the drawings and specifications as well. The design is based on the constraints of the codes. Standard codes, such as the International Building Code, Uniform Building Code, and the National Building Code, are modified by the local municipality or governing body. The contractor is expected to install the project elements in compliance with the locally enforced building, plumbing, electrical, energy, and local fire protection codes. It is assumed, however, that the construction documents comply to code and have been reviewed for such.

Material and equipment attributes also affect the installation of the construction elements. Each material and piece of equipment has installation parameters, instructions, and restrictions that must be followed to obtain a quality, durable installation. Most construction documents state that the installation of the material should be done in compliance with the manufacturer's recommendations and instructions. The latter are complementary documents to the construction documents. The contractor uses the manufacturer's recommendations, the construction documents (Figure 3–1), and the applicable codes and regulations to provide information for the construction of the project.

Figure 3–1   Jobsite Construction Documents
Don Mason/The Image Bank/Getty Images

The Construction Documents

Traditionally, construction documents consist of two major physical components: the project manual and the drawings. Various formats for both components are used, depending on the construction type and the local customs. The project manual normally includes the following:

- Invitation or Advertisement to Bid
- Request for Proposal, used with Design-Build and some Construction Management projects
- Instructions to Bidders
- Bid Forms
- General Conditions of the Contract
- Supplementary Conditions to the Contract
- Additional Information to Bidders (such as soil reports)
- General Requirements (Division 1)
- Technical Specifications (Divisions 2–48)

  Construction drawings for a building project normally include the following:

- Abbreviations and general notes
- Code-related compliance information
- Site surveys
- Site plans
- Utility plans
- Floor plans

- Building sections
- Wall sections
- Exterior elevations
- Interior elevations
- Details
- Equipment plans and details
- Structural engineering drawings
- Mechanical engineering drawings
- Electrical engineering drawings
- Special construction information

The project manual is usually in book form, often bound in plastic bindings. Some projects may include the drawings in the bound volume, particularly when there are few drawings for the project. There may be several volumes of the project manual. Drawings may be in several formats and sizes and can range in size from 8½" × 11" sheets to 48" × 36" sheets. Some projects reduce the drawings to half their size to conserve paper and to provide a more convenient size drawing for use in the field. Special care should be taken with reduced size prints to determine the scale used on the drawings. The original scale may be ¼" = 1'0", but in half-size reduction this scale becomes ⅛" = 1'0". The modified scale is rarely noted, so it is important for the user to observe if the drawings have been reduced. The project manual contains the qualitative information required to construct the project, and the drawings provide the quantitative and relational information required to construct the project.

Construction documents can also be made available on compact disk or online for computer access. Drawing files and specification files can be accessed using reader software, usually available on the disk or online. Electronic measuring tools are often included in the reader software. Paper copies of the files can be made, and hard copies of the drawings are usually necessary for estimating and construction purposes.

Many contractors have implemented electronic versions of the drawings on the jobsite in kiosks or job boxes for active use of the superintendent and onsite workers. The use of the full set of construction documents, such as drawings, specifications, change orders, approved submittals, and other pertinent documents, on the jobsite provides current access to any changes. It can also give the superintendent opportunity to record as-built information on the documents. When BIM is used on the project, the full detail from the BIM documents is available to the superintendent and foremen, facilitating complete and proper implementation of the work.

The primary purpose of construction drawings is to communicate the intended elements, systems, and relationships of the materials, equipment, and assemblies to the contractor in the construction of the facility. The documents also provide the necessary information for the contractor to compile a cost estimate and plan the construction process for the project. The construction documents also should provide sufficient information for the preparation of shop drawings and submittals for material suppliers and fabricators as well as provide information to the owner of the facility after the construction is completed for the maintenance and operation of the facility. Usually the construction documents are noted to reflect changes during the construction phase of the project, referred to as "as-built drawings," for use by the owner during the operation of the facility.

The owner of the project furnishes the construction documents to the contractor for the project. The owner, in most cases, does not prepare these documents but usually contracts with an architectural or engineering firm to design the project and prepare the documents. Some large corporate or public owners use in-house architects and engineers to design and prepare construction documents. Several different disciplines are involved in the design and document preparation, coordinated by the lead architect or engineer. Consultants employed by architects include geotechnical, structural, mechanical, and electrical engineers and specialty designers, such as industrial engineers, landscape architects, interior designers, and equipment consultants. The construction documents consist of several different components, some in written narrative and some appearing as graphical documents.

What follows is a discussion describing the information generally found in each section of the construction documents. As previously noted, the information found in these sections varies, according to local customs and the type of construction. Engineering type construction documents are generally a bit different than building construction documents. The mode of drawing in engineering documents, for engineering components such as bridges or roads, is more mechanical, reflecting critical attributes like location and elevation. Engineering drawings use an engineering scale, graduated in one-tenths of a foot, whereas architectural drawings use primarily an architectural scale, graduated in multiples of one-eighth of an inch. Many architects and engineers use some standard documents for certain parts of the project manual, such as the Invitation to Bid and General Conditions. The American Institute of Architects (AIA) has a standard set of documents used in building construction documents, just as the Engineers Joint Construction Documents Committee (EJCDC) uses a set of documents for engineering construction. These documents are somewhat similar but do have some differences based on custom in the appropriate fields. Many architectural and engineering firms use a master specification guide for technical specifications, resulting in similar specifications for projects.

Advertisement or Invitation to Bid

This section usually appears at the front of the project manual. The Advertisement or Invitation to Bid contains information about the project during the bid period. The information normally contained here includes the following:

- Project name, number, location, and description

- Owner name and address

- Architect/engineer name, address, and contact individual

- Bid date and time

- Bid security required

- Restrictions on bidders

- Anticipated price range of project (optional)

- Anticipated project duration (optional)

   Figure 3–2 illustrates an example of an Advertisement for Bids on a public works project.

Request for Proposal

In design-build and some construction management projects, a proposal of services is requested by the owner. This proposal is more extensive than a traditional bid, detailing the firm's experience and qualifications and approach to the project. The Requests for Proposals are evaluated by the owner and usually short-listed down to a few firms. Interviews of the firms are usually conducted, from which the owner selects the firm for the project.

Instructions to Bidders

This section contains information about the bid procedure. Both the AIA and the EJCDC have standard forms that can be used, with desired modifications, as instructions to bidders. Most of these bid procedures are standard. The bidder should review this section for each project, as specific information concerning the particular project will be contained here. Specific information concerning requests for substitutions, clarifications, bidder prequalification, bid period, and construction period duration can be included.

ADVERTISEMENT FOR BIDS

Sealed proposals will be received for the following project:

PROJECT NO.   98-250

TITLE: State Office Building
                     Centerville, WA

AGENCY: Department of Public Works

ESTIMATED BASE BID
COST RANGE: $ 2,500,000 to $ 2,600,000

TIME/DAY/DATE: BIDS WILL BE RECEIVED UP TO 3:00 PM
                     Wednesday, October 14, 2026

LOCATION: Department of Public Works, Olympia, WA

BID OPENING: Bid Center, Capital Center Annex
                     417 West 4th Avenue
                     Olympia, WA 98504-1112

Contractors may obtain plans and specifications from the office of the Consultant, NTG Architects, S. 400 Main Street, Centerville, WA 99345, telephone (509) 439-0478, upon the deposit of $ 100.00, or they may be view at the following locations: Associated Builders & Contractors, Inc., Centerville; Associated General Contractors, Seattle and Centerville; Centerville Plan Center, Centerville; Dodge/Scan, Seattle; Spokane Construction Council, Spokane. The State reserves the right to reject or accept any or all proposals and to waive informalities.

The bidding documents may contain mandatory requirements for Minority and Women Business Enterprises (MWBE) participation. The participating MWBE's must be certified, and the name and dollar amount for each participating MWBE must be included in the "Form of Proposal". MWBE firms qualified for certification but currently not certified are encouraged to contact the Office of Minority and Women's Business Enterprises (OMWBE) immediately regarding the steps necessary for certification. Only certification by OMWBE, State of Washington, will be accepted. For assistance verifying certification contact: OMWBE, 406 South Water, Olympia, WA 98504-4611, telephone (206) 753-9693.

A pre-bid conference and walk-through has been scheduled at the project site, Thursday, October 1, 2026, at 2:00 PM. General Contractors, subcontractors, and interested vendors are encouraged to attend this pre-bid conference.

Figure 3–2   Example Advertisement for Bids

AIA Form A701, Instructions to Bidders, includes the following types of information:

- Bidder representations, defining the obligations of the bidder
- Bidding documents: where and to whom they are available
- Interpretation: procedures for questions and interpretations of the documents
- Addenda: inclusion of addenda as part of the documents and procedures for addenda
- Bidding procedures, including the form and style of acceptable bids, the bid security required, procedures for submission of bids, and rules concerning modification or withdrawal of bids
- Bid opening, including procedures for bid opening
- Rejection of bids
- Award of project to successful bidder

- Requirements for post-bid information, such as bidder qualification and financial information, and product submittals
- Bonding requirements
- Form of contract to be used for the project

Bid Forms

The necessary bid forms and other certification forms usually are included in the project manual. Bid security forms may be included as well. Bid forms include information relevant to qualification as a responsive bidder, such as receipt of addenda, bid price, alternate pricing, proposed completion of construction, subcontractor information, and certifications of compliance to regulations. Many projects, particularly public works projects, require numerous certifications concerning affirmative action, Disadvantaged Business Enterprise utilization, and other compliance issues. Forms that are required to be submitted with the bid normally are included in the project manual. Figures 3–3A and B are illustrations of a bid form used in public works construction.

STATE OF WASHINGTON
DEPARTMENT OF PUBLIC WORKS
417 WEST 4TH AVENUE
OLYMPIA, WASHINGTON 98504-1112

P R O P O S A L

PROJECT NO. 04-250
State Office Building
Centerville, Washington

I/We, the undersigned, having read all the requirements of this call for bids, together with all the special and supplemental conditions, specifications, do agree thereto in every particular, and will furnish all labor and materials specified herein necessary for and incidental to the completion of the work in a workmanlike manner for the sum of:

_____Dollars ($_____)
(Base Bid shall be shown numerically and in writing)

ALTERNATE BIDS:

Alternate Bid No. 1: Water main and fire hydrants   Add $_____

Alternate Bid No. 2: Brick Pavers at Plaza   Add $_____

Alternate Bid No. 3: Plumbing Fixture Upgrade   Add $_____

TIME FOR COMPLETION:
The undersigned hereby agrees to complete all the work under the Base Bid (and accepted alternates) within 270 calendar days after the date of the Owner's letter of Notice to Proceed.
LIQUIDATED DAMAGES:
The undersigned acknowledges and agrees to abide by all provisions of the "Liquidated Damages" section of the General Conditions as it pertains to the Contractor for all work under this contract. The undersigned further agrees to pay the Owner as liquidated damages the sum of $ 500.00 for each consecutive calendar date that he shall be in default after the time for completion specified herein.

ADDENDUM RECEIPT:
Receipt of the following addenda to the specifications is acknowledged:

Addendum No. _____ Date_____   Addendum No. _____ Date_____

Addendum No. _____ Date_____   Addendum No. _____ Date_____

Figure 3–3A   Example Bid (Proposal) Form

Bid Form, Page 2

MINORITY AND WOMEN'S BUSINESS ENTERPRISE UTILIZATION CERTIFICATION:

To be eligible for award of this contract, the bidder must execute and submit with the bid the certification relation to MWBE Participation. This certification shall be deemed a part of the resulting contract.

The undersigned acknowledges that the goals for the new base bid work have been established for this contract in the amount of:

Minority Business Enterprise (MBE)	$ 225,000.00
Women Business Enterprise (WBE)	$ 125,000.00

The undersigned certifies that if they are the successful bidder on this project, the following MWBE firms will be utilized on the project and compensated in the amounts shown:

		DOLLAR AMOUNT	
FIRM NAME	DESCRIPTION OF UTILIZATION	MBE	WBE

TOTAL PARTICIPATION $_____ $_____

NOTIFICATION:

If written notice of acceptance of this bid is mailed, telegraphed, or delivered to the undersigned within the time limit noted in the contract documents after the date of bid opening, or any time thereafter before the bid is withdrawn, the undersigned will, within ten (10) days after the date of such ,mailing, telegraphing, or delivering of such notice, execute and deliver a contract on the State of Washington Public Works Contract Form.

This bid may be withdrawn at any time prior to the scheduled time for the opening of bids, or any authorized postponement thereof.

Enclosed is a certified check, cashier's check, or bid bond in the amount of 5% of the Base Bid. Bid deposits in cash will not be accepted.

BIDDER INFORMATION:

NAME OF FIRM: _____

SIGNATURE   _____

OFFICIAL CAPACITY _____

ADDRESS   _____

CITY AND STATE   _____ZIP_____

DATE   _____TELEPHONE_____

STATE OF WASHINGTON CONTRACTOR'S LICENSE NO. _____

NOTE: If bidder is a corporation, write State of Corporation below; if a partnership, give full names and addresses of all partners below:

Figure 3–3B   Example Bid (Proposal) Form

General and Supplementary Conditions of the Contract

The General Conditions of the Contract relate to a construction project as rules would relate to a football game. These conditions establish the relationship between the owner, its agents (architects and engineers), and the contractor and define the relationship and responsibilities of the parties to maintain this relationship. The conditions also establish the terms of the legal contract between the owner and contractor.

The Supplementary Conditions to the Contract are additional provisions or modifications to the General Conditions of the Contract that are specific to the particular owner and project.

Together, these form the Conditions of the Contract. All actions of the owner and contractor can be judged for compliance to the Conditions of the Contract. The General Conditions and the Supplementary Conditions of the Contract are the base of reference for determining responsibility—and resulting liability—for actions by either party during the project period.

The use of a standard form of General Conditions of the Contract is common in the construction industry. AIA Form A201 is the most commonly used form in building construction. Public works contracts usually use a custom set of conditions that is prepared for the particular branch of government, such as federal, state, or municipal. Corporate owners often will use a custom-prepared contract. The standard form of contract conditions is widely used, as the provisions are tested and well established. As the General Conditions of the Contract appear in preprinted form, they are occasionally included only by reference in the project manual. A copy of the General Conditions of the Contract and the accompanying contract agreement (AIA Form A101) should be readily available to the project manager and superintendent at all times for reference, whether bound in the project manual or not. Because there are several standard General Conditions of the Contract, the project management team must be aware of the particular form for their project. All project performance must comply with the General Conditions of the Contract and the modifications contained in the Supplementary Conditions.

As the basis for the legal contract between the owner and contractor, the General Conditions of the Contract is a very important document. Each sentence in the General Conditions and the Supplementary Conditions can have an impact on the construction project. Complete understanding of these documents is essential to project management. Because the purpose of this section of the book is to introduce the reader to various documents, a detailed discussion of the Conditions of the Contract is not included herein. The reader is encouraged, however, to carefully read and study the Conditions of the Contract that will be used, such as AIA Form A201.

The following is a list of the type of information contained in the General Conditions of the Contract:

- Definitions of the documents and their use in the construction project

- The rights and responsibilities of the owner, including information to furnish the contractor, fee payment, right to stop work, and the right to carry out the work

- The rights and responsibilities of the contractor, including the scope of work, supervision responsibilities, schedules, shop drawings and submittals, cutting/patching, and project cleanup

- Administration of the contract, including the responsibilities of the architect, engineer, and construction manager

- Procedures for claims and disputes during the contract, including method of dispute resolution

- Provisions regarding the use of subcontracts, including the contractor's responsibility for subcontractors

- Provisions allowing the owner use of separate contracts

- Provisions concerning changes in the work, including procedures for facilitating changes

- Provisions involving the timely completion of the project

- Payment procedures and methods

- Provisions regarding the completion of the contract

- Protection of persons and property related to the execution of the contract

- Provisions requiring insurance, including liability and property coverage

- Provisions requiring performance and payment bonds

- Provisions relating to testing, inspection, and correction of work

- Provisions for the termination of the contract

The Supplementary Conditions contain additional provisions and modifications to the General Conditions. A few examples of some modifications made in the Supplementary Conditions include the following:

- AIA Form A201, General Conditions of the Contract, which specifies arbitration as the remedy to dispute resolution. Some owners, due to their governing rules and regulations, cannot use arbitration as a remedy but must seek relief in the courts, in litigation. The Supplementary Conditions, then, would modify that section of the General Conditions.

- AIA Form A201 requires property insurance on the project itself (builder's risk insurance) to be carried by the owner. Many owners prefer that the contractor carry this insurance with a provision in the Supplementary Conditions modifying the General Conditions.

- AIA Form A201 does not contain specific monetary levels of insurance that the contractor is required to carry for the contract. The specific levels, such as "combined single limit, $1,000,000 per occurrence," are contained in the Supplementary Conditions.

- Prevailing wage rates, as determined by the public agency, also will be included in the Supplementary Conditions.

As the General Conditions and Supplementary Conditions are separate sections of the project manual, the project manager may want to annotate the General Conditions, indicating which articles and paragraphs have been modified by the Supplementary Conditions. Some contractors will "cut and paste" the provisions of the Supplementary Conditions into the General Conditions to provide a comprehensive set of Conditions of the Contract. By integrating these conditions, the contractor has a complete and quick reference for particular project situations.

Additional Information to Bidders

Many project manuals will include information to bidders that is not considered a contract document. The most common piece of information to bidders is the geotechnical or soils report. Because this report is prepared for use by the architect and engineer in determining the design of the foundations and not specifically for the contractor's use, the soils report is normally furnished only as information, without designation as a contract document. This information, however, may be the only available subsurface information. The contractor is responsible for making decisions about the information reasonably available. Many project manuals reference the soil reports, relating that they are available at the architect's and engineer's offices for examination.

Divisions 1–48, Technical Specification

The Technical Specification, which relates to labor, material, equipment, and procedures to accomplish the required construction work, is usually divided into 49 divisions as per MasterFormat (2004) published by the Construction Specifications Institute (CSI). MasterFormat is commonly used for most building construction specifications in the United States and Canada. This classification system has replaced the 16-Division format. There are some categories reserved for future items. The current specification divisions are the following:

Division 01 General Requirements

Division 02 Existing Conditions

Division 03 Concrete

Division 04 Masonry

Division 05 Metals

Division 06 Wood, Plastics, and Composites

Division 07 Thermal and Moisture Protection

Division 08 Openings

Division 09 Finishes

Division 10 Specialties

Division 11 Equipment

Division 12 Furnishings

Division 13 Special Construction

Division 14 Conveying Systems

Division 21 Fire Suppression

Division 22 Plumbing

Division 23 Heating, Ventilating, and Air Conditioning

Division 25 Integrated Automation

Division 26 Electrical

Division 27 Communications

Division 28 Electronic Safety and Security

Division 31 Earthwork

Division 32 Exterior Improvements

Division 33 Utilities

Division 34 Transportation

Division 35 Waterway and Marine Construction

Division 40 Process Integration

Division 41 Material Processing and Handling Equipment

Division 42 Process Heating, Cooling, and Drying

Division 43 Process Gas & Liquid Handling, Purification, & Storage Equipment

Division 44 Pollution Control Equipment

Division 45 Industry-Specific Manufacturing Equipment

Division 48 Electrical Power Generation

More detailed items, known as broad-scope and narrow-scope sections, are contained within each division. The CSI suggests a six-digit numbering system for these items. A typical broad-scope item is 033000, Cast-in-place Concrete. The first two digits indicate the division, which in this case would be Division 3, Concrete. The other four numbers indicate the broad- and narrow-scope sections for the item. Under the broad-scope classification of 033000, Cast-in-place Concrete, the following narrow-scope sections are standard:

033100 Structural Concrete

033300 Architectural Concrete

033400 Low-Density Concrete

033500 Concrete Finishing

033700 Specially Placed Concrete

033800 Post-Tensioned Concrete

033900 Concrete Curing

Knowledge of the organization of each specification will help project management personnel quickly and easily access appropriate information. For example, a field engineer who wants to find the specification on curing compound would look in Division 03, Concrete, Section 033000, Cast-in-place Concrete, with the material specification in section 033900, Concrete Curing. This organizational system strives to group items of similar properties, not to create work packages or subcontract packages. A typical subcontract may contain several broad-scope areas; for example, a floor covering subcontract might include the following broad-scope sections: 096400, Wood Flooring; 096500, Resilient Flooring; and 096800, Carpet.

Division 1, General Requirements

The General Requirements section specifies project-related overhead items for the particular project. The majority of these items are general items in that they relate to all phases of the work rather than an individual activity or a subcontract. This section specifies the necessary project facilities that are anticipated to complete the work. This division will relate to meetings, submittal requirements, construction schedule requirements, testing services, supervision requirements, temporary facilities, cleaning, and project closeout and warranty requirements. The majority of the cost items in this section would be included as "direct overhead" or "general conditions costs" for the contractor.

Some of the items included in this section are the following:

- Insurance and bond requirements, including procedures for submittal and completion

- Allowances (specific amounts to be included in the bid for items of work)

- Supervision and coordination requirements

- Field engineering and layout requirements

- Project meeting requirements, including meeting types, frequency, and minutes responsibility

- Submittal requirements for shop drawings, material data, material samples, photographs, and schedules

- Construction schedule requirements, including schedule type and procurement schedule

- Quality control requirements, including field testing services

- Temporary facilities, including temporary utilities, heat, field offices, barricades, and other temporary construction elements

- Temporary controls, including traffic, noise, and security

- Cleaning, including progress and final cleaning

- Closeout procedures and requirements, including operation and maintenance manuals, warranties, and certifications

This division is effectively used to prepare a checklist of required submittals early in the project and of closeout requirements at the end of the project. The contractor should assume that the owner intends that all of the procedures in this division will be completed. The information provided here provides a guide for the minimum overhead required for the project.

Divisions 2–48, Technical Specifications

The technical specification in Divisions 2–48 generally describes the products, equipment, and systems that are intended to be installed during the project. These specifications usually describe products that are shown on the drawings; however, there are some products that will be required and not shown.

The most common format for the technical specification is the "three-part" format consisting of Part 1, General; Part 2, Products; and Part 3, Execution. All three parts contain important information for the contractor to ensure that the proper product and systems are installed.

Part 1, General

This part contains several essential items that can help determine the scope of the product required. Included are the following components:

Related Work Specified Elsewhere: This describes other sections where related work is specified. For example, if the section being examined is section 033000, Cast-in-place Concrete, "related work specified elsewhere" would appear as follows:

Section 031000, Concrete Formwork

Section 032000, Concrete Reinforcement

Section 055000, Metal Fabrications

Description of Work: This normally is a short description of the work included under the section. For Cast-in-place Concrete, the "description of work" would appear as follows:

Cast-in-place concrete footings, foundation walls, walls, structural slabs, slabs-on-grade, and exterior concrete in location and dimension as shown in the architectural and structural drawings.

Quality Assurance: Several items can be included in this subsection, including Qualification of Manufacturer, Qualification of Workmen, Codes and Standards, and Inspection and Testing By Independent Laboratory. Not all products will require all of these items.

Submittals: This is a guide for submittals for particular products. For Cast-in-place Concrete, the submittals required would appear as follows:

Ready Mix Concrete: name of supplier; mix design for each type of concrete

Admixtures: product data, including name and address of manufacturer and supplier

Membranes: product data, including name and address for manufacturer and supplier

Product Delivery/Storage/Handling: This subsection would detail any special handling of the product.

Part 2, Products

This section details the products intended for the project. They may be generically described.

Curing and Sealing Coating: Clear, liquid acrylic based polymer compound for curing and sealing concrete slabs.

The product also may be specified using a brand name. To encourage competition, products often are specified with the brand name and the phrase "or approved equal." A procedure is usually specified in the Instructions to Bidders upon submitting a request for substitution prior to the bid. Using the brand name when specifying the product, the aforementioned specification would appear as follows:

Curing and Sealing Coating: "KURE-N-SEAL," manufactured by Sonneborn Building Products, Minneapolis, Minnesota, or approved equal.

Sufficient information should be provided in the specification to order the material. Care must be taken by the contractor to assure that the product desired is being furnished. Some products have true equal substitutions, and others do not. The architect's approval of a product helps ensure its acceptance, but the product still must perform as well as the specified standard.

Part 3, Execution

The construction documents rarely provide complete installation instructions for products and systems. The execution section may be as simple as "Follow manufacturer's instructions." In some instances, particularly with new or sensitive products or usage, there may be step-by-step instructions for installation. Generally, the contractor is assumed to have the expertise for installation of the material and the use of appropriate means and methods.

The execution phase can include information about suitable substrate, necessary preparatory work, tolerances of installation, quality of workmanship, type of finish, special techniques, weather and environmental limits, environmental constraints, curing and drying time, cleaning, and other necessary steps to achieve the desired product level.

The information contained in this section can be used as quality control checklists. The superintendent and project manager should carefully review this section for all subcontract work as well. Careful coordination of the work in progress to the specified requirements will substantially reduce punch lists at the end of the project.

Addenda

Addenda are bulletins of additional information that are germane to the contract documents issued during the bid period. This information is added to the contract documents after their completion and prior to the contract being awarded. Information contained in the addenda is considered part of the contract documents, and an acknowledgment of receipt of the addenda and inclusion of the information in the bid is required on the bid form.

The information contained in the addenda includes the following types:

- Clarification or correction of information contained in the contract documents. These clarifications result from a review by the designer, owner, and bidders. Answers to questions asked during the bid period are clarified in the addenda to provide the same clarification to all bidders. These clarifications can relate to both the project manual and drawings. Written and graphical clarifications are frequently made to make the documents more understandable to bidders.

- Approval of substitutions. Approval of substitutions for specified materials, usually listed "or approved equal." Items approved in the addenda are acceptable for use in the project.

- Additional information. Additional information is often distributed in the addenda. This could include supplementary specifications, drawings, or any other details relating to the contract documents.

As the information in the addenda becomes part of the contract documents, care should be taken to incorporate it into the contract documents used on the jobsite. Many contractors "cut and paste" the items of the addenda into the appropriate locations in the project manual and drawings. Merely including the addenda with the project manual rather than pasting the items into the documents in their relative locations is usually not effective, as the addenda tend to be misplaced. All documents used on the jobsite should be up to date, with the addenda and change order items noted in the appropriate locations.

The Drawings

The set of contract drawings has several sections, depending upon the nature of the project. Most commercial building projects will have, as a minimum, the following sections:

- Civil engineering and site survey documents, usually identified by a "C" designation

- Architectural drawings, usually identified by an "A" designation

- Structural engineering drawings, usually identified by an "S" designation

- Mechanical engineering drawings, usually identified by an "M" designation

- Electrical engineering drawings, usually identified by an "E" designation

Additional sections are added for special construction areas, when applicable, such as landscape architecture, commercial kitchen equipment, industrial equipment, detention equipment, and many other special construction considerations.

The drawings and project manual are considered a full set of documents. If something is shown or described once, in any of the drawings or contract documents, it is assumed to be covered by the documents, even though it may not be referenced in relating areas. Thorough knowledge of all of the documents is essential for contractor personnel.

Civil Engineering and Site Survey

These drawings are concerned with civil engineering concerns on the site, such as site drainage, site utilities, roads, bridges, and other related items. Plan views, contour drawings, cross sections, and details are usually contained in this section. Surveys of the construction site also are included. An existing site survey and the survey information for the constructed site could be shown as separate plans or could be included on the same plan drawing, with different designations for existing and new contours. These drawings normally are drawn in "engineer's scale," at 10, 20, 30, 40, 50, or 100 feet to the inch.

The information contained on these drawings usually is used for site layout, including location of site features and elevations. The contractor's surveyor, whether a licensed surveyor or the contractor's field engineer, will use information on these drawings to establish benchmarks and related elevations. Dimensions from these drawings often are used with larger-scale architectural drawings to establish the location of roads, improvements, and structures on the site.

Architectural Drawings

The architectural drawings normally are prepared by the architectural firm, occasionally with the consultant's input. The architectural drawings relate primarily to the buildings and structures, describing the building's location, size, form, systems, and materials. These drawings are always indicated with an "A" prefix. Several different numerical systems are found, such as A1, A2, and A1.1.2, A.2.1.2, as well as several other methods. Generally, architectural drawings include the following sections, usually in the sequence listed:

1. **Index, symbols, abbreviations, notes, location map:** The first one or two pages, after the title sheet, list this general information. The drawing index usually lists the drawings in the set and the type of information contained on the drawings. This index is convenient for individuals who are not particularly familiar with the specific project drawings. Most drawings list standard symbols and abbreviations, which usually do not list special symbols and abbreviations specific to the type project. The notes, however, should relate to the particular project. Some of the notes on the introductory sheets can contain information pertinent to the building permit for the project. Several project location maps may be included, with increasing detail.

2. **Site plans and details:** When civil engineering drawings are not necessary, the architectural drawings will include a site plan, locating the improvements and structures on the site. Contours, indicating elevations, often are included in these plans. Irrigation and planting plans also may be included.

3. **Demolition plans:** Indications of demolition areas often are included in the architectural drawings. These plans may illustrate large demolition areas or selective demolition, such as partition removal. For interior renovations, the removed partitions are often shown as dotted lines on the floor plan, with new partitions shown in heavier, solid lines.

4. **Floor plans:** It is customary to show every floor plan applicable to the project, even when the floors are similar. Floor plans should show: wall locations and types, window openings, door openings, dimensions (where necessary), cabinets, equipment, stairs, room numbers, detail and section locations, and various materials. Most material designations are usually shown on the sections and details.

5. **Roof plans:** These plans indicate drainage, equipment, penetrations, hatches, and so on.

6. **Ceiling plans:** These plans usually are reflected plans, as though the floor were a mirror and the ceiling an image in the mirror, coinciding in orientation with the floor plan. Ceiling plans indicate penetrations, light fixtures, grid configurations, and material types when there are a variety of materials within the same room.

7. **Building sections:** These sections are normally "cuts" through the building, indicated by symbols on the floor plan. They are usually fairly small-scale drawings, showing the full structure of the building. These drawings do not show details but rather provide a view of the relationship of building elements. By studying the building sections and elevations, an individual can visualize the three dimensions of the structure rather than the two dimensions of the floor plans.

8. **Wall sections:** These sections are larger-scale vertical cuts through the building that show and name the materials in the walls, floors, and roofs. These sections are very important when determining what materials and systems will be used in the building and the relationships of the material and systems.

9. **Exterior elevations:** The exterior elevations are two-dimensional drawings of the exterior of the buildings. These drawings illustrate a vertical picture of the building, showing materials, windows, doors, control joints, dimensions, and other information pertinent to the construction of the building. These are not renderings of the building but two-dimensional drawings. Occasionally, a three-dimensional rendering is available, either on the cover of the drawings or perhaps at the architect's office. Models of the building are occasionally built to convey to the owner the spatial aspects of the building and may be observed to obtain a three-dimensional perspective of the building. Occasionally, isometric drawings of specific areas will be included in the drawings to convey relationships not available from the customary two-dimensional drawings. Three-dimensional drawings, usually produced by computer-aided drafting (CAD), occasionally are used to illustrate the volume of the building elements.

10. **Schedules:** Schedules, in tabular form, often are included in the drawings. Some common schedules include door, window, louver, and finish. The schedules relate each particular feature, such as the door, window, or wall, to the material, style, detail, and color. They are commonly found in the project manual, usually near the applicable item specification, as well as on the drawings.

11. **Large-scale floor plans and accompanying sections and details:** Some areas will have large-scale drawings to show the complexities of the particular area. These drawings are usually found for toilet rooms, stairways, escalators and elevators, lobbies, and special-use areas.

12. **Exterior details:** Details of materials and systems, particularly at connections, are referenced from the plans, sections, and elevations.

13. **Interior elevations and details:** Interior details will relate to equipment, millwork, cabinetwork, and finish work shown on the plans and sections. These elevations and details are used primarily for finish work and for coordination of the various elements in the finishes of the facility.

Structural Drawings

The structural drawings represent the structural elements, such as foundations and structural frame. These normally are prepared by a structural engineer, either in-house with the architectural firm or on a consulting basis. The structural design is coordinated with the architectural aspects of the building. Structural drawings usually have definitive dimensions for the foundations and structural elements, both horizontally and vertically. These and the architectural drawings should be continuously coordinated, however, as both may contain information necessary for the location and construction of the building elements. The structural drawing is the primary document used in establishing the building's structural system and thus the basic dimensional attributes of the building.

The following elements usually are included in the structural drawings:

1. **Structural notes:** These notes are normally more specific in regard to the material strength and tolerances than are those in the project manual. The notes are often exactly related to the project. Typical details also are included in the notes. Many typical details are used in the structural drawings, relying on the shop drawings to coordinate conditions. The shop drawings are done by the contractor, subcontractor, or fabricator and are reviewed by the structural engineer.

2. **Foundation plan:** The foundation plan should indicate all subgrade elements, including piles, caissons, footings, and foundation walls. References are made to details.

3. **Framing plans for floors and roof:** The structural drawings will examine each floor structure, showing the necessary structure. In some structural drawings, the different system types, such as concrete, steel, and wood, will be separated. Some drawings will, however, combine all structural systems on the same drawings.

4. **Elevations and sections:** These structural drawings provide the three-dimensional aspect with the necessary elevations.

5. **Details:** These drawings provide the details of the systems, particularly connections of materials and systems. Structural details are normally provided for stair systems.

6. **Schedules:** Tabular schedules of structural elements, such as joists, beams, deck, and other elements, are commonly shown in these drawings.

Mechanical Drawings

Mechanical drawings normally include both plumbing and heating, ventilation, and air conditioning (HVAC) drawings. These drawings usually are accomplished through a mechanical engineering firm, which often acts as a consultant to the architect. A number of different subcontractors may use mechanical drawings, including the plumbing subcontractor, HVAC contractor, fire protection subcontractor, temperature control subcontractor, and other subcontractors or third-tier subcontractors. Information about the other drawing sections that is pertinent to the mechanical drawings is available. Therefore, full sets of the construction documents should be distributed to all subcontractors to facilitate information.

Although mechanical and electrical drawings use site and floor plans similar to architectural drawings, many mechanical and electrical drawings are much more diagrammatic than are architectural drawings. Plumbing riser diagrams, for instance, are not to scale or detail but indicate the plumbing system in a manner consistent with the plumbing craft. Additionally, different symbols and abbreviations are used in mechanical drawings rather than in other parts of the documents. A legend to the symbols is usually included in the mechanical drawings for clarification.

The following drawings are often included in mechanical drawings:

1. Mechanical site plans indicate the site utilities, such as water, sanitary sewer, storm sewer, and natural gas from the connection source to the building. Occasionally, the mechanical and electrical site plans will be combined.

2. Floor, roof, and reflected plans indicate the location of fixtures and piping.

3. Large-scale plans for mechanical and equipment rooms indicate equipment location, piping, and ductwork.

4. Floor plans indicate duct work locations.

5. Diagrams, such as plumbing riser diagrams, indicate piping flow and control diagrams.

6. Details are indicated for connections and special situations.

7. Fire protection drawings indicate fire risers, piping, and head locations. Because fire sprinkler systems normally are designed by the fire protection subcontractor, these drawings may be very diagrammatic and indicate the parameters of the system.

8. Schedules are indicated for equipment, piping, and fixtures. Depending upon the mechanical engineer, these schedules might be included in the project manual rather than on the drawings.

Electrical Drawings

The electrical drawings, like the mechanical drawings, are particularly diagrammatic. The former are also part of the entire set of documents and should not be separated from the documents. They also have their own symbols and abbreviations, which are usually defined within. Numerous systems are shown on the electrical drawings, such as fire alarm, communication, or security, which may be shown on separate drawings or integrated with the electrical drawings.

Electrical drawings will usually include the following:

1. Notes, symbols, abbreviations, and standard details
2. Site plan, indicating the utilities that connect to the building, such as power, TV cable, and telephone
3. Floor plans showing separate floor plans for power and lighting, though both may be included on the same drawing for smaller projects
4. Diagrams, such as power riser diagrams
5. Details
6. Schedules, such as panels, devices, special systems, and light fixtures
7. Special system drawings, such as intercom, security, centralized clock, TV cable, and data cable systems

Use of the Construction Documents

The construction professional uses the construction documents each day in managing the construction project. These documents are used for layout, clarification, direction, checklists, compliance inspections, communications, and verification in every stage of the construction process. The construction superintendent and field engineer need to know the documents in detail to be able to reference them quickly and efficiently. Some contractors will add reference tabs to the project manual to facilitate quick access to relevant information.

As previously mentioned, it is extremely important to have a complete and updated set of documents, such as the project manual, drawings, addenda, and change orders, at the jobsite, but other documents are essential for reference as well. Submittals and shop drawings should be complete, approved, and available at the jobsite. Product literature that is applicable to the project also is important. Current safety information, such as safety regulations, safety manuals, and Material Safety Data Sheets, should also be available. Copies of the local building codes and regulations should be readily available for reference by field management personnel, as should copies of subcontract agreements, detailing the responsibility of each subcontractor.

There are, of course, thousands of applications of construction document use and even more variations, depending upon the contractor and the situations on the jobsite. The following section illustrates the use of construction documents during a building project.

Familiarization with a Project

Construction professionals often are concerned with more than one construction project. Quick familiarization usually is necessary to provide a broad overview of the project, which enables one to intelligently interact with other workers. Obtaining detailed knowledge about the project requires considerable time and involvement. Steps for quick familiarization with a project, using the construction documents, include the following:

1. Review the site plan. Become familiar with the relationship of the structure to the rest of the site. Note the site limitations and access, as well as adjoining property and the relationship of the project to the adjoining property

2. Review the floor plans. Determine a two-dimensional size for the building and its floors

3. Review the building elevations. Determine a three dimensional size (volume of the building). Become familiar with the intended look of the facility. Additional nondocument information, such as renderings or models, may help gain a three dimensional perspective on the building.

4. Review the building sections, relating them to the floor plans and elevations. When reviewing the building sections and larger-scale wall sections, one should begin to understand the type of construction and structure for the building. Review the structural drawings, starting with the foundation plan; then examine the structural system of each floor and the building.

5. Review the mechanical and electrical drawings, determining an overview of the involvement of both areas in the construction.

6. Review the General Requirements section of the specification, determining the special circumstances for the project. Determine the completion date for the project.

7. Depending on the level of involvement with the project, review contractor documents, such as estimate, schedule, subcontracts, and work plan.

Preparing Crew Assignments

Many contractors will prepare "work packages" or "crew packages" to enable the crew to accomplish a task. This package information will vary, but could include the following:

- Drawings or references to drawings that are applicable to the particular task assigned to the crew. Because the document set is cumbersome to use in the field, many contractors condense the drawings into 8½" × 11" pages. These drawings may illustrate the task location, floor plans, sections, and details. Copies of the partial construction documents can be made and given to the crew. When CAD drawings are available, specific areas can be selected and printed on 8½" × 11" paper.

- Technical specification, including material and execution of the material, that can be copied and given to the crew.

- Material list, obtained from the drawings, according to material specification. Purchase order information is also normally included.

- List of necessary tools and equipment, usually determined by the superintendent for the assigned task.

- Information from the estimate and schedule that relates to the situation, such as man-hours available, work time frame, and other cost-related issues.

Problem Solving

Construction documents are used as a reference for solving problems that occur on the jobsite. They are continually referred to for everyday clarifications, particularly when confusion arises about the direction of the work. Usually, reviewing the documents clarifies the situation. Occasionally, further details are needed from the architect and engineer. The following section illustrates how essential construction documents are in problem solving (Figure 3–4).

Figure 3–4   Construction Problem Solving
iStock.com/PeterAustin

Example 1

During excavation for the building site, the excavation subcontractor encounters an existing large concrete footing about 10 feet below the existing grade and about 10 feet above the finish grade of the excavation. The subcontractor notifies the contractor's field engineer about the footing immediately upon discovery, explaining that this footing was not expected and probably would require additional work to remove it. Because the area surrounding the footing needs to be excavated, the field engineer directs the subcontractor to continue excavation to discover the size, all three dimensions, of the footing. The following steps could be taken to determine the extent of the problem and if additional payment is appropriate for this work:

1. The field engineer would immediately look at the construction drawings to examine the site, floor, and structural foundation plans to find any reference to the existing footing. In this case, the field engineer does not find any reference. The field engineer would then look in the specifications, Section 020100, General Requirements—Sitework; Section 02100, Site Preparation and Demolition; and Section 02200, Earthwork. No specific mention of the existence or removal of the concrete footing is made here. The notes in the structural drawings also are examined, again with no reference to the specific condition.

2. The next step the field engineer takes is examining the geotechnical report, contained in the project manual as information only. The boring reports are reviewed to determine whether any concrete was encountered in subsurface exploration. Four borings, 20 feet in depth, were taken on the building site. All four borings indicated a well-graded gravel strata between 7.5 feet and 15.3 feet below the existing grade. No mention is made of concrete footing in the boring report, although none of the borings were made in the location of the concrete footing.

(continued)

3. It is apparent to the contractor that this extra work is not covered in the construction documents. The field engineer then looks in the General Conditions and Supplementary Conditions to determine the procedures to follow for pursuing a change order. The field engineer examines the following clause:

> AIA form A201, General Conditions, 4.3.6: "If conditions are encountered at the site which are (1) subsurface or otherwise concealed physical conditions which differ materially from those indicated in the Contract Documents, or (2) unknown physical conditions of an unusual nature, which differ materially from those ordinarily found to exist and generally recognized as inherent in construction activities of the character provided for in the Contract Documents, then notice by the observing party shall be given to the other party promptly before conditions are disturbed and in no event later than 21 days after first observance of the conditions. The Architect will promptly investigate such conditions and, if they differ materially and cause an increase or decrease in the Contractor's cost of, time required for, performance of any part of the Work, will recommend an equitable adjustment in the Contract Sum or Contract time, or both."

The field engineer, upon direction from the superintendent, will then write a Request for Information (RFI) to the architect and engineer to notify them about the problem (see chapter 5 for a detailed explanation about Requests for Information). The field engineer could use the following description of the problem:

> On Monday June 12, 20xx, at 10:15 A.M. the excavation subcontractor encountered an existing concrete footing, 4'0" wide × 2'0" deep, at approximately grid 2-B at about 10'0" below existing grade. At this time, the extent of the footing is not known, and excavation is continuing to reveal the full extent of the footing affecting excavation at the building site.
>
> We have examined the following documents and find no mention of this footing: Site Plan, A-2; Basement Floor Plan, A-4; Structural Foundation Plan, S-2; Structural Notes, S-1; Sections 020100, 02100, and 02200 of the specification. We also have examined the Geotechnical Report, prepared by GO Engineering, Inc., and also find no indication of this footing.
>
> We feel that this concrete footing is a concealed condition, with no available information to the contractor prior to bidding concerning this footing. Our excavation contractor has indicated to us that there will be additional costs incurred to remove this footing. We will notify you of the extra costs when the full extent of the footing is known.
>
> As we feel that the removal of this concrete footing is additional work to our contract, we will not remove the footing until directed. Please respond as quickly as possible.

4. The field engineer sends the RFI to the architect via a fax. The architect then carefully reviews the construction documents and visits the site to verify the situation. After carefully examining the facts related to the problem, the architect discusses the problem with the owner's representative, and the owner decides to proceed with a change proposal from the contractor.

> The architect faxes a reply to the contractor:

> We have determined that the concrete footing mentioned in RFI-010, June 12, 20xx, must be removed from the building excavation location. Please prepare a change proposal for this work.

(continued)

5. The field engineer refers to the General and Supplementary Conditions for information concerning preparation of a change proposal. Paragraph 7.3.3, under Construction Change Directives, AIA Form A201, discusses three types of pricing for a change proposal: an itemized lump-sum proposal for the cost of the work; a unit-price proposal, when an unknown quantity of work needs to be accomplished; and a cost-plus-percentage arrangement, when unknown methods and quantities apply to the change. As the subcontractor has now discovered the length of the footing, 210 L. F., the field engineer decides to prepare an itemized lump-sum proposal and requests the appropriate information from the excavation subcontractor. The Supplementary Conditions for this particular project state,

> In subparagraph 7.3.6, the allowances for the combined overhead and profit included in the total cost to the Owner shall be based on the following schedule:
> For the Contractor, for work performed by the Contractor's own forces, ten percent (10%) of the cost.
> For the Contractor, for work performed by the Contractor's subcontractor, five percent (5%) of the amount due to the Subcontractor.
> For each Subcontractor or Sub-subcontractor involved, for work performed by the Subcontractor's or Sub-subcontractor's own forces, ten percent (10%) of the cost.

The field engineer would then prepare a change proposal, on the appropriate form, as follows:

> Remove and legally dispose of existing unknown concrete footing 4'0" wide, 2'0" deep, 210 L. F.

Excavating Subcontractor:

Labor	Operator	16 hrs.	@ $ 28.90	$ 462.40
	Laborer	16 hrs.	@ $ 24.63	394.08
Equipment 235C		16 hrs.	@ $120.00	1,920.00
Extra Trucking		6 hrs.	@ $ 40.00	240.00
Tipping Fees		124 tons	@ $ 50.00	6,200.00
Subcontractor Cost				9,216.48
Subcontractor Markup				921.65
Subcontractor Total				10,138.13
Contractor Markup				506.91
Total, Change Proposal				$10,645.04

As this work will delay the excavation work, which is on the critical path, we will also request a Two (2) calendar day extension to the contract.

6. The architect, upon receipt of the change proposal and after approval by the owner's representative, will issue a Contract Change Directive, in accordance to the General and Supplementary Conditions of the Contract.

Example 2

In the project described under Example 1, exterior and interior partitions have been framed. The insulation subcontractor is on the site and completing the insulation for exterior walls and ceilings. The insulation subcontractor foreman, in speaking to the field engineer, has mentioned that his crew is preparing to leave the jobsite, as their work is complete. The field engineer asks about installation of the acoustical insulation in the interior partitions. The insulation subcontractor foreman replies that the acoustical insulation is normally supplied and installed by the drywall sub-contractor, as the acoustical insulation is friction fit and needs one side of drywall complete to install it. The field engineer tells the insulation subcontractor foreman that he thinks the acoustical insulation is in the insulation contract, but he will verify it. At the jobsite office, the field engineer takes the following steps:

1. The field engineer telephones the project manager for the insulation subcon-tractor. The project manager confirms that he does not intend to furnish and install the acoustical insulation.

2. The field engineer checks the subcontract agreement with the insulation subcontract. Under description of work, the subcontract agreement reads,

   > Furnish and install insulation, as per Section 07200, Building Insulation, of the project manual. Furnish rigid perimeter insulation, no installation. (The subcon-tract agreement references all applicable work shown on the complete set of con-struction documents.)

3. The field engineer checks the subcontract agreement regarding the drywall subcontractor. There is no mention of Section 07200 in the drywall subcontract.

4. The field engineer examines Section 072100, Thermal Insulation. The following clauses are applicable to the situation:

   > Part 2, Products, Paragraph 2.04: Acoustical Batt Insulation: Fiberglass unfaced batts for wood stud walls where noted A. B. I. on drawings. Flame spread and smoke developed ratings of less than 25 and a noncombustible rating in accor-dance with ASTM E 136.
   >
   > Part 3, Execution, Paragraph 3.02.C: Friction fit acoustical batts into place between wood studs. Use multiple thickness as required to completely fill wall cavities. Batts shall be installed in walls indicated on drawings by A. B. I. designation.

5. The field engineer then examines the drawings to be sure that acoustical insulation is shown by the designation A. B. I. On drawings A2.1 and A2.2, the interior partitions on both the first and second floors are shown with a pattern, which in the legend on each page indicates A. B. I. for that wall type. The interior wall sections on A3.4.1 also indicate acoustical insulation.

6. As the drawings show acoustical insulation in definite locations, Section 07200 specifies the acoustical insulation, Section 07200 is listed in the subcontract agreement with the insulation subcontractor without exception concerning acoustical insulation, and the field engineer is certain that the acoustical insulation is required under the insulation subcontract. The field

(continued)

engineer then writes a letter to the insulation subcontractor project manager, faxing it immediately. The letter cites the subcontract agreement, the specification, and the location on the drawings.

7. The field engineer telephones the insulation subcontractor project manager after the fax is sent. The insulation subcontractor, although not particularly happy, agrees to install the acoustical insulation.

8. The next morning, the field engineer observes the insulation subcontractor delivering and installing the acoustical insulation.

In this example, the field engineer was able to effectively reference the construction documents and solve a dispute that could have delayed the project and increased the cost to the contractor.

Summary

The construction documents, although not prepared by the contractor, are an essential reference to the contractor when constructing the project. A thorough knowledge of these documents is necessary for the construction professional. As construction documents are quite complex, the construction professional should know where to locate the answers to questions in the documents. Construction documents should contain the following components:

- Advertisement/Invitation to Bid
- Instructions to Bidders
- Bid Forms and Certifications
- General Conditions of the Construction Contract
- Supplementary Conditions of the Construction Contract
- Additional Information for Bidders
- Technical Specifications
- Addenda
- Drawings (including civil, architectural, structural, mechanical, electrical, and specialty)

The documents can be used for the construction and organization of the project, as a general reference for all questions, and as an aid in solving problems on the jobsite.

Review Questions

1. What are some items of information that contractors might obtain from the Advertisement/Invitation to Bid that would influence their decision to bid a project?

2. What type of information is found in the Instructions to Bidders?

3. What is the purpose of the General Conditions of the Contract?

4. What is the standard form of the General Conditions of the Contract used in building construction?

5. What is the purpose of the Supplementary Conditions?

6. Name the 16 Divisions of the MasterFormat for the technical specifications.

7. What type of information is specified in Section 1, General Requirements?

8. What are the three parts of a technical specification section?

9. What are addenda?

10. Organize the following drawing types into the most likely organization in a set of construction drawings:

    Mechanical

    Index, Symbols, General Information

    Electrical

    Structural Drawings

    Site Plans

    Wall Sections

    Schedules

    Interior Elevations

    Roof Plans

    Building Sections

    Floor Plans

    Ceiling Plans

11. Assume that you are the field engineer on a project. The foreman for a painting contractor is unsure of the paint colors for the walls in office 110. Trace your steps to use the construction documents to find the answers.

Chapter 4

Submittals, Samples, and Shop Drawings

Objectives

This chapter discusses the important use of submittals, samples, and shop drawings in during the construction process. The objectives of this chapter are to:

- Illustrate the purpose of submittals in the construction process
- Describe the types of submittals used in the construction process
- Evaluate the information expected in submittals
- Outline the submittal process
- Review the use of the procurement schedule to control submittals to meet the construction schedule
- Recall the uses of submittals during the construction process

The construction documents, specifically the technical specifications, require the contractor to submit product data, samples, and shop drawings to the architect and engineer for approval. This is one of the first steps that is taken by the contractor after execution of the construction contract and issuance of the Notice to Proceed. Shop drawings, material data, and samples generally are referred to as **submittals**. The submittal process is very important, because it directly relates to the quality, schedule, and ultimately the overall success of the project. The submittal process can be complex because there are literally thousands of different materials, fabrications, and equipment used in a construction project.

Product data submittals, samples, and shop drawings are required primarily for the architect and engineer to verify that the correct products will be installed on the project. This process also gives the architect and sub-consultants the opportunity to select colors, patterns, and types of material that were not chosen prior to completion of the construction drawings. This is an occasion for the architect not to select different materials than specified but rather to clarify the selection within the quality level indicated in the specification. For materials requiring fabrication, such as reinforcing and structural steel, the architect and engineer need to verify details furnished by the fabricator. The contractor also uses this information in installation, using dimensions and installation data from the submittal.

Types of Submittals

Product Data Submittal

The **product data submittal** usually consists of the manufacturer's product information. The information that is necessary for such a submittal includes:

- Manufacturer, trade name, model, or type number: This information is necessary to compare the submitted item with the specified products and acceptable products listed in the specification and addenda.

- Description of use and performance characteristics: Information should be furnished describing the normal use and expected performance of the product. Both the architect and the contractor should review this information to confirm that the product is appropriate for the intended use.

- Size and physical characteristics: The size and physical characteristics, such as adjustment capabilities, should be reviewed by both the contractor and the architect. The contractor has the most available information for comparing adjoining materials and equipment. The contractor also needs to know the size and weight of the equipment for lifting and handling considerations.

- Finish characteristics: The architect should review the available finishes and select the appropriate finish, if the finish was not previously specified in the documents. The contractor should confirm that finish requirements in the specification are being met by the product.

- Specific request for jobsite dimensions: Some material is custom-fabricated to job conditions, requiring dimensions from the jobsite. These jobsite dimensions are provided by the contractor, prior to release of the product for manufacture.

Figure 4–1 is an example of a material data submittal.

PRODUCT DATA SUBMITTAL

PROJECT:	Downtown Center Office Building
SUBMITTED BY:	ABC Construction Company
SECTION NO.:	03250
PRODUCT TYPE:	Curing / Sealing Compound
PRODUCT SUBMITTED:	Sonneborn "KURE-N-SEAL"
MANUFACTURER:	Sonneborn Building Products, Minneapolis, MN
PRODUCT STATUS:	Meets ASTM C-309; Approved as equal, Addendum 2, 6/12/2010
PROJECT LOCATION:	Cure/Seal on Concrete floors, Rooms 110, 111, 114, and 116

KURE-N-SEAL

A Clear, Polymeric Liquid Compound That Cures, Seals, and Dustproofs All In One Application. Surfaces To Be Treated Can Be Damp or Dry; Horizontal or Vertical; Interior or Exterior

USE

Kure-N-Seal is specifically designed for curing and sealing freshly placed and finished concrete.

In addition to newly placed concrete floors, Kure-N-Seal is effective on:

> Exposed Aggregate
> Brick Floors and Walls
> Terrazzo
> Older Concrete Surfaces

Kure-N-Seal dries to a tough glossy membrane, resistant to construction traffic and workman abuse, adhesion of mortar droppings and paint, and many chemicals and stains.

Kure-N-Seal is highly resistant to discoloration caused by the effects of sunlight. Surfaces retain their brightness and color for longer periods of time without ugly yellowing.

DESCRIPTION

A liquid acrylic based polymer, Kure-N-Seal contains no oils, saponifiable resins, waxes or chlorinated rubbers.

It is a superior concrete floor sealing compound which, by locking in the moisture in freshly placed concrete and tenaciously adhering to the surface, cures the concrete and creates conditions for achieving maximum hardness of the concrete slab.

Simultaneously, Kure-N-Seal functions as a surface dustproofing sealer — producing a hard film with excellent resistance to traffic abrasion, water spillage, mild acids and alkalies. Helps prevent construction stains on concrete in new buildings.

The degree of gloss to the finish depends upon the porosity of the surface and the number of coats applied.

Note: After thorough curing, floors treated in accordance with directions with a single coat of Kure-N-Seal may be finished with resilient flooring according to the tile manufacturer's recommendations for tile and adhesive.

ADVANTAGES

- Cures, dustproofs and seals in one application.
- Eliminates dirt and construction stains.
- Protects against alkalies and mild acids.
- Quick drying — easy to apply and maintain.
- Construction work continues rapidly and economically.
- For interior and exterior concrete and masonry floors and walls.
- From construction through occupancy, maintenance and cleanup greatly simplified — housekeeping costs greatly reduced.

APPLICATION

New Concrete: Surface is application-ready when it is damp

KURE-N-SEAL — Continued

but not wet and can no longer be marred by walking workmen.

Aged Concrete: Surface must be free of any dust, dirt, and other foreign matter. Use power tools and/or strippers to remove any incompatible sealers or coatings. Cleanse as required.

Apply so as to form a continuous, uniform film by spray, soft-bristle pushbroom, long-nap roller or lambswool applicator. Ordinary garden-type sprayers, using neoprene hose, are recommended for best results.

For curing only, first coat should be applied evenly and uniformly as soon as possible after final finishing. Second coat should be applied when all trades are completed and structure is ready for occupancy.

Reducer 990 is used primarily to thin first coats when spraying or applying to aged floors. It is also used for cleaning tools and equipment with which Kure-N-Seal has been applied.

To seal and dustproof, two coats are required. For sealing new concrete, both coats are applied full strength. On aged concrete, when renovating, dustproofing and sealing, the first coat should be thinned 10% to 15% with Reducer 990.

At normal temperature and humidity, Kure-N-Seal will dry for application of additional coats in approximately two hours. Allow to dry hard...for normal traffic overnight drying. For maximum hardness, drying time of seven days is required.

LIMITATIONS

Kure-N-Seal should not be used on surfaces to receive concrete overlays and/or additional toppings. It can be applied to colored concrete, but mottling may occur. May rubber burn and highlight imperfections of dry concrete surfaces. Not recommended as a release agent or where other sealers or treatments are to be later applied.

Not for use where Kure-N-Seal will be subjected to immersion. Should not be used for a coating or interior lining of concrete tanks and pools.

COMPLIANCES

Kure-N-Seal is recommended for use on Class 1, 2, 3 and 4 concrete floors as classified in Table 1.1, ACI Standard 302-69. Product also meets the requirements for ASTM C-309. Asphalt and Vinyl Asbestos Tile Institute and AASHTO M-148. Available in conformance to Federal Specification TT-C-800A pigmented gray, and 30% solids. USDA approved.

COVERAGE

200 to 600 sq. ft. per gallon depending upon surface and type of application.

COLOR

Transparent

PACKAGING

5 gallon pails (18.93 liters) and 55 gallon drums (208.18 liters).

Figure 4–1 Example Product Data Submittal

Shop Drawings

A **shop drawing** is a drawing or set of drawings produced by the contractor, supplier, manufacturer, subcontractor, or fabricator. Shop drawings are not produced by architects and engineers under their contract with the owner. The shop drawing is the manufacturer's or contractor's drawn version of information shown in the construction documents. The shop drawing normally shows more detail than the construction documents. It is drawn to explain the fabrication of the items to the manufacturer's production crew. The style of the shop drawing is usually very different from that of the architect's drawing. The shop drawing's primary emphasis is on the product or installation and excludes notation concerning other products and installations, unless integration with the subject product is necessary.

Concrete reinforcing is one of the many items requiring specialized shop drawings for the fabrication of the material. Concrete reinforcing is custom-fabricated from 60-foot-long reinforcing bars. The reinforcing bars are cut to length and bent to specific configurations. The shop drawing and accompanying "cut sheet" list the quantity, sizes, lengths, and shapes of the reinforcing bar. This information is provided for review by the structural engineer to ensure that sufficient reinforcing is being supplied; fabrication of the bar by the supplier's shop; an inventory list for the contractor, upon delivery (the typical project has thousands of pieces of reinforcing steel that need to be organized for storage and installation); and placement by the ironworker. The Concrete Reinforcing Steel Institute has developed standard symbols, graphics, and formats for shop drawings and cut sheets that generally are used by reinforcing steel fabricators. Each fabricator, though, will have a particular style for shop drawings and cut sheets, depending on the drafts-people and computer-aided drafting (CAD) systems.

Figures 4–2A and B illustrate a simplified, comparative look at the reinforcing shown on a structural engineering drawing and reinforcing steel shop drawing. Figure 4–2A illustrates the typical information contained in structural drawings of contract documents. Shown is a partial plan view of a concrete footing and foundation, with the referenced Section A-A illustrating the reinforcing that is required for footing WF-1. Typically, dimensions and requirements for reinforcing are shown in the contract drawings.

Figure 4–2B shows the steel reinforcing supplier's shop drawing. The required length of the reinforcing bars is illustrated, as are the number and configuration of dowels and information needed for fabrication and placement of the reinforcing steel.

Each supplier or manufacturer will have specific information that should be included on shop drawings. This information includes the following:

1. **Comparison information for the architect and engineer:** The shop drawings should include information for the architect and engineer to compare to the specifications and drawings. The shop drawing should address the appearance, performance, and prescriptive descriptions in the specifications and construction drawings. The shop drawing often is more detailed than the information shown in the construction documents to give the architect and engineer the opportunity to review the fabricator's version of the product, prior to fabrication. References to the construction documents, drawings, and specifications assist the architect and engineer in their review of the shop drawings. Attachment of manufacturer's material specifications, "catalog cut sheets," and other manufacturer's information may be helpful to accompany these drawings. Because shop drawings facilitate the architect's and engineer's approval of the product, they should be as clear and complete as possible.

2. **Notes of changes or alterations from the construction documents:** Notes concerning changes or differences from the original documents should be made on the shop drawing for the architect's and engineer's approval. Ultimately, they are responsible for changes in these drawings and should have the opportunity to analyze any modifications. A dialogue should occur between the fabricator and the architect and engineer about any areas needing clarification. Successful installations are the result of collaboration between the designer, fabricator, and contractor.

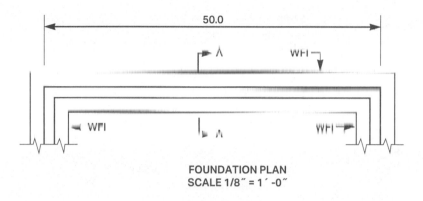

FOUNDATION PLAN
SCALE 1/8″ = 1′ -0″

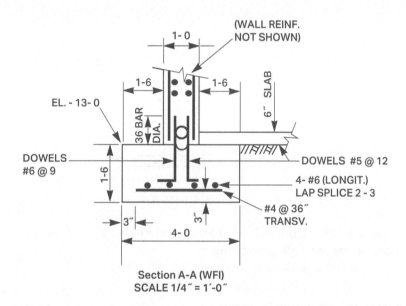

Section A-A (WFI)
SCALE 1/4″ = 1′-0″

Figure 4–2A Comparison of Structural Engineering Drawing
and Reinforcing Steel Shop Drawing

Courtesy of the Concrete Reinforcing Steel Institute

3. **Information needed to fabricate the product:** Dimensions, manufacturing conventions, and special fabrication instructions should be included on the shop drawing. It should be clear to fabrication personnel what will be manufactured from the shop drawing alone. The construction documents are rarely used as a reference in fabrication, with the fabricators relying on the shop drawing for all information.

4. **Indication of dimensions needing verification from the jobsite:** Most jobsite dimensions, such as the dimensions between two surfaces on the jobsite, need to be verified. A dimension may be shown on the construction drawings, but the actual dimension may vary, from very small to large increments, depending on jobsite conditions. It is extremely important that the fabricated item arrive on the jobsite ready to be installed without field modification. Special care must be taken by the contractor to measure and verify dimensions. In new construction, plan dimensions usually are sufficient for ordering many fabricated items such as structural steel or precast concrete. In remodel and renovation work, it is essential that field dimensions be verified prior to fabrication. Some fabricators, such as cabinet and casework suppliers, prefer not to rely on the contractor's verification and will verify the dimensions with their own personnel.

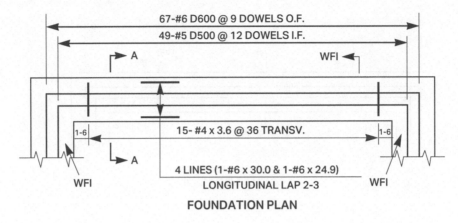

FOUNDATION PLAN

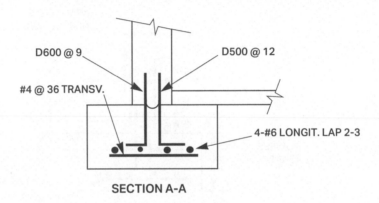

SECTION A-A

Figure 4–2B   **Comparison of Structural Engineering Drawing and Reinforcing Steel Shop Drawing**
Courtesy of the Concrete Reinforcing Steel Institute

5. **Placement or installation information:** Some fabricators and manufacturers will provide symbols, data, or instructions concerning installation. This can include a list of other materials, such as fasteners or adhesives, appropriate to but not included for the product.

6. **Samples:** Some fabrications will require a sample submittal with the shop drawing, primarily for color and texture selection of finishes.

Shop drawings are required, in various forms, depending upon the practice of the architect and engineer. A specific number of copies may be required by the specification. An example distribution of the completed and corrected shop drawing may include the following:

Owner—file or inspection copy

Architect—file copy

Architect—field or inspection copy

Consulting engineer—file copy

Consulting engineer—inspection copy

Contractor—file copy

Contractor—field copy

Supplier—original or one copy

(Total copies = eight)

Because writing comments on 8 to 10 copies is a tedious process and a waste of time for the architect and engineer, many times they will specify other methods for distributing their comments:

1. Submittal of one or two copies of the shop drawing. Corrections are made by the architect and engineer, and the shop drawing is corrected by the supplier; then the appropriate number of copies is distributed. This method can be time consuming, as the shop drawing is not approved until the corrections are made on it.

2. Submittal of a copy that can be reproduced, such as vellum or sepia. The architect and engineer make comments on the reproducible; then copies are distributed. This method facilitates the timely approval and distribution of the shop drawing. Review comments usually are obvious on the reproducible copy. When sepia copies are used, the reproduction of the sepia often is not as clear as a normal blue-line print. Because electronic forms of shop drawings are predominantly used currently, this method is rarely used now.

3. When the supplier and designer have compatible CAD software, the review can be made from a diskette or an electronic transfer. Comments can be made by the designer in a bold font, or changes can be boxed for emphasis.

Quick review is essential during the approval process. Any method that facilitates this, while providing ample opportunity for comment and complete distribution, should be considered. Although a procedure may be specified in the contract drawings, most architects and engineers are open to suggestions and innovations that speed up the process.

Samples

Many products require submission of samples. A **sample** is a physical portion of the specified product. Some samples are full product samples, such as a brick or section of precast concrete, or a partial sample that indicates color or texture. The product sample is often required when several products are acceptable, to confirm the quality and aesthetic level of the material. The size or unit of sample material usually is specified. For some materials, a mock-up or sample panel is necessary. A common example of a sample panel is a brick panel in a large enough mock-up to demonstrate the full appearance of the material. The brick panel might be 4 feet wide by 6 feet high, showing all the brick colors and materials, if there is a required variation in color and size. The sample panel also shows the mortar color and type of joint and, in this case, provides a completed version of the look of the wall that is not available from the brick sample alone.

Samples usually are required for finish selection or approval. Color and textures in the actual product can vary considerably from the color and textures shown in printed material. The printed brochure gives an indication of available colors, but the colors are rendered in printer's ink rather than in the actual material. A quality level may be specified, requiring a selection of color and/or texture from sample pieces of the material. Several acceptable manufacturers may be listed in the specification, and a level of quality also may be specified. The contractor, subcontractor, or supplier may prefer one of these products, based on price, availability, quality, workability, or service. The contractor would then submit the color samples for the preferred product for the color selection the designer chooses. Samples, especially color samples, for example, may have a two-submittal process. The first submittal, usually a color chart of all available colors in the specified line of product, is for "initial selection," and the second submittal, which could be a larger and actual sample, is for final selection.

Samples should be pursued as diligently as product submittals and shop drawings. They may take some time to obtain from the manufacturer. Most materials have substantial order, manufacture, and delivery periods that must be calculated along with the time spent to obtain samples. Sample processing should be accomplished as early as possible in the project, because delivery periods for construction materials can be considerable because of production schedules and transportation. In some cases, the architect may require all samples, especially color samples, to be submitted before final selection of colors, textures, or finishes to coordinate the finishes of the project as a whole.

Samples need to be stored at the jobsite and compared to the material delivered and installed. Confirmation of the correct material on the jobsite prior to installation of the product avoids costly delays. Comparison of samples with the product received is an important part of project quality control.

Requirements for Submittals, Shop Drawings, and Samples

The construction documents usually indicate which product data submittals, shop drawings, and samples are required by the architect for a particular project. The contractor can require these in purchase orders and subcontract agreements, whether or not they are specified in the construction documents. Submittals, shop drawings, and samples are used by the contractor and the architect as a reference for monitoring quality control.

The General Conditions of the Contract require product data submittals, shop drawings, and samples. AIA Form A201, General Conditions of the Construction Contract, requires the aforementioned in Section 4.12, which defines each. The Conditions also require that the contractor review these submittals prior to transmitting them to the architect. The contractor is required to verify that the materials to be used are the correct ones for the project. Article 4.12.8 requires that all submittals be approved prior to the commencement of work associated with the submittal. The Supplementary Conditions to the Construction Contract may add provisions relating to the submittals required for the particular contract.

Specification Section 013300 in the General Requirements section of the Project Manual defines the information required in the product data submittals, shop drawings, and samples. This section also specifies the necessary format for project submittals. Many architects will list the required submittals for the project in this section, providing a handy checklist for the contractor. A checklist can be compiled by examining each product specification in the Project Manual. Part One of the material specification should list the submittal requirement for the product.

Review of Submittals, Shop Drawings, and Samples

Definite processing lines are required by most projects for approval of all submittals, shop drawings, and samples. The procedures can seem very cumbersome and time consuming; however, there are substantial reasons for review steps by all parties. The designer is ultimately responsible for the design of the facility to meet occupancy needs and must ensure that the products being installed are suitable to meet these needs. Any change in material or fabrication needs to be reviewed for its acceptability with the original design. Both the architect and the contractor need to be able to coordinate the product and installation of the product with other systems.

Figure 4–3 is a flowchart showing the typical process used in processing submittals for approval.

Each level must review, add information as necessary, and stamp that the submittal was examined and approved by that party. After the submittal reaches the primary reviewer, the sub-consultant in the earlier example, it is returned through the same steps, which provides an opportunity for further comment and ensures that each party is aware of the approval, partial approval, notes, or rejection. Obviously, this approval process is cumbersome and time consuming.

Typically, the architect will review the submittal for compliance to the requirements in the construction documents. Revisions may be noted on the submittal. Colors and other selection items will be made by the architect during this review. Sometimes the architect will reject the

THE SUBMITTAL PROCESS IN
CONSTRUCTION

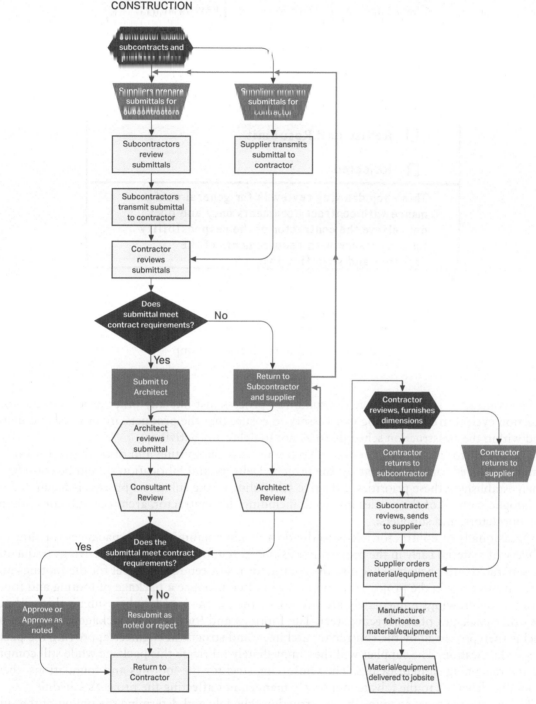

Figure 4–3   The Submittal Process in Construction

entire submittal and other times will request re-submittal of some of the items. The architect also will make corrections, which normally do not need to be resubmitted but which do need to be applied to the product. A typical architect's submittal stamp is shown in Figure 4–4, recognizing that each architect will have a slightly different stamp and wording. It must be noted that most contract documents indicate that the architect's approval of a submittal does not relieve the contractor from meeting all contract requirements. If the submittal varies from the specified product, it must be brought to the architect's attention. If the variance is substantial, a formal substitution request may be required.

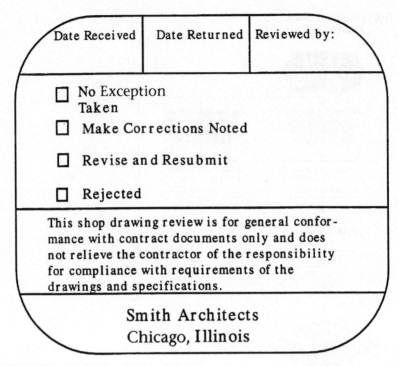

Date Received	Date Returned	Reviewed by:

☐ No Exception Taken

☐ Make Corrections Noted

☐ Revise and Resubmit

☐ Rejected

This shop drawing review is for general conformance with contract documents only and does not relieve the contractor of the responsibility for compliance with requirements of the drawings and specifications.

Smith Architects
Chicago, Illinois

Figure 4–4   Example Architect's Review Stamp

The contractor should manage the submittal process just like any other process in the construction cycle. Careful planning is necessary to ensure that the products are ordered and delivered within the construction schedule so as not to delay any activities.

The contractor must prioritize the submittal process, submitting and obtaining approval for materials needed for the first part of the project. Delivery and fabrication should be considered when establishing these priorities. Effective scheduling of the submittal process is facilitated by a dialogue with all of the parties involved, including the contractor, architect, sub-consultants, subcontractors, and suppliers.

Occasionally, a contractor needs to divide a product submittal into packages, facilitating delivery of material early in the project. For example, reinforcing steel shop drawings frequently are separated into packages. Because the contractor needs reinforcing steel for the footings and foundations early in the project, the supplier will often produce a package of footing and foundation shop drawings immediately after receiving the purchase order, then submit this without the other packages of reinforcing steel. The footings and foundations package of reinforcing steel is then processed by the contractor, architect, and structural engineer approving the package for fabrication. The supplier will then immediately fabricate this package while still compiling the remaining shop drawings. The reinforcing steel for the footings and foundations, then, should be delivered to the jobsite in a timely manner, not affecting the project's schedule.

The contractor must examine the construction schedule and determine the timing of the submittals and shop drawings so that the material will be delivered to the jobsite prior to the scheduled installation activity.

The Procurement Schedule

The contractor will coordinate the submittal schedule with procurement and installation schedule requirements to ensure that the product will be delivered to the jobsite to coincide with the appropriate installation activity. AIA Form A201, General Conditions of the Contract, requires that the contractor provide a schedule of submittals to coordinate with the construction schedule:

> 1.10.2 The Contractor shall prepare and keep current, for the Architect's approval, a schedule of submittals which is coordinated with the Contractor's construction schedule and allows the Architect reasonable time to review submittals (A201, General Conditions of the Contract, 1987 edition, *American Institute of Architects*)

The contractor needs to acquire data from the various parties concerning the durations used in a procurement schedule. The **procurement schedule** is a schedule of activities for particular products from submittal through delivery to the jobsite. The contractor must discuss the time that is necessary for the approval of submittals with the architect. Some of the factors that apply when determining the necessary time frame for these approvals include the following:

1. The size of the submittal package to be submitted. If a submittal is divided into packages, the approval time would be less per package than it would be for the entire submittal.

2. The complexity of the submittal has a large influence on the review and approval time.

3. The timing of the submittal. If all the project submittals are given to the architect on the same date, it would take considerable time to process the submittal.

4. The number of consultants reviewing the submittal will influence the processing time. Occasionally, several consultants will review the submittal, which requires additional time for reviewing, handling, and mailing.

5. Some of the architect's consultants may live in other geographical areas; thus, mailing time should be considered in the approval process.

The architect should have the opportunity to provide input and review the time frames allowed for approval of the submittals. The actual approval cycle will closely achieve the approval schedule if the contractor and architect first develop a realistic schedule.

The contractor also needs to obtain input from the supplier of the products or fabrications for the following information:

- Amount of time necessary to produce the necessary submittal, shop drawing, or sample

- Amount of time necessary to order the product after receipt of approved submittals

- Amount of time necessary for manufacture and fabrication and delivery of the product to the jobsite

After receiving input from the architect and suppliers, the contractor can compile a procurement schedule. Figure 4–5 is a sample procurement schedule. Additional information can be added to this schedule, depending upon the contractor's needs and the use of the schedule. This information can include the following:

- Vendor, supplier, fabricator, or subcontractor name and location

- Additional steps in the process, such as approval by consultants

- Actual dates achieved to be used for comparison with the scheduled dates

- Correlation with the construction schedule activities, by number and description

The **submittal log** is used for tracking the actual progress of the submittal. Many contractors use this only for the dates the submittal was received by the appropriate parties. A more complete and useful submittal log would compare the projected dates with the actual dates, as shown in Figure 4–6. By comparing the actual and scheduled dates in a single form, variances are easily determined. The submittal log is used as documentation to indicate unnecessary delay

Procurement Schedule

Sect. No.	Item	To Contractor	To Architect	To Contractor	Order Date	Delivery Date
02150	Shoring Shop Drawing	1-May-26	2-May-26	9-May-26	9-May-26	15-May-26
02730	Drywell Submittal	1-May-26	2-May-26	9-May-26	10-May-26	24-May-26
02850	Irrigation Submittal & S.Dwg.	1-Jul-26	2-Jul-26	15-Jul-26	20-Jul-26	1-Mar-26
02900	Landscape Shop Drawing	1-Jul-26	2-Jul-26	15-Jul-26	20-Jul-26	1-Apr-26
03201	Rebar: Footings Shop Drawing	1-May-26	2-May-26	5-May-26	6-May-26	10-May-26
03202	Rebar: Found.Wall S.Dwg	4-May-26	5-May-26	10-May-26	11-May-26	20-May-26
03203	Rebar: Slabs Shop Drawing	10-May-26	11-May-26	15-May-26	16-May-26	26-May-26
03204	Rebar: T/U Panels, S.Dwg.	10-May-26	11-May-26	20-May-26	21-May-26	2-Jun-26
03300	Concrete Mix Design	1-May-26	2-May-26	3-May-26	4-May-26	10-May-26
03350	Cure/Seal Submittal	15-May-26	16-May-26	21-May-26	22-May-26	26-May-26
03400	Tilt-Up Panel Shop Drawings	15-May-26	16-May-26	22-May-26	23-May-26	2-Jun-26
04200	CMU Samples	15-May-26	16-May-26	18-May-26	19-May-26	1-Jun-26
04200	CMU Test Reports	15-May-26	16-May-26	18-May-26	19-May-26	1-Jun-26
05001	Steel: Embed, Bolts S.Dwg	1-May-26	2-May-26	12-May-26	13-May-26	20-May-26
05002	Steel: Columns Shop Drawing	15-May-26	16-May-26	20-May-26	21-May-26	28-May-26
05003	Steel: Beams Shop Drawing	1-Jun-26	2-Jun-26	15-Jun-26	17-Jun-26	10-Jul-26
05200	Steel Joist Shop Drawing	1-Jun-26	2-Jun-26	15-Jun-26	17-Jun-26	12-Jul-26
05300	Metal Deck Shop Drawing	1-Jun-26	2-Jun-26	15-Jun-26	17-Jun-26	12-Jul-26
05500	Steel Stair Shop Drawings	15-Jun-26	17-Jun-26	1-Jul-26	6-Jul-26	1-Oct-26
06400	Millwork Shop Drawings	15-Jun-26	17-Jun-26	1-Aug-26	15-Aug-26	1-Feb-26
07500	Roofing Submittal	15-May-26	16-May-26	1-Jun-26	2-Jun-26	1-Aug-26
07600	Flashing Submittal	15-May-26	16-May-26	1-Jun-26	2-Jun-26	1-Aug-26
07900	Joint Sealant Submittal	1-Jun-26	3-Jun-26	10-Jun-26	11-Jun-26	1-Aug-26
08200	HM Drs, Frs Shop Drawing	15-May-26	16-May-26	23-May-26	24-May-26	5-Jun-26
08300	Overhead Door Submittal	1-Jul-26	2-Jul-26	10-Jul-26	20-Jul-26	1-Nov-26
08500	Metal Window Shop Drawing	1-Jul-26	4-Jul-26	20-Jul-26	23-Jul-26	1-Oct-26
08700	Finish Hardware Submittal	1-Jun-26	2-Jun-26	15-Jun-26	16-Jun-26	1-Oct-26
09250	Drywall Submittal	1-Jul-26	2-Jul-26	10-Jul-26	15-Jul-26	15-Aug-26
09300	Ceramic Tile Samples	1-Jun-26	2-Jun-26	10-Jun-26	12-Jun-26	15-Sep-26
09500	Ceiling S. Drawings, Samples	1-Jun-26	2-Jun-26	10-Jun-26	12-Jun-26	1-Oct-26
09680	Carpet Samples	1-Jun-26	2-Jun-26	1-Jul-26	15-Jul-26	1-Jan-26
09900	Paint Submittal, Samples	1-Jun-26	2-Jun-26	1-Jul-26	5-Jul-26	1-Sep-26
10150	Toilet Partition Submittal	1-Jun-26	2-Jun-26	1-Jul-26	5-Jul-26	1-Dec-26
10800	Toilet Access. Submittal	1-Jun-26	2-Jun-26	1-Jul-26	5-Jul-26	1-Dec-26
15010	Plumbing R/I Submittal	1-May-26	2-May-26	9-May-26	10-May-26	11-May-26
15300	F.Sprinkler S. Dwgs.	15-Jun-26	16-Jun-26	1-Jul-26	2-Jul-26	15-Jul-26
15400	Plumbing Submittal	20-May-26	21-May-26	1-Jun-26	5-Jun-26	15-Jun-26
15500	HVAC Submittal	20-May-26	21-May-26	1-Jun-26	5-Jun-26	15-Jun-26
15950	Temp. Controls Submittal	15-Jul-26	16-Jul-26	1-Aug-26	2-Aug-26	1-Nov-26
16100	Electrical R/I Submittal	10-May-26	11-May-26	18-May-26	19-May-26	20-May-26
16200	Electrical Submittal	20-May-26	21-May-26	1-Jun-26	5-Jun-26	15-Jun-26
16700	Fire Alarm Shop Drawing	15-Jul-26	16-Jul-26	1-Aug-26	2-Aug-26	1-Nov-26

Figure 4–5   Example Procurement Schedule

in the submittal process. As the material and fabrications cannot be ordered until the approvals are received, any delay in the submittal process, whether by the subcontractor, supplier, contractor, or architect and engineer, can result in a delay of the delivery of the item to the jobsite. This delivery delay also can impact the construction schedule. The submittal log and procurement schedule are useful tools for the contractor's personnel, enabling them to track submittals at any given point in time and follow up with the individual who is responsible so that the material will be ordered on schedule.

SUBMITTAL LOG

Sect. No.	Item	Scheduled: To Contractor	Actual: ACTUAL	To Architect	ACTUAL	To Contractor	ACTUAL	Order Date	ACTUAL	Delivery Date	ACTUAL
02150	Shoring Shop Drawing	1-May-26	30-Apr-26	2-May-26	1-May-26	9-May-26	5-May-26	9-May-26	6-May-26	15-May-26	14-May-26
02730	Drywell Submittal	1-May-26	1-May-26	2-May-26	2-May-26	9-May-26	2-May-26	10-May-26	6-May-26	24-May-26	24-May-26
02850	Irrigation Submittal & S.Dwg.	1-Jul-26	15-Jun-26	2-Jul-26	16-Jun-26	15-Jul-26	25-Jun-26	20-Jul-26	28-Jun-26	1-Mar-26	1-Mar-26
02900	Landscape Shop Drawing	1-Jul-26	15-Jun-26	2-Jul-26	16-Jun-26	15-Jul-26	25-Jun-26	20-Jul-26	28-Jun-26	1-Apr-26	1-Apr-26
03201	Rebar: Footings Shop Drawing	1-May-26	4-May-26	2-May-26	4-May-26	5-May-26	6-May-26	6-May-26	7-May-26	10-May-26	10-May-26
03202	Rebar: Found.Wall S.Dwg	4-May-26	4-May-26	5-May-26	6-May-26	10-May-26	7-May-26	11-May-26	8-May-26	20-May-26	18-May-26
03203	Rebar: Slabs Shop Drawing	10-May-26	10-May-26	11-May-26	11-May-26	15-May-26	20-May-26	16-May-26	20-May-26	26-May-26	27-May-26
03204	Rebar: T/U Panels, S.Dwg.	10-May-26	10-May-26	11-May-26	11-May-26	20-May-26	20-May-26	21-May-26	20-May-26	2-Jun-26	27-May-26
03300	Concrete Mix Design	1-May-26	28-Apr-26	2-May-26	1-May-26	3-May-26	3-May-26	4-May-26	4-May-26	10-Jun-26	10-May-26
03350	Cure/Seal Submittal	15-May-26	1-May-26	16-May-26	5-May-26	21-May-26	7-May-26	22-May-26	10-May-26	26-Jun-26	24-May-26
03400	Tilt-Up Panel Shop Drawings										
04200	CMU Samples	15-May-26	5-May-26	16-May-26	10-May-26	18-May-26	14-May-26	19-May-26	15-May-26	2-Jun-26	4-Jun-26
04200	CMU Test Reports	15-May-26	5-May-26	16-May-26	8-May-26	18-May-26	12-May-26	19-May-26	13-May-26	1-Jun-26	1-Jun-26
05001	Steel: Embed, Bolts S.Dwg	1-May-26	10-May-26	2-May-26	11-May-26	12-May-26	18-May-26	13-May-26	19-May-26	30-Jun-26	22-May-26
05002	Steel: Columns Shop Drawing	1-Jun-26	28-May-26	16-May-26	29-May-26	20-May-26	11-Jun-26	21-May-26	19-Jun-26	28-May-26	27-May-26
05003	Steel: Beams Shop Drawing	1-Jun-26	28-May-26	2-Jun-26	29-May-26	15-Jun-26	10-Jun-26	17-Jun-26	11-Jun-26	10-Jul-26	5-Jul-26
05200	Steel Joist Shop Drawing	1-Jun-26	28-May-26	2-Jun-26	29-May-26	15-Jun-26	10-Jun-26	17-Jun-26	11-Jun-26	12-Jul-26	5-Jul-26
05300	Metal Deck Shop Drawing	15-Jun-26	30-Jun-26	2-Jun-26	29-May-26	15-Jun-26	10-Jun-26	17-Jun-26	11-Jun-26	12-Jul-26	5-Jul-26
05500	Steel Stair Shop Drawings	15-Jun-26	30-Jun-26	17-Jun-26	3-Jul-26	1-Jul-26	17-Jun-26	6-Jul-26	29-Jul-26	1-Oct-26	28-Sep-26
06400	Millwork Shop Drawings	15-Jun-26	15-May-26	17-Jun-26	16-May-26	1-Aug-26	20-Jul-26	15-Aug-26	4-Oct-26	1-Aug-26	15-Feb-26
07500	Roofing Submittal	15-May-26	15-May-26	16-May-26	16-May-26	1-Jun-26	28-May-26	2-Jun-26	29-May-26	1-Aug-26	1-Aug-26
07600	Flashing Submittal	15-May-26	15-Jun-26	16-May-26	16-May-26	1-Jun-26	28-May-26	2-Jun-26	29-May-26	1-Aug-26	1-Aug-26
07900	Joint Sealant Submittal	1-Jun-26	16-May-26	3-Jun-26	17-Jun-26	10-Jun-26	30-Jun-26	11-Jun-26	1-Jul-26	1-Aug-26	1-Aug-26
08200	HM Drs, Frs Shop Drawing	15-May-26	15-May-26	16-May-26	18-May-26	23-May-26	18-May-26	24-May-26	24-May-26	5-Jul-26	10-Jun-26
08300	Overhead Door Submittal	1-Jul-26	1-Jul-26	2-Jul-26	17-May-26	10-Jul-26	25-May-26	20-Jul-26	27-May-26	1-Dec-26	23-Nov-26
08500	Metal Window Shop Drawing	1-Jul-26	15-Jun-26	5-Jul-26	10-Jun-26	20-Jul-26	24-Jun-26	23-Jul-26	28-Jun-26	1-Oct-26	25-Sep-26
08700	Finish Hardware Submittal	1-Jun-26	1-Aug-26	2-Jun-26	25-Jun-26	15-Jul-26	5-Jul-26	16-Jun-26	10-Jul-26	1-Sep-26	25-Sep-26
09250	Drywall Submittal	1-Jul-26	1-Jun-26	2-Jul-26	3-Aug-26	10-Aug-26	3-Aug-26	15-Jul-26	15-Aug-26	15-Aug-26	16-Aug-26
09300	Ceramic Tile Samples	1-Jun-26	1-Aug-26	2-Jun-26	3-Jun-26	10-Jun-26	3-Jun-26	12-Jun-26	12-Jun-26	15-Sep-26	15-Sep-26
09500	Ceiling S. Drawings, Samples	1-Aug-26	1-Jun-26	2-Jun-26	5-Aug-26	10-Aug-26	5-Aug-26	12-Jun-26	17-Aug-26	1-Oct-26	1-Oct-26
09680	Carpet Samples	1-Jun-26	15-Jun-26	2-Jun-26	3-Aug-26	1-Aug-26	3-Sep-26	15-Jul-26	10-Sep-26	1-Jun-26	1-Feb-26
09900	Paint Submittal, Samples	1-Jun-26	15-May-26	2-Jun-26	17-Jun-26	1-Jul-26	17-Jun-26	5-Jul-26	20-Jul-26	1-Sep-26	1-Sep-26
10150	Toilet Partition Submittal	1-Jun-26	15-May-26	2-Jun-26	20-May-26	1-Jul-26	3-Jun-26	5-Jul-26	5-Jun-26	1-Dec-26	1-Nov-26
10800	Toilet Access. Submittal	1-Jun-26	1-Jun-26	2-Jun-26	20-May-26	1-Jul-26	3-Jun-26	5-Jul-26	5-Jun-26	1-Oct-26	1-Nov-26
15010	Plumbing R/I Submittal	1-May-26	17-Jun-26	2-May-26	7-May-26	9-May-26	7-May-26	10-May-26	8-Jul-26	11-Nov-26	11-May-26
15300	F.Sprinkler S. Dwgs.	15-Jun-26	15-May-26	16-Jun-26	17-Jun-26	1-Jul-26	1-Jun-26	2-Jul-26	1-Jun-26	15-May-26	16-May-26
15400	Plumbing Submittal	20-May-26	15-May-26	21-May-26	16-May-26	1-Jun-26	16-May-26	5-Jun-26	1-Jun-26	15-Jun-26	15-Jun-26
15500	HVAC Submittal	20-May-26	15-May-26	21-May-26	16-May-26	1-Aug-26	29-May-26	5-Jun-26	29-May-26	15-Jul-26	15-Jul-26
15950	Temp. Controls Submittal	15-Jul-26	7-Jul-26	16-Jul-26	16-May-26	1-Aug-26	29-May-26	2-Aug-26	11-Aug-26	1-Dec-26	1-Dec-26
16100	Electrical R/I Submittal	10-May-26	8-May-26	11-May-26	9-May-26	18-May-26	15-May-26	19-May-26	5-Jun-26	1-Nov-26	1-Nov-26
16200	Electrical Submittal	20-May-26	20-May-26	21-May-26	7-Jun-26	1-Jun-26	21-May-26	5-Jun-26	8-Jun-26	20-Mar-26	1-Jun-26
16700	Fire Alarm Shop Drawing	15-Jul-26	1-Aug-26	16-Jul-26	10-Aug-26	1-Aug-26	30-Aug-26	2-Aug-26	1-Sep-26	1-Nov-26	5-Nov-26

Figure 4–6 Example Submittal Log

Submittal Review by the Contractor

Although the submittal process is intended primarily for the architect's review of material and fabrications, the contractor is quite involved in the submittal process. The contractor reviews submittals for:

- Compliance to specifications

- Dimensional conformance to the construction assemblies

- Interface with other materials and assemblies, avoiding duplication or omission of elements in the process

- The constructability of the assembly, recognizing the steps necessary in constructing the system

The contractor receives the submittal from the supplier or subcontractor prior to forwarding it to the architect and is expected to review the submittal and stamp it as having been reviewed prior to transmitting it to the architect. The contractor acts as a first-line filter with the submittals, refusing products that do not comply to the project's specifications, and reviews the submittal for compliance with the contract documents. Many architects will not accept product submittals for products that have not been approved for substitution. Because the architect has selected products and approved substitutions, many contractors are reluctant to suggest further substitutions. If the product is specified as a primary product, listed as an approved equal, or approved in the addenda, it will comply with the contractual requirements. The contractor then needs to confirm that the product is acceptable for its intended use and compatible with the other products specified. If the product does not meet contract requirements, the contractor should immediately return the submittal to the supplier or subcontractor to avoid wasting valuable time in the submittal, order, and delivery processes. Some architects and owners will accept substitutions for products after the contract is awarded, but usually only with an appropriate deduction from the contract amount.

The contractor also is responsible for providing field dimensions for openings and items that are installed in instances where other construction elements determine the size of the material. Many materials have a very small tolerance in dimensional variance, requiring exact dimensions of the constructed elements rather than relying on those in the construction documents. The field dimensions necessary may not be available at the time the shop drawings are submitted, requiring the contractor to hold the shop drawings until all are available or provide them at a later date. Some suppliers and fabricators will measure the field dimensions themselves rather than relying on the contractor for the dimensions. When fabricators visit the jobsite to obtain dimensions, they also are able to familiarize themselves with other aspects of the project that may affect their product's fabrication.

The contractor is able to determine the interface of the systems from the shop drawings and material submittals, occasionally becoming aware of duplication of material by more than one supplier. The contractor also may find that additional material is necessary to complete the assembly. In these cases, changes to the original purchase orders or subcontracts may be necessary.

By reviewing the shop drawings and submittals, the contractor will become aware of the means and methods of installing the construction materials, systems, and assemblies. When installing the material and equipment with their own forces, the contractor will use the submittals to determine the necessary equipment and workforce to construct the assembly. Although the contractor should have determined a plan for installation during the estimating phase, a detailed examination of the procedures is necessary during the construction phase. The information in the submittal should indicate the size, weight, configuration, and installation details of the material and equipment. It is possible that the material is not compatible with the construction methods intended for use on the project, requiring either a different material or different construction methods.

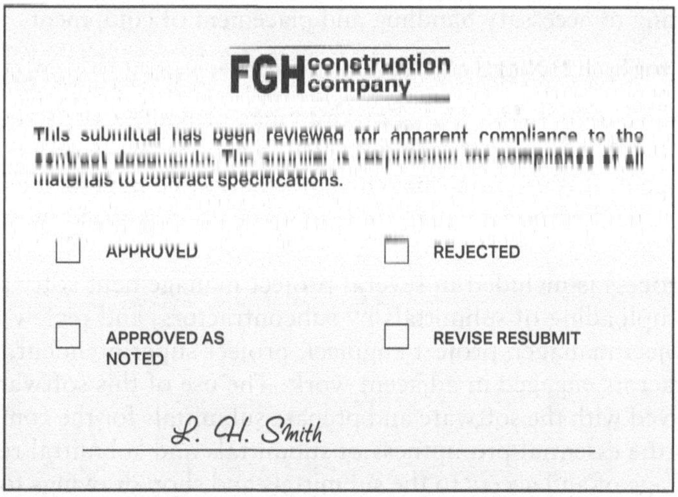

FGH construction company

This submittal has been reviewed for apparent compliance to the contract documents. The supplier is responsible for compliance of all materials to contract specifications.

☐ APPROVED   ☐ REJECTED

☐ APPROVED AS   ☐ REVISE RESUBMIT
   NOTED

L. H. Smith

Figure 4–7   **Example Contractor's Review Stamp**

Each construction project generates many submittals, usually early in the progress of the project. The chaos presented by the large submittal flow can be overwhelming to the engineer assigned to review the documents. There is a tendency to quickly process the documents, without a complete detailed review. It is essential to the process for the engineer to prepare a detailed review of the submittals to determine compliance to the specifications and if the product is appropriate for the installation, compatible with adjacent materials and systems, and available within the construction schedule, in a timely manner.

Review of shop drawings and submittals for the contractor should be done by an individual who thoroughly understands the project's requirements. The project manager often reviews the submittals on smaller projects, but on larger projects, the field engineer or office engineer reviews and processes the submittals. Because many submittals are received during the same period, a larger project will have several engineers reviewing submittals and shop drawings.

The contractor normally stamps the submittals, indicating that they have been reviewed. Some contractors prefer a brief statement on the stamp to avoid the transfer of liability. Some of these simple stamps may contain the following information:

- "Reviewed" statement

- Contractor

- Date reviewed

- Project

- Signature

Some contractors prefer to stamp the submittals with more information, as shown in Figure 4–7.

The Use of Submittals During Construction

The contractor will use submittals at the jobsite for several different applications:

- Information for preparation of openings, support, adjoining assemblies, and general construction details

- Quality control information to ensure that the correct product has been supplied

- Placement diagrams for installation of the material

- Information relating to necessary handling and placement of equipment

- Jobsite reference for architect and owner

The information in product data and shop drawings provides essential information that is usually beyond that of the contract documents, which facilitates the proper installation of the material and equipment. It is essential that this information be kept at the jobsite; normally it is kept in file cabinets and plan racks that are systematically organized by specification section number.

The submittal process is included in several project management software programs. This software facilitates uploading of submittals by subcontractors, and review by the appropriate parties, such as project manager, project engineer, project superintendent, architect/engineer, and other subcontractors engaged in adjacent work. The use of this software requires the participants to be involved with the software and prepare submittals for the computerized use. This software facilitates the essential promptness of submittals and submittal reviews. It also provides organized storage of and access to the submittals and shop drawings for the project team.

Summary

Submittal of product data, shop drawings, and samples in a complete and timely fashion is essential for the smooth execution of the construction contract. Submittals are used for approval for compliance to the contract and for quality control to ensure that the appropriate products are being used in the constructed facility.

Complete information needs to be shown in the product submittal or shop drawing, regarding physical characteristics, finishes, and installation details or restraints. Samples and mock-ups are normally used to ensure that the product and installation will meet the expectations of owners and designers.

Submittals are required in the following areas of contract documents:

- General Conditions of the Construction Contract

- Supplementary Conditions

- Section 013300 of General Requirements

- Individual Product Specification in the Technical Specification

The approval process for submittals involves several steps and can be very time consuming, but it is one of the first steps in the quality control process. A procurement schedule, listing approval steps, order date, and delivery date, is required by some contracts and can be helpful in monitoring and managing the submittal process. Cooperation by all parties will aid in a smooth submittal process.

The contractor reviews submittals for several reasons:

- As the first-line review for compliance to the contract

- For interface with other materials and systems

- To determine the necessary equipment and procedures for installation

- To provide jobsite information, such as field dimensions

The contractor uses the submittals in the construction process for:

- Placing details

- Determining installation techniques

- Inventory of material

- Quality control

Review Questions

1. What are the purposes of product data submittals, samples, and shop drawings?

2. What are five types of information provided on a product data submittal?

3. What are two purposes of the shop drawing, other than for A/E approval?

4. When samples are required, what characteristics are usually examined by the architect?

5. What is the process for approval of submittals?

6. What is a procurement schedule?

7. Why would a contractor prepare a procurement schedule?

8. What information would be included in a procurement schedule?

9. What additional information would be added to the procurement schedule for a submittal log?

10. What are five uses of submittals during the construction process?

Chapter 5

Documentation and Record Keeping at the Jobsite

Objectives

This chapter discusses documenting the construction process and keeping records at the jobsite. The objectives of this chapter are to:

- Present the reasons for keeping accurate records at the jobsite
- List the goals of documentation and record keeping
- Recommend the types and appropriate content of documentation and record keeping
- Illustrate the use of documentation and record keeping in the construction process

As the contractor approaches the actual construction of the project, documentation will be needed for all activities. When preparing for the project, the contractor begins the documentation process by keeping logs and schedules for product submittals, as discussed in the previous chapter. This process continues throughout the construction project.

Accurate documentation of the construction project is essential in the current contracting climate. There was a time, within recent memory, when the contractor was able to pursue only the construction of the project, and the project itself spoke for its success. Today, however, the contractor operates within tight cost and time constraints. A number of activities beyond the control of the contractor can influence the contractor's performance, whether by actions of the owner, architect, subcontractor, supplier, building inspector, or other parties. An activity deviation may not appear to impact on the contract at the time it happens; however, it may be felt at a later date. Because disputes can occur with the owner, architect, subcontractors, and code enforcement officials during the course of the project, clear documentation can assist in finding quick and equitable solutions.

All documentation should be clear and concise, as many individuals will be referring to it and using it as a basis for other actions. Documentation such as daily reports and meeting minutes may be the only contact that some individuals, such as those in upper-tier management, have with the project; thus, clear, objective, and complete reporting is necessary. Documentation should be objective and convey the facts truthfully, without bias. The personal diary may be slightly subjective, however, because it may be opinion oriented, but this is a necessary part of the diary, as it will provide a larger perspective regarding particular situations. Keeping this in mind, the individual should try to be as objective as possible when using this type of documentation.

Some keys to effective jobsite documentation and communication include the following:

- Objectivity and truthfulness—Provide a fair and honest assessment of the situation, without bias.

- Timeliness—Distribution of documentation, as required for the particular documentation tool, should be made as quickly as possible. Upper management needs current data to keep pace with the project.

- Retrievability—The documentation must be readily accessible and closely tied to the specific issue. A good, updated manual filing system or computerized search and sorting capability facilitate documentation.

- Appropriate distribution—Each piece of documentation has different distribution requirements, depending on the nature of the issue and the parties involved. It is important to distribute applicable information to the parties but to not send too much irrelevant information. Some parties may need weekly or monthly progress summaries rather than a daily report.

- Standard, uniform information—Each piece of documentation should contain certain information for quick retrieval. For example, if one needs to know how many roofing subcontractor employees worked on a project on a specific date, the daily reports would provide the information. There would be no need to search other documents for this information. Standard forms save time for all levels of management. They also ensure that company standard procedures are being followed at the jobsite. Standard information from project to project helps management evaluate conditions quickly, efficiently, and accurately.

- Completeness and comprehensiveness—The description of the event or issue should be as complete as possible at the time, without excessive elaboration. The entire documentation system for the construction project must include recording all facets of the project, without gaps in the information. The documentation must be continuous, from the beginning of the project to the end.

When documenting the construction project, the primary areas covered include the following:

- Events—An event can be defined as an occurrence that should be documented during the project. These events can vary, from the number of employees on the project during a specific day to a catastrophic event such as a structural failure. Documentation of the events of the project might include documentation of its progress, specific occurrences, and other information that might relate to the work.

  Documentation types—These consist of daily reports, weekly and monthly reports, diaries, accident reports, subcontractor logs, photographs, videos, time-lapse photography, progress schedules, schedule updates, and document control logs.

- Conversations—Included here are written records of conversations, including the parties involved, topics covered, and any directions or solutions. These records should be as objective as possible but may also reflect a subjective view of the discourse. Conversations can occur by telephone or through direct personal contact. Formal meetings usually are covered by meeting minutes, but all conversations that concern the project should be documented.

  Documentation types—These consist of daily reports, diaries, telephone logs, and memos to the file.

- Costs—The contractor needs to track all costs on the jobsite and compare them to the estimated cost. All labor, material, and equipment used by the contractor must be reported and associated with work items. The cost data accumulated on the jobsite is used by the contractor's accounting department as well as by the project management team. Cost information is accumulated during the work as a tool to determine the crews' productivity, which allows managers to alter the production factors during the process to control the cost within the budget that was established through the estimate.

  Documentation types—These include the bill of materials, purchase order, receipt of delivery, delivery logs, time cards, labor reports, labor packages, labor cost control, equipment logs, and rental logs.

- Correspondence—Throughout the duration of the project, written correspondence is transmitted between the parties through hard copy via the mail, hard copy via a fax, or via e-mail. This correspondence should be sorted by party and issue. The contractor corresponds with the architect, the owner (usually through the architect), subcontractors, suppliers, building officials, and other parties active in the construction process. This correspondence ranges from a transmittal, indicating delivery of an item, to letters concerning serious contractual issues.

  Documentation types—These include transmittals, transmittal logs, submittal transmittals, submittal logs, requests for information (RFIs), letters, faxes, e-mail notes, speed letters/with responses, punch lists, payment requests, schedules, and schedule updates.

- Contractual requirements—Several items of documentation are required by the contract documents. Although these documents serve specific purposes, they also document certain events throughout the project. Specific forms will be specified for areas such as progress payment, change orders, and substantial completion.

Documentation types—These include progress payment requests, schedules of values, contract change orders and proposals, certified payrolls, certificates of substantial completion, and photographs.

- Meeting minutes—Numerous meetings occur throughout the construction process. Some are regularly scheduled progress meetings and some may be special-topic meetings. A written record, or the minutes of the meeting, should always be saved and later distributed to meeting participants and other interested parties.

Documentation types—These include meeting minutes for preconstruction, construction progress, special installation, subcontractor, and special-issue meetings.

Report Types and Content

Event and Conversation Documentation

Complete and accurate documentation about what actually occurred on the jobsite during the construction process is perhaps the most important record keeping done. This documentation illustrates the actual sequence of the project, personnel on the job, materials delivered to the jobsite, equipment used on the jobsite, and many other factors. These reports are necessary to remain consistent in content and consecutive throughout the duration of the project, without time gaps between documentation. Although this record keeping seems burdensome at the time, it is extremely useful in recreating a realistic picture of the jobsite at a later date, as is often necessary in the settlement of disputes. These records can be transmitted to individuals who are not directly involved on a daily basis with the project, keeping management aware of jobsite activities. Much of the event documentation is recorded by the field engineer or superintendent on the jobsite.

Daily Reports

The daily report is the consecutive record of events on the jobsite. Its purpose is to provide a snapshot of the day's activities and conditions. The daily report records information objectively. The data are normally recorded on a preprinted form and contains consistent, daily information. The information and format will vary from contractor to contractor and even from project to project.

The contractor's daily report is, in most cases, an internal document, distributed only within the contractor's firm. All of the contracting entities at the jobsite, such as the owner's inspector, the architect's inspector, and the subcontractor's foremen, should keep daily reports for their own use as well. Although this seems like unnecessary duplication, each of the parties is particularly aware of the events and activities that the other parties may not be informed about. Most firms want to rely on information from their own representatives rather than from another firm.

The daily report is a jobsite report, normally completed by the superintendent or field engineer. The daily report could be completed at all levels, that is, by the project manager, superintendent, and field engineer, with different contents for each report. Typical distribution of the daily reports would include the following:

- One copy on file at the jobsite

- One copy to the project manager; copy to remain in project file

- One copy, or a summary by week or month, to the company officer (partner, owner) in charge of the project

Information will be different for each contractor's daily report. Realistically, the report should be limited to one page. One of the objectives of any documentation system is to accurately record the information but to minimize the amount of time spent by field personnel in documenting the events. Some forms have preprinted categories, such as types of subcontractors—roofing, drywall, painters, and so on—so only a number has to be added by the form preparer. Other forms require more information.

The daily report can be hard copy, with photocopies sent to the home office by mail, usually on a weekly basis. The daily report is commonly prepared on the jobsite computer and is transferred by modem or fax to the home office. Immediate transfer of this report and others helps home office personnel obtain an accurate picture of the current status of the project.

Typical information included in the daily report is the following:

- Date—The date reported and the date the report is written should be the same. Sequential numbering of the report also is required by some firms.

- Project name and number—The project may have several numbers. Because this is an internal document, the contractor's project number should be attached.

- Individual making the report.

- Weather information—Weather information is extremely important for project documentation. It indicates project conditions that can explain why work was not done on a specific date. This information should reflect the particulars of each work shift, such as the temperature at the start of the shift, at midshift, and at the end of the shift. It also could reflect the temperature during activities that are temperature sensitive, such as concrete pours. Barometric readings help predict immediate changes in the weather. The weather section of the daily report should describe precipitation during a 24-hour period, including the period before the shift, such as overnight. The amount of precipitation, if known, and the time period, for instance, 10 A.M. to 2 P.M., should be mentioned as well. The effect of the precipitation also should be noted, such as mud, ice, or the amount of snow on the ground. General wind conditions, such as speed and direction, should be noted, as should the time, duration, velocity, and direction of unusual wind conditions. Because radiated heat can affect some materials, particularly concrete, notes should indicate whether it was clear and sunny, cloudy, partly cloudy, and so on. If there is a disruption in work activities, including stopping work, extraordinary measures to protect work, or rescheduling of the activity because of weather conditions, the duration of the disruption should be noted.

    Most of these data are available through observation at the jobsite. Additional information can be acquired through the U.S. Weather Service or several online databases. The contractor may wish to use a simple weather station on the jobsite, consisting of a thermometer, barometer, and rain gauge. An example of weather information that could be used in the daily report follows.

Example

Weather: 42°F, 7 A.M.; 65°F, 12 P.M.; 70°F, 2 P.M. Concrete Pour

Precip: None; Month accum: 1.75"

Wind: Calm morning, 10 mph wind from south, afternoon

- Description of activities in progress—This includes a brief description of the work in progress on the jobsite during the report period (for the day or shift).

Example

Carpenters, laborers, ironworkers, and electricians setting tilt-up panel forms 5 through 16 on Building A. Excavator digging foundation on Building B.

- Contractor's labor on the jobsite—This area should list the trades directly employed by the contractor on the jobsite and indicate the number of employees. This is not a time card or hourly listing but provides an indication of the size of the crew on the jobsite.

Example

Carpenter	5	Ironworker	2
Laborer	4	Truck driver	1

- Subcontractors on the jobsite—Some daily reports classify the type of craftsmen and/or the number of people working for the subcontractor. Actually, both pieces of information are valuable to obtain a full picture of the available productivity potential. This information is not meant for time cards or to track time and material accounts for subcontractors. It is used primarily to determine if subcontractors have adequately staffed the project. Personal observation of the subcontractors' crews is the most common method to determine crew size. The subcontractor's foreman also could be a source for obtaining the number of crew members. Occasionally, the contractor will require that daily reports be submitted from each subcontractor working on the site.

Example

ABC Masonry, Inc.		FS Insulation	
Bricklayer	4	Carpenter	3
Hodcarrier	1	Laborer	1
City Plumbing, Inc.		State Electrical, Inc.	
Plumber	2	Electrician	3
Apprentice Plumber	1	Apprentice Electrician	1
Pipefitter	1		

- Equipment at the jobsite—The contractor should list the equipment used on the jobsite and indicate whether it is being used or it is idle. If a piece of equipment is not being used, its rental might not be applied to the cost item if the equipment is owned by the contractor. Equipment logs normally are used to establish hours for the contractor's use of the equipment. The list of equipment indicates the capabilities to perform the work at the time. Information from the equipment records can be used for cost control, for estimating historical data, and for availability costs. Idle subcontractor equipment should be noted because a record needs to be kept for equipment charges or cost-plus items. Normally, equipment listed in this area is larger and does not account for tools such as saws, drill motors, or hand tools.

Example

Equipment	In Use (Hrs.)	Idle (Hrs.)
Our Equipment		
Concrete Pump	4	4
Forklift	8	
Tower Crane	8	
ABC Masonry, Inc.		
All-terrain Forklift	8	
Scaffolding: 200 frames	8	
Mixer	8	
City Plumbing, Inc.		
Hi-Lift	4	4

- Material deliveries to the jobsite—The material at the jobsite indicates the ability to pursue construction activities. Delivery of material also shows compliance with purchase orders and subcontract agreements (the delivery of material will be included in the purchase order records). Delivering large amounts of material to the jobsite can be disruptive, requiring the crew's time to unload and store material. Delivery of material also indicates the amount of crane time necessary for unloading material, which will detract from work activities.

Example

Material Delivery

From	For	Time	Items
Valley Lumber	Our Firm (P.O. 293–124)	10–11 A.M.	2,000 BF 2 × 4
			3,000 BF 2 × 6
Smith Plmbg. Sply	City Plumbing, Inc.	11–11:30 A.M.	1,000 LF 2" PVC
			24 P-2 Fixtures
Iron City Steel	Our Firm (P.O. 294–003)	1–2 P.M.	4th shpt. Rebar

- Visitors to the jobsite—Verification of the dates for visits from the owner's representatives, building officials, architects, engineers, and other interested parties is necessary in some disputes. Job security also is maintained by requiring visitors to register with the field office. A separate visitor's log, which records the visitor's signature, could be kept in addition to or in lieu of this activity item on the daily report. The contractor's purpose for this log is to monitor visitors to the jobsite in compliance with the safety program. It is important that the person be identified and that the name of the firm, the purpose, and the time and duration on the jobsite be recorded. Documentation of visitors' conversations normally is addressed in records such as the personal diary.

Example

Visitor	Firm	Purpose	Time
A. J. Jones	OSHA	Safety Inspection	9–11 A.M.
M. Smith	ABC Architects	Construction Observation	1–2:30 P.M.
O. K. Anderson	Anderson Safety Sply.	Salesman, Safety Protect	2–3 P.M.

- Occurrences on the jobsite—This section is used to describe occurrences that fall outside of the description of "work in progress." This area could indicate an action or a conflict on the jobsite, an accident, discovering an unknown condition, or another notable event. Most of these items also will be covered in other reports, such as accident reports, diary conversations, or an RFI to the architect. It is essential, however, that the occurrence be noted in the daily report. The date of occurrence is crucial to any potential change or claim when establishing the time frame for processing either. Specific information should be included here, including reference to other reports. Each occurrence item should include what happened, who was involved, when it happened, how it happened, where it happened, and the resolution, if any, that was reached.

Example

Occurrences

10:15 A.M.: John Smith, AAA Excavation, notified us that they have encountered solid rock in the excavation of Building B, between grids A2 and G4 at about an elevation of 1567.0. Excavation is intended to go to 1560.5. Called M. Smith, ABC Architects. Faxed RFI 034.

2:35 P.M.: Jack Johnson, carpenter, cut hand with circular saw, in forming of building A. Art Anderson, foreman, administered first aid and took him to emergency room at City Hospital. Eight stitches necessary, bandaged, and back at the jobsite; able to perform tasks. See Accident Report 294–010.

3:15 P.M.: Conflict between plumbing rough-in and electrical panel in room A-103. RFI 035 faxed to architect.

- Signature and date—A signature and date usually are necessary to establish the report as an official document. Initialing the report also may indicate authorship by the preparer. Electronically produced documents do not provide the opportunity for a signature. A signed or an initialed hard copy in the job files should provide enough legal credence to the document.

As previously mentioned, contractors should develop their own forms containing information needed for project management. Blank and completed sample forms for the daily report are shown in Figures 5–1 and 5–2.

FGH Construction Company

DAILY REPORT

Project:	Project No:	Date:	No.
Report by:	Weather:	Temp.	
	Wind:	Precipitation:	

WORK IN PROGRESS:

Labor: FGH Employees:		
Carpenters________	Laborers________	Operators________
Truckdriver________	Cement masons________	Iron workers________
Labor: Subcontractors:		

Equipment:			
Item ________	Firm________	Hrs. In use________	Hrs. Idle________

Material delivery:			
From________	For________	Time________	Items________

Visitors:			
Visitor________	Firm________	Purpose________	Time________
Occurrences:________			

*Signature:*________

*Date:*________

P.O. Box 3888, New City,
CA 93478(805) 444-9900,
FAX: (805) 444-9901

Figure 5–1 Blank Daily Report Form

Weekly and Monthly Reports

Some contracting firms require weekly or monthly summaries of the project, usually to inform upper management of the project's progress. Daily reports are read by those who are involved on a day-to-day basis with the project, but the weekly or monthly report or summary keeps upper management aware of the project and enables them to assist when necessary. Occasionally, such reports also are required to be submitted to the owner. Obviously, different types of information will be contained in a report to the owner than in a report intended for internal management.

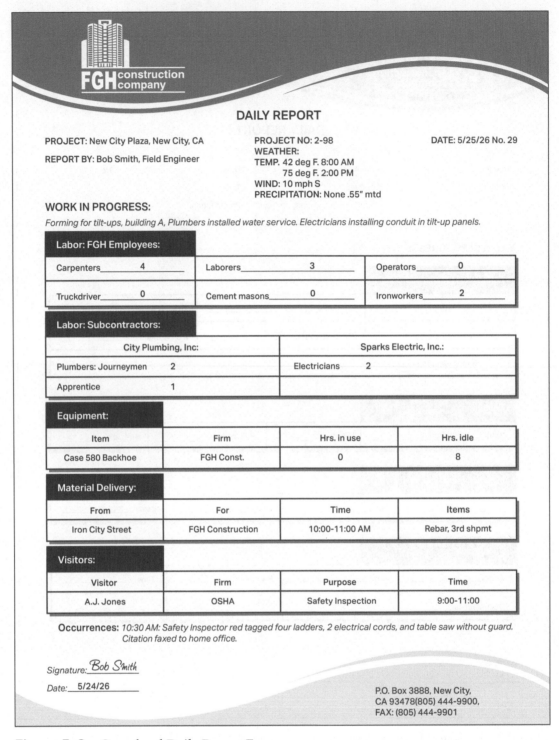

Figure 5–2   Completed Daily Report Form

The weekly or monthly report for internal management is normally written in narrative form, with some organizational parameters, rather than on a form such as the daily report. The organization of each report should be similar. The following areas examine some of the topics that could be included in a weekly or monthly report:

• Identification of the project—This includes the project name, location, and internal project number.

• Summary of activities—A summary of the activity progress since the last report. A discussion of site conditions, such as weather and the results on the site, also should be included here.

- Schedule analysis—This determines the relationship with the construction schedule, identifying the areas that are not meeting the schedule, what impact they will have on the overall schedule, and what can be done about those areas

- Cost analysis—This briefly analyzes the profit picture for the project to date and clearly delineates any areas of concern and the steps that can be taken to minimize the impact

- Subcontract and purchase order management—This involves any problems or project impact caused by subcontractors, vendors, or fabricators. Concerns about subcontractors could include the number of personnel on the project, competency of jobsite personnel, schedule compliance, and potential areas of dispute. Concerns about vendors and fabricators could include delivery date compliance, amounts of material delivered, and quality of material delivered.

- Change orders—These are used to describe the change order progress and problems that might result in change orders.

- Summary—This is used to describe any additional problems or positive aspects relating to the project. Areas of interest or concern are noted, particularly unresolved issues that may become claims.

- Signature of preparer—The preparer should be the superintendent or project manager, as the information submitted requires management insight.

Longer reporting periods, such as monthly, can provide a forum for further analysis than can shorter-term, or weekly, periods. A firm may want only weekly reports to keep abreast of progress, without the detail of daily reports, or a monthly report may be desired for problem-identification and problem-solving analysis. Some firms may want all three levels—daily, weekly, and monthly. Figures 5–3 and 5–4 show weekly and monthly reports, written by the superintendent to the project manager.

Diaries

Diaries are the personal records of conversations and occurrences that are kept by each management individual on the jobsite. Although this is a personal journal concerning the individual's contact and activities, it really is the property of the employer, as it concerns the record of the individual who is employed at the firm.

The diary should be as factual as possible in relating conversations and occurrences. Memory alone, in most cases, is not enough to recall specific conversations and events that took place weeks, months, or even years earlier. The diary is used primarily for disputes that involve specific events or conversations. As it is often used in arbitration, depositions, and court appearances, the writing should be clear and businesslike, and the facts should be accurate. A business diary or journal is a legal record and can be subpoenaed in court cases; therefore, the construction professional should be mindful of the importance of each diary entry.

Traditionally, an individual's daily diary should be as follows:

- Written in the individual's own hand to prove authenticity

- Bound so that pages cannot be inserted

- Consecutively written with each day dated

The form of this diary varies greatly but usually conforms to the aforementioned guidelines. Some individuals use a 12-month hardcover book, with consecutively dated pages. Several commercially produced diary-type books are available, including the spiral-bound type. Some firms use a bound book with duplicate copies, so one copy is kept in the bound book and the other in the job file.

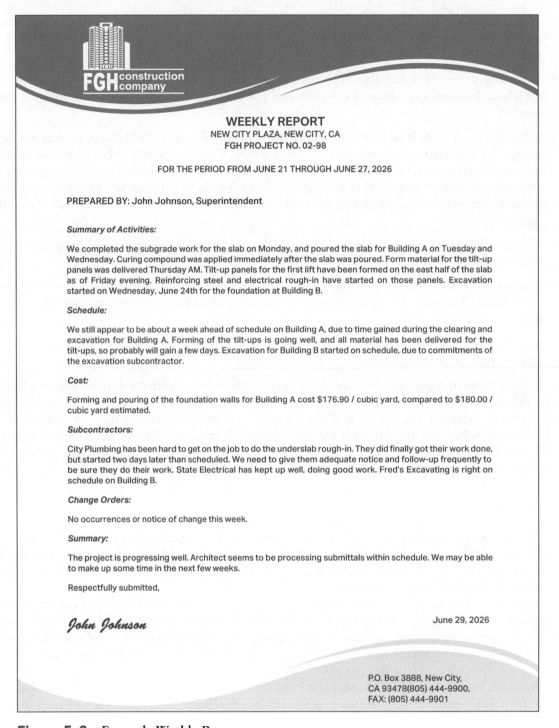

WEEKLY REPORT
NEW CITY PLAZA, NEW CITY, CA
FGH PROJECT NO. 02-98

FOR THE PERIOD FROM JUNE 21 THROUGH JUNE 27, 2026

PREPARED BY: John Johnson, Superintendent

Summary of Activities:

We completed the subgrade work for the slab on Monday, and poured the slab for Building A on Tuesday and Wednesday. Curing compound was applied immediately after the slab was poured. Form material for the tilt-up panels was delivered Thursday AM. Tilt-up panels for the first lift have been formed on the east half of the slab as of Friday evening. Reinforcing steel and electrical rough-in have started on those panels. Excavation started on Wednesday, June 24th for the foundation at Building B.

Schedule:

We still appear to be about a week ahead of schedule on Building A, due to time gained during the clearing and excavation for Building A. Forming of the tilt-ups is going well, and all material has been delivered for the tilt-ups, so probably will gain a few days. Excavation for Building B started on schedule, due to commitments of the excavation subcontractor.

Cost:

Forming and pouring of the foundation walls for Building A cost $176.90 / cubic yard, compared to $180.00 / cubic yard estimated.

Subcontractors:

City Plumbing has been hard to get on the job to do the underslab rough-in. They did finally got their work done, but started two days later than scheduled. We need to give them adequate notice and follow-up frequently to be sure they do their work. State Electrical has kept up well, doing good work. Fred's Excavating is right on schedule on Building B.

Change Orders:

No occurrences or notice of change this week.

Summary:

The project is progressing well. Architect seems to be processing submittals within schedule. We may be able to make up some time in the next few weeks.

Respectfully submitted,

John Johnson

June 29, 2026

P.O. Box 3888, New City,
CA 93478(805) 444-9900,
FAX: (805) 444-9901

Figure 5–3   Example Weekly Report

Because most writing is currently done on word processors and computers, it seems logical that this would be true for the diary as well. Some computer software programs are in journal format, which does not allow the writer to rewrite comments at a later date. However, even a running diary done in a word processing program can provide a historical context to a problem, enabling the writer to recollect conversations and events that relate to a particular issue. It is generally held that this type of documentation is valid, although it does not have the weight a traditional diary does.

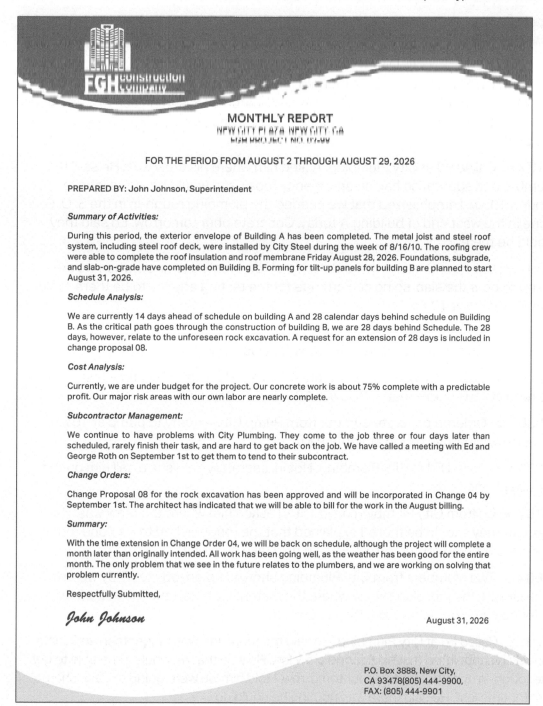

Figure 5–4 Example Monthly Report

There is a further benefit, not always obvious, to the contractor who keeps a daily diary. In writing, the individual concentrates on the events of the day and selects the most important items, thus establishing priorities when problem solving. Solutions to problems often are reached in this way.

What follows is an example of the type of information contained in a superintendent's diary.

Example

Wednesday, June 2, 2026

Our crew working to complete subgrade for slab, west part of building A. Three laborers backfilling and spreading gravel. Two carpenters setting screeds. Plumber not here to finish underslab rough-in. Two electricians completing underslab conduit.

9:10 A.M.: Called Ed at City Plumbing. Asked him where his crew was. He said the plumber and apprentice had an emergency repair and would be at the jobsite around 10 A.M. I emphasized that we needed the plumbing rough-in in the S. O. G. done in the west end of building A today. Concrete pour tomorrow. Ed said they would be there.

9:30 A.M.: Call from Smith at the architect's office. Wanted to know when we are going to pour the slab, so he can arrange for the testing agency to be there. I told him tomorrow at 10 A.M.

10:30 A.M.: Screeds set, subgrade done, except in area of plumbing. Moved crew to building B. Finishers to be here tomorrow for slab pour.

11:00 A.M.: Ordered 75 cu. yds. concrete 4,000 #, ¾" gravel, 4" slump—first truck to be here at 10:00 A.M.—rest to follow in 10-minute intervals.

11:30 A.M.: Ordered concrete pumper from Pump City—ready to pump at 10 A.M. tomorrow, will arrive on job at about 9 A.M.

11:35 A.M.: Called Ed at City Plumbing. Not in, secretary said she'd call him on the mobile phone.

1:15 P.M.: Ed from City Plumbing on jobsite. I asked him where the crew was. He thought they should be there. I explained that the rough-in had to be done today, concrete ordered for tomorrow. Ed said he'd take care of it.

2:00 P.M.: Two plumbers from City Plumbing showed up on jobsite. They weren't familiar with the job, didn't know where the material was, left the job at 2:20 P.M. I tried to keep them there, but they snuck off.

2:20 P.M.: Called Ed at City Plumbing. He said the repair job was bigger than anticipated. He was disappointed that his second crew left. He said that he wouldn't be able to get the rough-in done before the pour tomorrow. I told him we were going to back charge him for time lost. He said there was nothing he could do.

2:45 P.M.: Notified Fred at home office of problem with City Plumbing. He will follow up. Agrees that I have to put off the pour.

3:00 P.M.: Canceled concrete for tomorrow. Canceled inspection for pour.

3:10 P.M. Canceled order for pumper from Pump City. Guy at the desk said they will charge me a cancellation charge. I asked for Bud, but not in—he will call me.

4:45 P.M.: Bud at Pump City called. He said he wouldn't charge cancellation charge, but went on for a while that I should get my act together.

5:05 P.M.: Called Ed at City Plumbing: No answer.

Many firms and individuals prefer to keep a log of telephone conversations, separate from the diary, because the log entry would be made during or immediately after the phone call was made. This also can be accomplished with the diary, as most individuals write their diary entries at the end of the workday. The advantage of combining the diary and telephone conversation record is having a complete record of what occurred in one source.

Logs

Many logs can be kept on the jobsite to collect specific information. These logs are kept in addition to other reports. They can contain a mix of information in each form of document. Many firms will include all telephone call information in a telephone log, while some firms list the calls in a diary. A visitors' log often is kept separate from the daily report. Subcontractor information can be kept in either the daily report or the daily diary. The method usually is chosen based on which method works best for the individuals who are recording the information. The method is not as important as providing complete, accurate, and up-to-date information about the activities and conversations at the jobsite.

Telephone Log

The telephone log can be an accurate account of telephone conversations, or it can be a list that contains the time of the call, the person called, and the person calling. If used for recording the content of the call, information should be accurate and should include when the call was made, who called, who received the call, topics discussed, and promises made. Entries in the telephone log normally are made at the time of the call. When telephone discussions are recorded in the diary, they are included with other events that occur on the jobsite.

Visitors' Log

Many contractors maintain a notebook in the jobsite office for visitors to sign as they enter the area. This practice is probably not as effective as assigning a member of the jobsite team to track visitors and enter their names on the daily report.

Subcontractor Log

Some contractors like to keep a close count of the subcontractors used on the jobsite. A subcontractor log can be organized to record on a daily basis the manpower for each subcontractor. The log can be organized by the date, listing the subcontractors and employees, or by the subcontractor, listing the date and number of employees. This is an important tool when determining whether subcontractor staffing is adequate for the project.

Document Control Log

Construction documents often are changed and supplemented during the construction phase of the project. A document control log records these revisions, with dates and reference-associated documents, such as change orders. This log is very important when organizing large projects.

Accident Reports

Accident reports are specific reports written about particular incidents or accidents. These reports are part of the company's safety program, which is discussed in chapter 9. Safety activities, including occurrences and documentation of meetings and safety programs, are performed throughout the construction phase. (See chapter 9 for a discussion about documentation information and a description of safety activities.)

Progress Photographs

An essential part of jobsite documentation is to photograph the project. Still photographs should be taken at specific intervals throughout the project. Weekly photographs are probably adequate to record the project's progress. Photographs of a special condition, such as defective work, should be taken when the occurrence is encountered. Photographs are used to communicate certain situations both before and after the project. If a dispute arises, a photograph can radically change a person's idea about events and conditions. The old adage that a "photograph doesn't lie" is mostly true in that the photograph accurately portrays its subject.

Because a contractor takes thousands of photographs during a project, a primary concern is labeling and identifying photographs. The following information should be recorded when taking jobsite photographs:

- Date and time the photograph is taken—Some cameras are equipped with an automatic date and time stamp that appears on the negative and the actual photograph.

- Location of the project—The location of the photograph should be noted, as many jobsites look similar. Notation should be made regarding the direction of each photograph, such as "looking northwest from corner G-9."

- Subject matter—Notation should be made regarding the subject that was photographed.

There are numerous ways to record the aforementioned information. A photograph log can be kept, recording pertinent information, including film speed, lens aperture, and shutter speed, although these details are recorded by only the most serious photographers. Electronic (digital) photographs that can be transferred into the computer also are used on the jobsite. These photographs can be processed by a computer, inserted into reports or documents, and electronically transmitted to a remote location, such as the contractor's home office or the architect's office.

After the photograph is developed, it needs to be cataloged. Positive identification is ensured when information about the photograph is contained on the back. Because that information alone is not very retrievable, a computer database of information that has retrieving capabilities can facilitate the labeling of photographs and provide a database that can be sorted or searched for particular information. Typical data fields that might be made for a photograph database include the following:

- Photograph number

- Date, time, and photographer*

- Project, location*

- Subject*

- Issue

- Stage of completion

- Construction system

- Subcontract

   * This information can be added to a label and attached to the back of the photograph.

Video Recordings

Video recordings are an excellent way to document project activity. Any activity that involves motion within a relatively short duration is a good subject for a video recording. Video recording does have some limitations in low-light conditions, however. Most recorders have a time and date feature that permanently stamps the video. Although video can be a good representation of some areas, it involves a time and equipment investment, whereas a few photographs may be all that is needed to quickly tell the story. Some areas where video can provide good records include the following:

- Discovering an unknown condition. The camera operator can record while describing the condition.

- Showing a process, such as an excavation, that can be used on the project. The video can show the equipment used and how long the process took. This type of video is useful for doing time and productivity studies. Real-time recordings should be made for activities of a fairly short duration, considering the cost of the recording media and the likelihood that anyone would watch hours and hours of these recordings.

- Recording existing conditions. Particularly in renovation or remodeling projects, the contract may require the contractor to restore an area to its original condition if it was damaged during construction. The contractor can perform a video walk-through, recording the original conditions. At the end of the project, this video can be reviewed to determine what damage was actually done.

- Videotaping installation techniques that can be used for reference by other superintendents on future projects.

- Videotaping special installations that can be referenced by maintenance personnel. Some special installations should be recorded to provide maintenance personnel with information about how the system was built.

- Videotaping operating and maintenance instructions during the closeout of the project. Videotaping these instructions provides not only a record of but a reference for maintenance personnel.

Like photographs, videotapes should be carefully labeled and stored where they will not be damaged by heat, light, or moisture. Indexing the videos, possibly in a computerized database, makes the information more accessible.

Time-Lapse Photography

Time-lapse photography involves a series of still pictures taken at 1- to 4-second intervals by a special camera from a fixed location. This process provides an accelerated view of the construction process compared to real-time video recordings. This type of recording shows the flow of the process but not the details. Time-lapse photography is used primarily for information in disputes, showing the sequence, equipment, and flow of the project; in productivity studies, showing the effect of jobsite layout and facilities; and in public relations for the contractor, showing how the facility was constructed.

Special attention should be paid to the initial placement of the camera. It should be placed in a location that will show the entire process for the duration of the project, or at least until the exterior work is complete, without the camera being moved during the project. Recording is automatic, but care must be taken to maintain its operation.

Progress Schedules and Schedule Updates

The progress schedule can be used as a record of progress and sequence as well as a plan for the project. Actual events, activities, and occurrences can be tracked and entered on the schedule, providing a record of what actually was done on the project. Chapter 12 provides a detailed description of the uses of the project schedule during construction.

Cost Documentation

Much of the documentation that is done in the field for a contractor relates to tracking cost information. Documentation of cost information has two primary purposes: to transmit information to the company's accounting system for disbursement of funds and to accumulate information to control the project's costs. Both types of cost information are usually collected and disseminated from accounting.

The objective of cost data reporting is to report the information in a manner that will permit cost control during the project and establish a cost database for future reference. Cost information should be assigned to cost codes that correspond with estimating activities to enable the contractor to compare the actual cost with the estimated cost. If this comparison is done quickly and accurately, the contractor can use this information to control the cost during the activity by taking positive action concerning labor, material, subcontractors, or compensation for the item.

Because a wide variety of methods of construction cost accounting exist, many methods of reporting are used. Time is of the essence in most cost reporting, because there are finite periods defined for payment of wages, materials, and subcontracts. Time also is important because problems need to be recognized immediately for activities where cost is exceeding estimate. Accounting systems that provide immediate compilation of data to the jobsite and to accounting are preferred by most contractors. Cost control information available to the jobsite after the activity is completed is not as valuable in project management as is current information.

The following section describes the types of cost documentation that are taken during the construction of a project.

Labor

The field needs to report labor hours to the accounting system. Because this information needs to be specific for payroll information, the accounting office needs to know the number of hours attributable to each employee for established payment periods. For the cost control system, the labor hours and classification need to be reported for specific construction activities. The following example shows information for payroll purposes, submitted weekly.

Example

Name	Soc. Sec. #	Classification	Rate	Hours
Smith, Robert	547-09-8905	Carp 1	$18.57	40

This information is used by accounting to determine the amount of the payroll check, applicable fringe benefits, insurance premiums, and taxes for each employee.

The next example shows additional information that is needed for the cost control system.

Example

Name	Hrly. Cost	Activity	Hours	Quantity
Smith, Robert	$25.40	03101-03	16	2,000 SFCA
	$25.40	03101-05	24	5,000 SFCA

Hourly cost is the cost to the contractor, including wages, fringe benefits, insurance, and taxes. The activity number is a cost code for a specific construction activity. In this case, the construction activity would be concrete forming, with two different form types or locations. The quantity would indicate the amount of production related to the hours worked.

Material

Prior to beginning project construction, the contractor normally prepares a bill of material that lists the types of material, the amount, the vendor, and the cost. The bill of material also should relate the material to the specific construction activity. Purchase orders are generated from the bill of material. A purchase order is an agreement to purchase items from a vendor and may include several different materials and activity codes and multiple delivery dates. The purchase order is used for ordering material and for payment by accounting. The following example shows a bill of material for concrete formwork, footings.

Example

Code	Material	Quantity	Vendor	Cost	PO #
03100-01	2 × 6 F&L, 2+	3,000 BF	Acme Lumber	$1,500	294-03
	1 × 2 stakes × 18	500 ea	Acme Lumber	$ 100	294-03
	2" Waterstop	1,500 LF	U.S. Concrete Co.	$ 750	294-10

Some computerized estimating software produces a bill of material that automatically combines all activity code items for the material classification, similar to the bill of material that follows.

Example

Description	Takeoff Qty.	Order Qty.	Unit Price	Amount
Carpentry-Lumber:				
2 × 4 × 8 Standard & Better	45.00 each	26 MBF	$475/MBF	$123.50
2 × 4 × 10 Standard & Better	21.00 each	15 MBF	$475/MBF	$ 71.25
2 × 4 × 12 Standard & Better	34.00 each	29 MBF	$475/MBF	$137.75

This information also can be sorted by vendor to provide information for purchase orders.

The purchase order, because it is a purchase agreement, details the terms of the agreement and references the construction documents as necessary. The purchase order also specifies the terms of payment for material. It cites the date of the bid or pricing and who made the offer. A list of the material, its cost, its anticipated delivery date, and the activity code for the contractor's code also should be provided. In addition to this information, other particulars may be included, such as the catalog or inventory number and the sales tax amount. Further information on the bill of material and purchase orders can be found in chapter 10. The following example shows a list of materials for a purchase order.

Example

Code	Material	Quant.	Unit Price	Cost	Delivery Date
03100-01	2 × 6 F&L, 2+	3,000 BF	$500/MBF	$1,500.00	5/22/26
03100-01	1 × 2 stakes × 18"	500 EA	$ 20/C	$ 100.00	5/22/26
03100-10	2 × 4 F&L, 2+	10,000 BF	$450/MBF	$4,500.00	5/29/26
Total P.O. 294-03				$6,100.00	

Equipment

The contractor's owned equipment has certain rates associated with it, reflecting the computed cost of investment, fuel, repair costs, and miscellaneous costs, recognizing that the equipment does not work full-time. Reporting the hours of usage then relates to the amount of time the equipment is actually being used for its intended tasks. As described previously in the daily report, it is important to record the presence of the equipment and its immediate availability on the jobsite.

Owned equipment at the established internal rental rate is charged to the actual work activities. Operating labor is usually not included in the rate because the labor reporting should be done separately from the equipment reporting. The following is a weekly report on the activities of a Caterpillar D-7N bulldozer on the jobsite.

Example

Act. Code	Description	Rate	Hours
02210-01	SITE GRADING, GRID A2-G4	$63.40	16
02210-02	SITE GRADING, GRID G5-J10	$63.40	16
02210-03	SITE GRADING, GRID J10-K12	$63.40	8

Some equipment is rented from outside sources. In this case, the rental cost and miscellaneous costs, such as fuel, should be invoiced to accounting for payment, with cost information going to cost control accounts.

Correspondence

Correspondence with other parties in the construction process is a major form of documentation of the construction project. Each construction contract and agreement requires that all requests, directions, and changes be in written form. Although legal agreements can be made orally and confirmed by a handshake, current construction customs dictate that all discussions be recorded, or written, to provide proof of the existence of such an agreement. The construction process is complex and can extend into several years, requiring reliance on written documents rather than on human memory.

All correspondence should be well crafted by the author. Written correspondence needs to accurately convey the message completely while being as brief as possible. Care must be taken by the author to avoid misinterpretation of the intent or content of the message. The correspondence probably will be reviewed by people other than the addressee; thus, a clear, objective statement of all of the information is required in the correspondence. Humor, emotional appeals, threats, and strong language are inappropriate for the majority of construction correspondence. These elements can be easily misconstrued by the reader, who may attach an unintended meaning to the text. The writer must always be polite and professional despite the emotion that may be generated by an incident.

Most construction correspondence, with the exception of transmittals, address specific issues or problems encountered during the project. The following guidelines can be used for construction correspondence:

1. **Reference:** Reference the project name and number. When writing to the architect and owner, the contractor should list both the official project number and the contractor's project number. Further reference may be added to a letter, RFI, particular issue, or other previous correspondence.

Example

Re: Construction of New City Plaza; Project No. 2010-001-NCP

FGH Construction Project No. 2-2010

RFI from FGH Construction Co., dated 5/28/26

Unsuitable Soil at Building B

2. **Description and Location:** For problem resolution, it is essential that the situation be described exactly, without confusion. Many times an incident can cause several problems that need to be solved independently. The exact location of the problem needs to be detailed as accurately as possible. It is not uncommon for the same problem to occur in more than one location on the project, which requires an accurate description of the location for each instance. Detailed information about a particular problem normally will expedite its solution. A description of the condition, references to drawings and specifications, quantities, and even pricing information are appropriate when explaining the problem. Withholding information as a strategy to avoid showing the firm's full position usually confuses and lengthens the discussion, turning it into a dispute.

Example

As per our RFI dated 5/28/26, faxed to your office, our excavator located solid rock and rock described as solid rock, larger than a ½ yard bucket, in the rock clause, Section 02200, paragraph 4, page 2-2-1 of the Project Manual, on May 28, 2026. This solid rock appears at elevation 1556.0 at grid G-0 and appears to extend to about Grid E to the north and Grid 4 to the east, at Building B. The bottom-of-slab elevation in this area is intended to be 1550.0. Test pits in the area of Building B do not indicate solid rock. Elevation 1556.0 is below the bottom of the nearest test pits, B-11 and B-2. We estimate the rock to be 1,068 cubic yards in quantity; however, the exact amount of rock will vary from this amount, due to the irregular rock formation, which will be revealed during the rock removal.

3. **Objective of Correspondence:** Without clearly stating the objective of the correspondence, the description of an occurrence could be ambiguous. The writer needs to state, with certainty, one's position and justification and what is desired. Some individuals try to avoid being direct in an effort to be polite. Being direct is not impolite but rather a route to resolution. If a monetary settlement is sought, the amount, or at least the method of payment, should be specified.

Example

FGH Construction Company feels that the removal of this material was not required in the contract documents and that we should be compensated for the removal of the rock material, as per the specified rock removal rate, as per our proposal of 2/23/26, in the amount of $114/bank cubic yard. Using an

(continued)

approximate quantity of 1,068 bank cubic yards, the resulting addition to the contract would be $121,752 for the removal of this rock. We suggest that your on-site inspector accurately measure the exact quantity of the rock excavation, with our surveyor's assistance, as excavation progresses to provide an accurate estimate of the rock quantity.

4. **Summary:** The summary of the letter should clearly indicate what has happened or what is expected to happen. Most decisions or actions, within contractual confines, have further actions associated with them. If the construction firm feels they deserve extra compensation for additional work, they should request a change order. If the architectural firm rejects a request for a change order, they normally will request that the work be done at no additional cost. When further action is requested, usually a stipulated time restraint is added as well.

Example

FGH Construction Company is hereby requesting a change order to the contract for the removal of the solid rock encountered in Building B. We feel that this contract change order should be compensated for the amount of rock removed, inspected, and measured by your inspector and our surveyor, at a previously negotiated price of $114/bank cubic yard. Excavation work can continue for a brief period of time before we are delayed by a decision. Please notify us on June 1, 2026, of your decision for this additional work.

5. **Signature:** Every piece of correspondence should be signed by the originator of the document. Some correspondence, such as a request for a change to the contract, has significant contract implications and should be signed by the authorized party.

The construction contractor uses a number of vehicles to correspond with other parties in the construction process, depending on its purpose. Some of the most common forms of correspondence are described next.

Letter of Transmittal

The letter of transmittal is a dated record of when a particular document or item was sent to another party. It is necessary proof that a particular piece of information was sent from one party to another, but it is not conclusive proof that the item was received. To ensure receipt, the contractor should request that the document be sent by certified mail, with a return card showing the signature of the receiving party. A wide variety of couriers and delivery services that obtain signatures of receipt are available. Signed receipts usually are necessary for important documents, such as contracts; time-sensitive documents, such as change order documents or payment documents; security items, such as keys; and valuable items.

The letter of transmittal usually contains the minimum following elements:

• Name and address of sender

• Name and address of intended receiver

- Project number (both project numbers, if applicable)
- Item sent (full description)
- Number of copies of the item
- Notes relating to the item

Preprinted forms are available for transmittals. Special forms are available for contractors, containing boxes for the most commonly sent items, such as submittals, shop drawings, contracts, change orders, and so on; what they are being sent for (review, recipient's use, and so on); and what should be done with them, such as "return four approved copies." Prepared from templates or form-making software that are available for word processors and computers, these forms are convenient to fill out at the computer.

Fax transmittals are common in construction correspondence. As the fax message is instantly received rather than being received several days later, it is currently used for most construction correspondence. Fax transmittals also can be customized for the contract's specific needs. Many businesses send faxes directly from their computers, with a computer-generated fax transmittal sheet.

RFI

The contractor has numerous questions throughout a project concerning documents, construction, materials, and numerous other items. Traditionally, a phone call or informal conversation with the architect solved the problem. It is now necessary, however, to document every request and reply. Extra costs or complications can arise during the process, requiring use of the RFI to substantiate a project's direction.

RFIs have a number of uses, several of which do not have cost implications. The request for clarification can be a non-change item and can merely require information about something shown in the documents. It can be a simple query to the architect regarding a particular in the construction document. Initially, the RFI normally just asks for clarification. It also can be a notice to the architect about an occurrence or knowledge of an occurrence as well as a notice of latent, or unknown, conditions.

Most RFIs are brief questions requesting clarification. It is important, however, that the RFI contain all of the necessary information and not be too brief. If the contractor is requesting a clarification, the architect needs to know exactly what is unclear. If multiple issues are contained in the RFI, then each one should be clearly delineated, requesting a reply for each one. When asking for clarification, all relative facts should be presented. Complete and honest representation of conditions and factors will result in timely and fair responses.

The guidelines for correspondence, mentioned earlier, apply to the RFI, although the RFI is usually considered a short communication. It is important that the RFI clearly state the problem and define what type of response is desired. Each RFI is numbered in the sequence issued, the number being used as a reference. Coordination among members of the jobsite team is necessary to avoid double numbering or leaving a gap between actual RFIs. The RFI is a time-sensitive document that requires immediate information. The date the RFI was sent should be included, as a dated response is needed.

The RFI (sometimes called the request for clarification) also is available in preprinted form. Most contractors custom-prepare their forms and include specific information relevant to their business. Multiple copy forms, using carbon paper or NCR forms, can be used. A template form can be prepared for the computer, which facilitates communication. Some integrated document management programs, such as Expedition (discussed in chapter 13), include a form for RFIs. RFIs are commonly faxed to parties to speed communications. Most RFI forms use the top half of the sheet for the request and the bottom half for the reply. Figure 5–5 illustrates a sample blank RFI form, with the completed information shown in Figure 5–6.

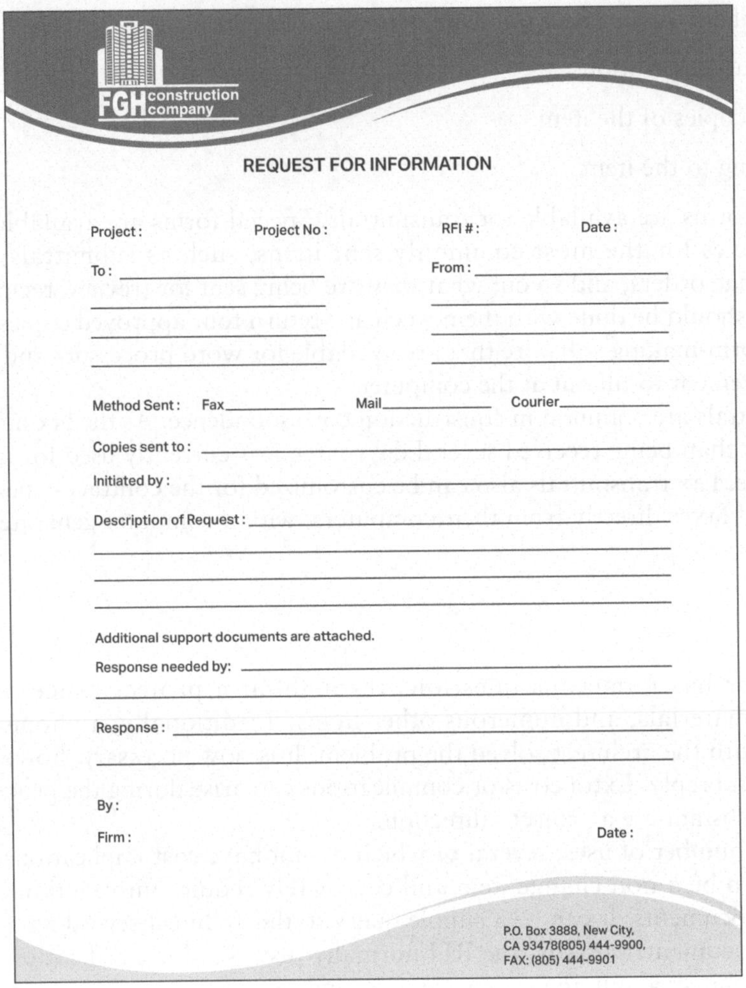
FGH construction company

REQUEST FOR INFORMATION

Project: Project No: RFI #: Date:

To: From:

Method Sent: Fax____ Mail____ Courier____

Copies sent to:

Initiated by:

Description of Request:

Additional support documents are attached.

Response needed by:

Response:

By:

Firm: Date:

P.O. Box 3888, New City, CA 93478(805) 444-9900, FAX: (805) 444-9901

Figure 5–5 Example Request for Information Form (Blank)

An increasing belief in the industry is that the contractor should be compensated for time spent processing RFIs, as the majority of them relate to errors, omissions, and conflicting information in the construction documents. Further, many contractors feel that the mere number of RFIs indicates incompetent completion of the documents that warrants an award for damages. Most of these cases need to be determined in the courts. The RFI should be used as a request for further information or clarification rather than as a vehicle for a claim. Documentation of the clarification is necessary to eliminate unnecessary disputes.

Letters

Letters are used to provide and obtain information, request action, reply to a request for action, or present an explanation. They are used to encourage activity by parties in the construction process as well. The telephone call is the quickest form of communication, whereas the letter is probably the most powerful. A letter, as a valid piece of documentation, can make demands or state facts more strongly, thus having more of an impact than a telephone conversation. Both forms of communication should be used to obtain results, but obviously the letter is more time consuming and expensive than the telephone.

The previously mentioned guidelines for correspondence also apply to letter writing. The letter should address a specific issue, using standard language in most cases. Inconsistencies

REQUEST FOR INFORMATION

PROJECT : New City Plaza   PROJECT NO : 2-98   RFI # : 082   Date : August 21, 2026
                           98-001-NCP

To : R.G. Smith   From : F.W. Johnson
      Smith Architects   FGH Construction
      P.O. Box 2334
      Atascadero, CA 93784
      FAX: (805) 834-0987

Method Sent :   Fax_____X_____   Mail_____   Courier_____

Copies sent to : City Printing

Initiated by :   F.W. Johnson

Description of Request :

The Finish Schedule shows the north wall of Room 245, Building A, to be painted Canary Yellow. The drawings, on sheet A-22, detail 4, note that the color of the north wall in 245 is to be "Robin's Egg Blue." The painter will be in this area on 8/23/2026; and we need to know the proper color to get the paint mixed.

Additional support documents are attached.

Response needed by: 8/22/2026 12:00 PM

Response :

The color of the North wall in Room 245, Building A, is intended to be "Robin's Egg Blue." Please submit a sample of this paint prior to application.

We are assuming that this is a non-cost clarification. Please change the notation in the Finish Schedule to Robin's Egg Blue.

By : R G Smith   R.G. Smith   Date : August 21, 2026 3:00 PM

Firm : Smith Architects   Sent via Fax

                                                    P.O. Box 2356
                                                    New City, CA 93209
                                                    FAX: (905) 342-7654

Figure 5–6   Example Request for Information Form (Completed)

and unnecessary language can result in the letter not being taken seriously by the reader. Form letters, although appropriate in some situations, always read as such and do not get the recipient's attention. There are situations, however, where mail-merging functions in the computer can personalize a form letter, avoiding the tedious task of writing individual letters. In the example that follows, the contractor is sending letters to all of his subcontractors requesting shop drawings or submittals. In the database, the contractor has included the subcontractors' names and addresses, the type of submittal they are required to submit, and the date the submittal is due.

Example

Database Listing:

First/Last Name	Firm	Address	City	Submittal	Date
A. C. Jones	AC Acoustical	P.O. Box 3456	New City, CA	Ceiling drawings	6/10/26
Fred Nelson	Nelson Tile	P.O. Box 3478	New City, CA	Ceramic tile sample	6/01/26
Dave Anders	Anders Plbg.	P.O. Box 1233	New City, CA	Plumbing submittal	5/14/26

A letter to all of the previous subcontractors can be written using the mail-merge function in the word processor. The items inserted from the database are underlined in the sample letter shown in Figure 5–7.

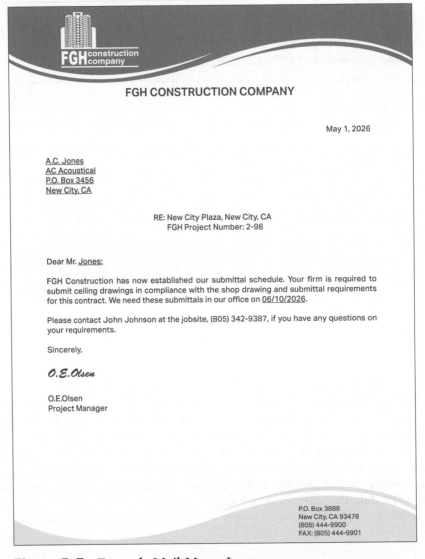

Figure 5–7   Example Mail-Merge Letter

Several types of letters are used in the construction industry, the most familiar being the standard letter form on company letterhead. Numerous other forms, such as speed letters with multiple copies and carbons and space for a reply, are frequently used for short notes. Regardless of the form, all correspondence needs to be filed and retained. The filing system may reflect the particulars of outgoing correspondence, such as who is writing the letter or the issue that is involved. Whatever the filing method, it should be consistent for document retrieval, as needed. Integrated document systems allow immediate retrieval of the document, or parts of the document, by issue.

E-mail

E-mail is becoming more popular for business correspondence as well as for personal correspondence. It is instantly available and convenient for both the sender and the receiver. However, the same considerations for other types of communications apply to e-mail. E-mail often is a short, abbreviated message, but it can be a full letter as well, using the guidelines previously discussed. Software is available for sending a variety of documents, including schedules, via a modem. Because of the fragile nature of computer hardware, all electronic correspondence should be copied to avoid the risk of losing documents.

Contractual Requirement Documentation

Numerous pieces of documentation of the construction process are required by contract documents. Most follow a required standard format, whether on a form or not. These documents, while conveying a particular purpose within, provide a record of the activities of the project. Progress payment requests are specifically formatted documents the contractor uses to show the amount earned during the construction period. Progress payment requests also provide a record of the contractor's progress. A list of the types of contractually required documents follows:

Start

Project Start-Up:

Construction Schedule

Schedule of Values

List of Subcontractors

Product Submittals, Shop Drawings, and Samples

Construction Progress:

Progress Payment Requests

Construction Schedule Updates

Certified Payrolls

Contract Change Orders: Proposals, Directives, and Change Orders

Project Closeout:

Certificate of Substantial Completion

Lien Releases

Consent of Surety

Warranties

Operation and Maintenance Manuals

Spare Parts

Punch Lists

Meeting Minutes

Meetings are frequent occurrences during the construction process. A meeting provides several people the opportunity to discuss current matters of concern about the project, face to face. The construction meeting is formal, with an agenda, a leader, and some structure. Different types of meetings during the construction process include partnering meetings and workshops, preconstruction meetings, progress meetings, subcontractor meetings, special installation meetings, schedule coordination meetings, safety meetings, and postconstruction meetings. All have various purposes and thus have different participants and a unique atmosphere. (See chapter 7 for a further discussion about these meetings.)

Because important discussion occurs in the aforementioned meetings, careful minutes should be taken to reflect the conversation and any resolution of issues. Minutes provide not an exact record of the meeting but rather an accurate summary of the major points and who made them. They are as objective and truthful as possible. Because topics are summarized, redundant discussion, trivial points, or long explanations are avoided.

The minutes taker has a certain amount of control of the project. The primary goal when taking minutes is to be as objective as possible. Even the most objective minutes taker will be biased to some extent. Most individuals who participate in project meetings view taking minutes as a burden rather than an opportunity. Recording, editing, writing, and distributing the minutes does take extra effort but, as stated earlier, can result in subtle control advantages.

Occasionally the minutes taker does not accurately report the action that occurred at the meeting. If this should happen, any objections should be sent to the recorder and discussed in the subsequent meeting. When the minutes are consistently inaccurate, concerned individuals should keep their own notes and write and distribute an alternative set of minutes.

Progress meetings are the most common during the construction phase of the project. The elements that follow are key to progress meeting minutes, which also are similar for other meeting types.

Title

The title should address the type of document, type of meeting, date of the meeting, and sequential number of the meeting. The time and location of the meeting also should be included.

Example

Minutes of the Meeting

Construction Progress Meeting

Meeting #4

May 6, 2026, 9:00 A.M.

FGH Construction Co. Conference Room

Project Designation

Project name and project number (may be several numbers), as in the other documents.

Example

Project: New City Plaza, New City, CA Project No. FGH Const #2-2010

Smith Architects # 2010-001-NCP

Parties in Attendance

There are two ways to record the parties in attendance at a meeting. The first method is to list the parties at the meeting. The minutes taker should note who is present and the time individuals arrive or leave. The list of individuals also should include their firms. This method ensures that all parties are recorded, as long as the recorder is familiar with all meeting participants.

Example

Parties in Attendance: Thomas Thompson, New City Plaza Development Corp.; R. G. Smith, Fred Stone, Smith Architects; O. E. Olsen, John Johnson, FGH Construction; George Roth, City Plumbing (arrived at 9:45 A.M.); Charlotte Smith, State Electric; A. C. Jones, AC Acoustical (left at 9:30 A.M.).

The second method is to provide an attendance roster or sign-up sheet for all meeting participants. This method documents attendance in the event that a dispute later arises. It does not, however, ensure that all attendees will sign the sheet, particularly if they arrive late. The minutes taker should follow up to obtain the signatures of all parties listed on the roster.

Example

Parties in Attendance: See Attached Attendance Roster (Figure 5–8).

Minutes from the Previous Meeting

This section indicates any additions or corrections to the previous meeting. Usually there are none, which also should be noted. This section may seem like a waste of time, but it provides corrections that complete the validity of the minutes as a viable project document.

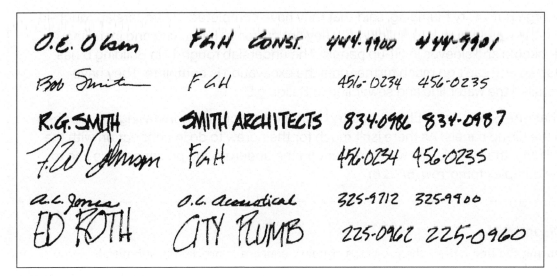

Figure 5–8   Example Meeting Attendance Roster

Example

Minutes from the Previous Meeting: No corrections or additions were made to the meeting of April 28, 2026.

Example

Minutes from the Previous Meeting: George Roth noted that he had stated that City Plumbing was complete with the underslab plumbing rough-in in Building A and just starting the rough-in in Building B, not "complete with the rough-in in Buildings A and B," as shown in the minutes.

No other corrections or additions were made.

Project Progress

This section can be handled in a number of different ways, in a full section or in an items of business section. One of the most important elements of a construction progress meeting is the update of current construction progress. This is an item of interest to the parties attending the meeting and to those reading the minutes who are not able to attend the meeting, thus creating a record of the project's progress.

Example

Project Progress:

John Johnson, FGH Construction Co., updated the progress of the project. The slab-on-grade for Building A was poured on May 4, 2026. They are now starting forming for the tilt-up panels. Tilt-up drawings have been approved for Building A. Tilt-up drawings for Building B will be submitted on May 10, 2026. All of the reinforcing steel for Building A has now been delivered to the jobsite. Excavation has started for Building B. Johnson's only concerns are about some of the submittals (next section).

George Roth, City Plumbing, said that they have completed the underslab rough-in and the water service to Building A. They are currently furnishing and installing blockouts and sleeves in tilt-up panels. The underslab rough-in in Building B has started and can't go much further until the excavation is complete. They have installed the water line and sewer line to Building B.

Charlotte Smith, State Electric, stated that they are currently installing the rough-in in the tilt-up panels. As there isn't much for their crew to do in connection with the building, the electricians will start work on the underground power service line to the complex tomorrow (5/7/26).

Submittals

During the first half of the project, a primary concern is processing submittals, samples, and shop drawings. The timely processing of these items relates to the release for ordering and fabrication of the material and equipment. Discussion about submittals normally occurs in a construction progress meeting. In addition to the discussion on changes in submittals, a submittal log might be attached to the minutes to concerned parties to indicate the status of any submittals.

Example

Submittals:

The mechanical submittal in total has been submitted, reviewed, and returned to FGH Construction. AC Acoustical submitted the ceiling drawings at this meeting to FGH Construction. They will be forwarded to Smith Architects immediately, following review by FGH Construction.

The Submittal Log Is Attached:

Section #	Item	To FGH	To Smith	To FGH
03200	Rebar Dwgs.	4/15/26	4/17/26	4/28/26
03350	Tilt-up Dwgs.	4/20/26	4/28/26	5/4/26
05100	Str. Stl. Dwgs.	5/1/26	5/6/26	
06400	Cabinet Dwgs.			
07400	Roofing Sub.			
08200	HM Doors	4/10/26	4/11/26	4/15/26
08700	Fin. Hdwe.	4/10/26	4/11/26	4/15/26
09300	Cer. Tile			
09500	Acoust. Clgs.	5/6/26		
09650	Carpet			
09900	Painting			
15000	Mechanical	4/10/26	4/11/26	5/4/26
16000	Electrical	4/28/26	5/1/26	

More information might be included in the submittal log, such as scheduled dates, delivery schedule, actual delivery date, activity relationship, and start of activity. (For a broader discussion about the submittal or procurement schedule, see chapter 4.)

Change Orders

The progress of change orders is a major project issue for both the contractor and the subcontractor, who are interested in the authorization of the change order, so that work can proceed, and in the final approval of the change order, work can be billed on the monthly progress payment request. The current status of change orders should be discussed in the progress meeting. A log of the current progress of change orders, attached or included in the minutes, prevents many problems when answering phone calls for subcontractors who are inquiring about their status. (See chapter 14 for a more complete discussion about change orders.)

Example

Change Orders:

Change Proposal 06, "Additional floor hardener, Bldg B" has been submitted and approved, directive issued. It will be combined with other items in C. O. 2.

The change order log is attached:

C.P.#	Descrip.	Submit	Approve	Direct.	C.O.#	Date
01	Brick type	3/28/26	4/2/26	4/2/26	1	4/15/26
02	Drain Tile	4/1/26	4/3/26	4/3/26	1	4/15/26
03	Water PR Valve	5/5/26	Resubmit			
10	Sprinkler Cont.	4/5/26	4/16/26	4/18/26	2	5/6/26
05	Lt. Fixt. F-12	4/15/26	4/28/26		2	5/6/26
06	Hardener, B	4/28/26	5/5/26	5/5/26	2	5/6/26

The distribution of minutes goes beyond the contractual line among the owner, architect, and contractor. It should be noted that the amount of the change orders is not included in the minutes and is basically confidential information. Depending on the change order structure, other items may be included in the log as well.

Old Business

The old and new business areas relate to discussions about project issues. Each item of business should be numbered (with the meeting number and item number). This system indicates the age of the item in old business. All items that have not yet been resolved should be included here.

Example

Old Business:

298-02-03: Water Pressure-Reducing Valve: The price on the pressure-reducing valve included in Change Proposal 03 is unacceptable to the owner. The mechanical engineer has suggested pricing an "ACME" valve, #304, and resubmitting.

298-03-01: Power Interruption: The owner still needs to know the date of the power interruption with the underground connection. Charlotte Smith, State Electric, stated that the connection should be made in the next 2 weeks and will establish a date with the maintenance staff.

New Business

All new business should contain the following information: who introduced the problem, a description of the problem, who will take action, what action will be taken, and when the action will be taken. Common practice at construction progress meetings is for any individual present to introduce items.

Example

New Business:

298-10-01: R. H. Smith, Smith Architects, mentioned a concern about proper curing on the slab on grade. John Johnson stated that a curing compound was applied the day after the slab was poured. Smith agreed that the curing compound was adequate. No further action necessary.

298-10-02: John Johnson, FGH Construction, mentioned that the excavator found what appears to be solid rock in Building B. He will notify the architect by RFI if there is a significant rock problem, probably by 5/8/26.

298-10-03: A. C. Jones, AC Acoustical, asked if ¼" scale was adequate for the ceiling shop drawings. Smith indicated that it was adequate. Jones submitted the shop drawings to FGH Construction at the meeting.

Meeting Adjourned, Next Meeting

The minutes should indicate the time the meeting was adjourned and should announce the next regularly scheduled meeting. Including the meeting date in the minutes, assuming that the minutes are issued immediately, saves an additional meeting announcement.

Example

Meeting adjourned at 10:45 A.M.

Next Meeting: May 14, 2026, 9:00 A.M., FGH Construction Conference Room

Meeting minutes are traditionally distributed to those in attendance and the three major participants in the project. Normally the architect is responsible for forwarding copies to sub-consultants and the contractor for forwarding copies to subcontractors. The contractor should carefully review the contents of the minutes and send them to the affected subcontractors if blanket mailing is not a standard.

Immediate distribution of the minutes minimizes confusion. Minutes should be read, noted, and corrected (if necessary) and kept on file for future reference. Meeting minutes are among the most important documentation, indicating the direction of the construction project.

Summary

Project documentation is an essential function of project administration. Several different areas need to be documented:

- Events, occurrences, and conversations—documented by daily reports, weekly reports, monthly reports, diaries, telephone and other logs, accident reports, photographs, time lapse photography, videotape recordings, and schedules.

- Costs—documented by purchase orders, subcontracts, material reports, labor reports, and equipment reports.

- Correspondence—documented by transmittals, RFIs, and letters.

- Contractual requirements—documented by payment requests, schedules of values, change orders, punch lists, and certificates of substantial completion.

- Meetings—documented by meeting minutes.

- Documentation should be honest, accurate, complete, and usually sequential. Careful documentation, considering all aspects of the events, helps the contractor solve problems on the project and facilitate budget and duration goals.

Documentation is also the foundation for successful claims, arbitration, and litigation.

Todays' modern construction project documentation is written, saved, shared, and stored with use of computers and computer software. There are a number of project management tools available to the project management team today, and they all seem to be growing and adding new features to their original configuration. There is even a trend to add main office functions, such as estimating and additional connections to legacy accounting systems.

Documentation is essential for all construction projects. It helps to ensure that everyone involved in the project is on the same page. It is the tool for collaboration, and decimating information to all stakeholders, clarifying and solving issues. It lets the owners know how their projects are progressing as well as the construction firm's main office.

There are many different types of construction documentation, but four main categories stand out, they are:

- **Contract documents:** These documents outline the terms of the contract between the owner and the contractor. They include the scope of work, the schedule, the budget, and the payment terms.

- **Design documents:** These documents are created by the architect or engineer and show the design of the project. They include drawings, specifications, and other technical documents.

- **Construction documents:** These documents are created by the contractor and show how the project will be built and is being built. They include drawings, schedules, and other technical documents.

- **As-built documents or record drawings:** These documents are created during and after the project is completed and show how the project was built. They are used for future reference, such as for maintenance and repairs. Today these are generally required to be in electronic and digital form, i.e., an AutoCad-like format.

The Importance of Accurate and Timely Documentation

- Accurate documentation is essential for any construction project. It helps to avoid disputes and delays, and it can help to protect the owner, the contractor, and the subcontractors.

- Timely documentation is also important. It helps to ensure that the project is completed on time and within budget. If documentation is not completed in a timely manner, this can lead to delays and cost overruns. Often end-of-job completion and further commissioning may not start without full documentation.

The Importance of Electronic Documentation

Electronic documentation is becoming increasingly common in the construction industry. There are many advantages to using electronic documentation, including:

- **It is more efficient:** Electronic documents can be easily shared and updated, which saves time and effort.

- **It is more secure:** Electronic documents can be password-protected and backed up, which helps to protect them from theft and damage.

- **It is more accessible:** Electronic documents can be accessed from anywhere, which makes it easier for everyone involved in the project to stay up to date.

And one cannot overemphasize its importance for the resolution of changes, claims, arbitration, and litigation.

- **Dispute resolution:** Construction documentation can be used to resolve disputes by providing a clear and concise record of the project. This can help to identify the facts of the dispute and to reach a fair and equitable resolution.

- **Litigation:** Construction documentation can be used in litigation by also providing a clear and concise record of the project. This can help to support the claims of the parties involved in the litigation.

Construction claims are a common occurrence in the construction industry. They can arise from a variety of sources, such as:

- Changes in the scope of work

- Delays in the project schedule

- Defective materials or workmanship

- Negligence or misconduct by a party to the contract

When a claim arises, it is important to have good construction documentation in order to support the claim. This documentation can include:

- The contract documents

- Change orders

- Correspondence

- Photographs

- Inspection reports

- Test results

If a claim cannot be resolved through negotiation, it may be necessary to file a lawsuit. In litigation, the construction documentation will be critical in proving the merits of the claim. A party that does not have good construction documentation is at a significant disadvantage in litigation.

The outcome of a construction claim, or litigation can vary depending on several factors, but good construction documentation will make a significant difference in the outcome of a claim or litigation. By taking the time to create and maintain good construction documentation, you can help to protect your interests in the event of a dispute.

Here are some additional tips for creating and maintaining good construction documentation:

- Keep all documentation in one place. This will make it easier to access the documentation when needed.

- Date and label all documentation. This will help to establish the timeline of events and the sequence of events.

- Keep the documentation organized. This will make it easier to find the information you need.

- Make sure the documentation is accurate and complete. This will help to strengthen your case in the event of a dispute.

By following these tips, you can help to create and maintain good construction documentation that can protect your interests in the event of a dispute.

DroneDeploy is a company that is using technology to revolutionize construction documentation. DroneDeploy provides a platform that allows users to capture and process all reality capture data, including drone maps, drone media, 360 media, post-processed media tours, and scan data, and supports autonomous captures with robots. This platform can be used to create accurate and up-to-date documentation of construction projects, which can help to improve efficiency, safety, and quality.

Here are some specific ways that DroneDeploy and StructionSite's technologies are being used to improve construction documentation:

- **Accurate and up-to-date documentation:** DroneDeploy and StructionSite's platforms can be used to create accurate and up-to-date documentation of construction projects. This documentation can be used to track progress, identify potential problems, and make informed decisions.

- **Improved safety:** DroneDeploy and StructionSite's platforms can be used to improve safety on construction sites. For example, drones can be used to inspect high-risk areas, such as roofs and bridges, without the need for workers to climb up.

- **Improved quality:** DroneDeploy and StructionSite's platforms can be used to improve the quality of construction projects. For example, drones can be used to create 3D models of buildings, which can be used to identify potential construction flaws.

Overall, DroneDeploy and StructionSite's technologies can be a valuable tool for construction companies that are looking to improve their documentation practices. By using these technologies, companies can create accurate, up-to-date, and secure documentation of their projects, which can help to improve efficiency, safety, and quality.

Another example of modern construction software that helps the overall process is called Clearstory.

Traditionally, the change order process relied heavily on paper, e-mail, and excel to track costs between companies.

Clearstory is the construction industry's only change order communication network. It helps general contractors, specialty contractors, and owners communicate project change order requests and time and material tags in an easy-to-use collaborative cloud-based log so companies can always be on the same page. Along with a powerful communication platform, Clearstory includes features such as digital time and material tags, easy-to-use change order templates, and more to streamline the process further between companies.

Here are some specific ways that Clearstory can help:

- **Shareable source of truth:** Clearstory automatically structures all CORs sent on a project in a shareable cloud-based log between parties. This log automatically stores all change order documentation and keeps a digital paper trail of all events related to that COR.

- **Speed up change order processing:** Clearstory digitizes many workflows in the change order process, such as digitally tracking field-directed change order work on a mobile app and distributing design changes for pricing through a structured workflow. These speeds up time to visibility for surfacing costs for all parties.

- **Facilitate change order review:** Change orders can be a big source of risk for construction projects. Clearstory automatically organizes all change orders and brings in modern tools such as real-time messaging, PDF markups, and more to allow general contractors to review the documentation to check for valid scope, accurate rates, etc.

- **Proactive decision making:** Because Clearstory captures changes in project costs in real time, all parties can make value-based decisions with all the information at their fingertips. These tools include data analysis, project scheduling, and risk management.

Here are some additional benefits of using Clearstory for construction documentation:

- **Increased productivity:** Clearstory can help to increase productivity by automating many of the tasks associated with documentation. This frees employees to focus on other tasks, such as managing the project and completing the work.

- **Reduced risk:** Clearstory reduces the risk for all stakeholders by surfacing costs faster and adding transparency. This helps specialty contractors speed up cash flow and protect revenue, general contractors reduce the risk of fee erosion, and owners get fair value on what they pay for.

- **Improved relationships:** Construction is a people industry. One of the biggest sources of conflict can come from change order disputes. By adding trust and transparency Clearstory helps all stakeholders proactively avoid these issues making construction a better industry for everyone.

And to end this chapter, one of the leaders in construction management software should be mentioned along with what it can provide today's construction firm. Procore is a construction management software that provides a comprehensive suite of tools to help construction firms manage their projects more effectively. Procore's features include:

- **Project management:** Procore provides a centralized platform for managing all aspects of a construction project, from planning and budgeting to scheduling and execution.

- **Procurement:** Procore's procurement module helps construction firms manage their purchasing process, from sourcing and bidding to contract management.

- **Quality control:** Procore's quality control module helps construction firms track and manage their quality assurance processes.

- **Safety:** Procore's safety module helps construction firms track and manage their safety procedures.

- **Document control:** Procore's document control module helps construction firms store and manage all of their project documentation.

- **Cost management:** Procore's cost management module helps construction firms track and manage their project costs.

- **Reporting:** Procore's reporting module provides construction firms with the ability to generate reports on all aspects of their projects.

Procore is a powerful tool that can help construction firms improve their efficiency, productivity, and profitability. If you are looking for a construction management software that can help you take your business to the next level, I encourage you to consider Procore.

Overall, Procore is a valuable tool for construction firms that are looking to improve their efficiency, productivity, quality, safety, and compliance.

The future of construction documentation is bright. As technology continues to evolve, new and innovative ways of documenting construction projects will be developed. These new technologies will help to make construction projects more efficient, more secure, and more accessible.

Review Questions

1. What are six keys to effective jobsite documentation and communication?

2. What types of activities in the construction project need to be documented?

3. What is the purpose of maintaining daily reports?

4. What are some important items of information that need to be recorded in the daily report?

5. What are the purposes of weekly and monthly reports?

6.   What is the purpose of a jobsite diary?

7.   Name several logs that could be kept on the jobsite.

8.   What are some items of information that should be recorded concerning jobsite photographs?

9.   What are some instances where the use of video recordings is useful?

10. What are the two primary purposes of jobsite cost documentation?

11. What are five basic elements of any correspondence?

12. What is an RFI?

13. What are some items that would be included in project meeting minutes?

Chapter 6

Jobsite Layout and Control

Objectives

This chapter discusses the factors that affect the jobsite plan and layout. The objectives of this chapter are to:

- List the goals of cost-effective jobsite layout
- Relate the relationship of material handling to labor cost
- Compare the relationship of the jobsite layout to labor productivity and the profitability of the project
- Recognize the physical attributes of the site and community affecting the project
- Examine the equipment considerations and needs of the jobsite
- Determine the organization of the jobsite to optimize productivity and profitability

Jobsite organization is essential for a productive construction project. Because estimated profit margins are small, the relative efficiency of the construction site can influence the profitability of the project. The jobsite layout affects the cost of material handling, labor, and the use of major equipment by the general contractor and the subcontractors working on the site. A well-organized jobsite has a positive effect on the productivity of the entire jobsite workforce. Productivity and worker morale are optimized by an effective jobsite layout. An efficient jobsite is a good indication of high-quality professional management by the contractor.

The **jobsite layout plan** is a plan for temporary facilities, material movement, material storage, and material handling equipment on the jobsite. It is similar to the construction plan and schedule and is a long-term system that considers all factors of the construction project. Although the jobsite layout plan is planned, funded, and implemented by the general contractor, it should consider the needs and requirements of all of the subcontractors working on the site. Some of the provisions of jobsite implementation, such as transportation of materials, are often the financial responsibility of subcontractors but should be included in the overall plan established by the general contractor.

The jobsite layout plan includes the following aspects:

- Jobsite space allocation—areas on the jobsite for material delivery, material storage, temporary offices, and facilities

- Jobsite access—access to and from the jobsite and to work areas within the jobsite, including haul roads

- Material handling—including material movement on the jobsite, both horizontally and vertically; lifting equipment, including forklifts and cranes

- Worker transportation—personnel movement and access on the jobsite

- Temporary facilities—temporary offices, storage facilities, dry shacks, sanitary facilities, temporary water, power, and heat

- Jobsite security—temporary fencing, guard dogs, security patrols, electronic alarm systems, and watchmen

- Signage and barricades—protection of the public from construction hazards on the jobsite

Based on the aspects of the jobsite layout plan, the following four areas should be taken into consideration:

1. Material handling
2. Labor productivity
3. Equipment constraints
4. Site constraints

All these areas have considerable impact on the decisions made concerning the jobsite layout plan. An optimum jobsite layout plan minimizes on-site labor in material movement, travel, and transportation, allowing workers to spend the maximum amount of time possible performing their construction activities. If a worker has more time to spend on the work activity it follows that more production will be accomplished during the work shift. A well-organized, clean jobsite provides a working environment that is conducive to completing work tasks for all jobsite personnel, including direct-hire and subcontractor employees.

Material Handling

Efficient material handling is extremely important in optimizing the construction worker's productivity. Ideally, the necessary material should be within reach for the craftsperson as it is needed for the installation. Obviously, this rarely happens. Material could be stored on-site in a remote location, it could be delivered as it is used, or it might not even be available on the jobsite. The primary concern is to have the craftsperson complete the construction activity as quickly as possible.

Guidelines for material handling on the jobsite follow:

Example

A wood-framing crew consists of two journeyman carpenters, a first-year carpenter apprentice, and a laborer. The laborer and carpenter apprentice will move the lumber and equipment where necessary, and the two journeyman carpenters will do the framing. Because the laborer and carpenter apprentice are not both needed 100 percent of the time to move material and equipment, the carpenter apprentice can assist the carpenters with the framing when not moving lumber and equipment. The laborer can collect scrap material and clean the worksite when not moving material and equipment.

- *Always move material with the least expensive labor possible.* Normally, the lowest-paid member of the crew, such as a laborer, apprentice, or helper, should be responsible for moving material. The craftsperson, such as the carpenter, is paid a higher wage to do a specific type of work. The crews should be organized to avoid using the journeyman craftsman for moving material.

Figure 6–1   Material Handling at the Jobsite

- *Deliver material as close as possible to the location of installation.* When possible, material should be stored near the installation location, making it ready for installation without much extra labor. This is a common practice when gypsum drywall is "stocked" on the jobsite. The drywall usually is initially distributed to the different floors or locations where installation will occur.

- *Deliver the material to its location with delivery people.* Material delivery to the jobsite and even to the location within the jobsite is most economically done by delivery people employed by the supplier of the material. Although there is normally a delivery charge, the material supplier's delivery crew probably will receive a lower wage than the jobsite labor. The delivery crew knows how to handle material efficiently and usually is interested in the prompt delivery of material. The delivery truck often comes with a boom or fork attachment that assists in the placement of the material. For example, drywall is normally delivered and "stocked" by the delivery crew. The crew will, as directed, put portions of the order in specific rooms and on specific floors. They also can use the fork boom on the delivery truck to deliver drywall to a second floor opening, if desired.

  Within unionized jurisdictions, however, delivery people usually will deliver to the jobsite but not within the jobsite, as they usually are not union employees. Union laborers would claim material movement on the jobsite. Under union jurisdictions, only certain union craftspeople can move material or equipment on the jobsite. Usually, laborers will have the authority to move material, while operating engineers run the lifting equipment. Some trades, however, move their own materials, depending upon the language in the agreements. To avoid jurisdictional disputes, the contractor should realize which craft claims each of the tasks on the jobsite.

- *Deliver from the truck to the installation location, if possible.* There are some instances when delivery can be made from the delivery truck to the material installation location. This is often done with structural steel. The steel fabrication, such as a column assembly, is lifted by the tower crane directly to the installation location and immediately bolted into place. Large equipment, such as air handlers and fans, often is lifted directly from the truck to its ultimate destination. This method avoids on-site storage of material and is used extensively when little or no on-site storage is available. Extra coordination is needed, however, to ensure that the correct fabrication is available and shipped at the time needed and the installation location is ready for the material or equipment upon its arrival.

- *Avoid moving the material more than once.* When material is stored or stockpiled on site, it should go from the storage area to installation. Too often on construction sites a storage pile of material has to be moved to another location because of other storage needs, providing access to work or excavation or for any other number of reasons. Material piles rarely need to be moved if prior planning is done. Anticipation of the work schedule and delivery of material can help create a storage plan that does not need to be changed during the project. Material that is placed haphazardly on the jobsite usually results in relocation of the material prior to its installation.

- *Anticipate equipment needs for the entire project and ensure that the proper equipment is available.* The contractor should anticipate the amount, size, and packaging method of the material and have the appropriate means of moving the material on the jobsite prior to delivery. Planning at the start of the project can provide adequate provisions for lifting equipment through the duration of the project. Permanent equipment should be selected for the majority of lifting and material handling. Some equipment needs may be temporary and require special machinery such as a mobile crane, for a few hours or days, because of the size, location, or amount of material delivered to the jobsite. Some lifting equipment will be the subcontractors' responsibility, such as the crane for erecting structural steel or for lifting a chiller unit to the roof of the building. Although the subcontractor is responsible for the cost of the lifting equipment, the general contractor should provide a location for the lifting equipment and for the delivery of the equipment. The contractor must consider all of the material that is to be installed on the project, including that furnished by subcontractors, when establishing a jobsite plan.

- *Select the optimum equipment for moving the material.* There are many ways to move and lift material into place. Most construction lifts and moves can be performed manually rather than by using a crane, forklift, or other method. Cost, of course, is the prime consideration, but a number of other factors should be considered. The following aspects should be considered when analyzing how to use equipment:

1. **Cost:** The rental cost of the necessary equipment, including minimum rental (4 hours, 8 hours, and so on) time and travel time to and from the jobsite, should be considered. All necessary accessories, such as rigging and chokers, should also be considered.

2. **Availability:** The availability of lifting equipment within the community. A one-time lift may appear to require a piece of equipment that is not readily available within the community. Any piece of equipment can be shipped to a community, but the shipping costs may greatly exceed the cost of an alternative. Sometimes, for small lifts, a gin pole with a block and tackle can replace a crane that is not available in the area. For example, when setting a precast bridge section, a contractor needs a large mobile crane to set the precast section. The mobilization cost to bring the crane into the community is quite expensive. Thus, the contractor uses two smaller cranes, one on each side of the river, resulting in a quick, efficient pick for a much lower cost.

3. **Capacity of the equipment:** The contractor needs to be sure the equipment has the appropriate capacity, including the safety factor to move and lift the equipment necessary. Cranes are selected according to the location of the pick and the designated target. Each piece of equipment has a certain capacity that should be considered with exact jobsite conditions. All the qualities of the equipment need to be considered, including load capacity and the reach or size of the equipment.

4. **Safety:** Safety is of paramount concern on the jobsite. Safety considerations always supersede cost issues. A more expensive method may have to be used to protect workers from a riskier one. A little more expense during the initial lift is a much better investment than a lift or move that endangers the lives or well-being of the workers.

5. **Quantity of material:** The relative quantity of material to be moved also is a factor when deciding what equipment to use. High mobilization costs can be absorbed if a large amount of material is to be moved. For small quantities, the contractor will probably use a labor-intensive method rather than pay travel or setup fees for lifting or moving equipment.

6. **Access to the point of use:** Situations arise where equipment must be used because access is not close to the point of use. The most efficient and cost-effective way to pour concrete is to do it directly from the ready-mix truck into the concrete form. This is not always possible, as the form may be too far from the nearest truck access or above the pouring level of the truck, requiring alternative methods. Some of these methods might include a series of gravity chutes, a concrete pump, a bucket lifted by a crane, or possibly a conveyor. Having the space for delivery of material and sufficient room for trucks and vehicles to maneuver also should be considered. This analysis is made by considering the factors discussed in this section.

7. **Provide adequate delivery routes:** The route for delivery should be clearly marked from the main roads and streets to the jobsite entrance. Construction sites often are located in remote areas, but firm and well-maintained roads to the point of delivery are needed. The majority of delivery trucks to the construction site are semi-truck-trailer setups, requiring wide turns and standard roadway width. The roadway, even if it is temporary, needs to be firm and stable. (See Figure 6–2 for some indications of truck size and weight.) The jobsite entrance for deliveries should be clearly designated, and internal site roads should be adequate for deliveries at the times they will be made.

8. **Coordinate deliveries:** Deliveries should be scheduled and coordinated, even though exact delivery times are not always available, particularly when the delivery is to be made from a long-distance hauler or common carrier. Because the typical jobsite will receive many deliveries during the day, scheduling the time of deliveries will ensure that

Delivery	Truck Type	Load Capacity	Truck Length	Truck Width	Truck Weight, Loaded	Vertical Clearance	Remarks
Gravel	Dump	16 tons (8 to 9 CY)	27 feet	8'-2"	53,180 lbs.	9'-9"	
	Dump w/ pup	30 tons (15 to 17 CY)	63'-2"	8'-2"	91,800 lbs.	9'-9"	"Pup" is trailer to dump truck
Concrete	Mixer truck	9 CY (36,458 lbs.)	40 feet	8'	66,000 lbs.	12'-0"	
Lumber	Tractor/trailer flatbed	48,000 lbs. 12 units lumber or 16 units plywood	16' tractor + 42' trailer = 58'	8'	80,000 lbs.	13' max.	Unload with forklift needs 16' clearance each side
Masonry	"Maxi" Semi w/ pup	CMU: 22 pallets, 1900 ea Brick: 14,000 ea	85 feet	8'	103,000 lbs.	13'-6" minimum	Forklift unload, 16' clearance each side Cannot back up (drive through)
Drywall	Flatbed w/boom	16,000 lbs. 160 sheets drywall 5/8" x 4' x 12'	30 feet	8'	48,000 lbs.	11'4"	Boom: 37' from roadway extended

Figure 6–2   Delivery Truck Size Data

equipment and personnel are available to promptly unload the truck. The contractor should prepare for the delivery by having available the appropriate amount and type of labor and equipment. Quick handling of the delivery facilitates the optimum number of deliveries, as necessary, and also frees up labor and equipment to accomplish work tasks.

On jobsites with limited receiving facilities, schedules for the delivery area and lifting equipment should be established. Because several subcontractors require deliveries, certain times should be set aside for these. This schedule needs to be set up early in the project so that the contractor and subcontractors can stipulate delivery restraints in their purchase orders. An example of a delivery schedule follows.

Example

7:00 A.M. to 10:00 A.M.	General contractor deliveries
10:00 A.M. to 12:00 P.M.	Mechanical contractor deliveries
1:00 P.M. to 2:00 P.M.	Electrical deliveries
2:00 P.M. to 4:00 P.M.	Miscellaneous subcontractor deliveries (varies, depending on the work being done)

A delivery schedule should be flexible to allow for special construction events and activities. Long-distance deliveries can arrive at any time and should be accommodated, if possible. The contractor should establish daily schedules and coordinate deliveries in addition to the project delivery parameters. Because scheduling is a major item of concern on the jobsite, the superintendent or projected manager should make scheduling decisions and provide that information to their own forces and to the subcontractors.

- *Make arrangements for material or equipment to be placed in the installation location.* Certain materials or pieces of building equipment are too large to be taken through conventional routes to the area of installation at the time of delivery. The constructor should always try to place this equipment or material in the space provided prior to the installation of walls and doorways, which prevent the material from entering the space.

Example

1. A large air handler, about 30 feet long, was designed for installation in the subgrade lower level (basement) of the building. Realizing the problem well before construction, the constructor preordered the air handler and lifted it into place prior to the installation of the first floor slab. The air handler needed to be covered and protected during construction operations.

2. In a high-rise building, transportation of gypsum drywall in the traditional 4' × 12" sheets is difficult after the installation of the exterior curtain wall. Moving large sheets by elevator also is difficult, requiring a large amount of labor, if that is even possible, depending upon the size of the elevator car. The easiest way to stock drywall on the floors is to use a tower crane or material lift prior to the installation of the exterior curtain wall. The drywall also needs to be covered and protected until its installation. The large size of the sheets may be in the way of some installations, such as ductwork, electrical rough-in, and suspended ceilings. Care should be taken when stocking drywall on elevated slabs to distribute the drywall to avoid overloading the slabs.

Equipment and material delivery cannot always be timed to arrive at the jobsite prior to the installation of constraining elements. When possible, the constructor can leave openings for the material or equipment to be moved into its assigned space. It also may be possible to have a piece of equipment broken down into smaller sections to enable it to be moved into the space.

Example

1. The exterior precast concrete panels of a building have been installed prior to the delivery of a large exhaust fan on the upper floor. Provisions are made to omit a panel until the fan is delivered and lifted into place. The precast panel is then installed after the fan is lifted into place. Care must be taken to not interrupt the structural integrity of the exterior cladding. A structural relationship between the cladding panels may exist, requiring additional supports to accommodate a temporary opening.

2. An air handler is scheduled for a small upper-floor mechanical room. The air handler, fully assembled, is too large to fit into the building's elevator and through the door into the mechanical room. The air handler is custom-made for the project, fully assembled and tested at the factory. It is scheduled to be delivered after the curtain wall is in place and the interior walls, including doors and frames, are installed. The air handler can be separated into sections that can be transported in the elevator car and through the door into the mechanical room. There is an additional charge from the manufacturer for breaking down the air handling unit. Extra cost is also incurred to reassemble the air handler in its place. An analysis and comparison of costs to create openings as well as to partially disassemble a piece of building equipment should be made to determine the most feasible alternative.

- *Storage of material on the jobsite should be systematic.* Most on-site storage areas are fairly small, requiring consolidation of material. The storage of material should be organized in a manner that is accessible. Deliveries are not necessarily made in sequential order for the material needed. An effective, well-organized storage area requires knowledge of the construction schedule and of the materials used for construction.

  Unless well-organized, fabricated materials, such as reinforcing steel and structural steel, can become a serious storage and access problem at the jobsite. Literally thousands of pieces of reinforcing steel, even in fairly small projects, are delivered to the jobsite. The following steps can help organize the storage of material:

  1. *Coordinate shop drawings and fabrication with the supplier.* The contractor should work closely with the fabricator to establish a schedule of shop drawing production and fabrication that coincides with the construction activities. The sequence of the construction and the timing of the delivery of the material are not always obvious to the fabricator. For the fabricator, the ordering of production of fabricated items relates to the availability of raw material and economy of mass cutting, bending, and connecting rather than the construction schedule. Delivery pertains to the completed fabrications rather than the construction need. The contractor needs to clearly establish the progression of construction with the fabricator and ensure that the fabricator produces shop drawings and fabrications in a timely manner; that is, delivered to the jobsite prior to the construction activity.

Because of the physical location of the jobsite, the contractor decides to construct Building B, a warehouse building with a slab-on-grade, first, then Building A, an office building with a basement. This may not be the way in which the fabricator envisioned the project would be constructed. After completing the construction schedule, the constructor then establishes a sequence and timetable for the reinforcing steel fabrications that will be needed for the project. Specific information rather than the entire construction schedule will help the fabricator understand what is required to comply with the contractor's needs. A sample schedule of information the contractor can give to the fabricator is shown in Figure 6–3.

The fabricator can use this information to prepare a shop drawing and fabrication schedule to meet the required delivery dates.

2. *Establish areas for the delivery of each major material.* Establishing organized subareas in the storage yard for each major material, such as an area for reinforcing steel, a separate area for structural steel, and so forth, is essential. Mixing materials in the storage area causes chaos when identifying and retrieving items as the project progresses. A discussion with the supplier, concerning the timing of the delivery and the material being delivered, will help determine how much space to allocate for each material. The type of access needed when moving the material also needs to be examined when allocating space. If the material needs to be moved with a forklift, wide-enough aisles should exist between the materials to maneuver the forklift. The area needed for the storage for each material will vary depending upon the stage of the project. During the first third of a building project, the area needed for storing reinforcing steel is quite large. In the subsequent two-thirds of the project, though, storage needs for reinforcing steel are considerably less, reduced to little or no space for the final third of the project. The construction schedule is a useful tool when determining the relative amounts of storage space needed during the project. The term **laydown area** is frequently used to indicate the storage area on the jobsite.

3. *Sort the material upon its delivery to the site.* The material needs to be sorted as it is unloaded from the truck. Material that is needed first should be most accessible. The material pile should be ordered sequentially for materials that have a definite order in the installation. For example, the reinforcing steel previously discussed would be stored in this order: Building B footings, Building B foundation wall, Building B slab-on-grade,

Building	Component	Schedule Date	Deliver Date
B	Footings	May 23, 2026	May 19, 2026
B	Foundation Wall	May 31, 2026	May 26, 2026
B	Slab-on-grade	June 13, 2026	June 9, 2026
A	Footings	June 13, 2026	June 9, 2026
B	Tilt-up Panels	June 20, 2026	June 16, 2026
A	Foundation Wall	June 20, 2026	June 16, 2026
A	Foundation Wall 2	June 27, 2026	June 23, 2026
A	Basement Columns	June 30, 2026	June 27, 2026
A	Slab-on-grade	July 8, 2026	July 5, 2026

Figure 6–3 Example Reinforcing Steel Delivery Schedule

and so on. The material for Building A and Building B may be stored in separate areas as well. Some material, such as lumber, may be used throughout the process, so organizing by size is probably the most efficient method to use, with 2 × 6s in one pile, 2 × 4s in another pile, and so on. Easy access should be provided to each stack of lumber, as it will be used throughout the process.

4. *Allow adequate space for sorting and storage of waste materials.* There was a time when all construction waste was accumulated and taken to a landfill. Sorting materials is now necessary to economically dispose of the construction waste. Materials should be sorted according to general types, such as wood, drywall, metal, and so forth, and then recycled. Adequate provisions should be made for sorting and accumulating in separate bins for major recyclable materials.

5. *Protect storage material, as necessary.* Many materials are sensitive to environmental conditions and should be adequately protected from rain, snow, wind, heat, freezing temperatures, and other adverse environmental elements. Most materials should be set on pallets or skids to protect them from ground moisture. Some materials can be covered by a tarp or polyethylene sheet; however, moisture tends to condense in some of these conditions. Some materials are inappropriate for outside storage and should be stored either in the facility or warehouse. Portable storage trailers can be used to protect material on the jobsite, depending upon the space available.

Labor Productivity

Labor cost is the most unpredictable for the contractor. Although a fixed rate per hour is easy to determine, the number of hours and crew makeup to complete a task vary. The contractor estimates the number of hours each task will take at a certain rate under assumed conditions. Because the contractor is held to the estimate, the amount actually estimated for labor will be the budget for the item. If the actual labor equals the amount estimated, the contractor will achieve the estimated profit. If labor cost exceeds the estimated amount, the contractor will not achieve the estimated profit and could possibly lose money on the project. Concentration for labor then should focus on the work task, keeping all other activities minimal.

As previously mentioned, higher productivity rates will be achieved if time is spent installing the material rather than moving it. The craftsperson should be instructed to perform the work for which they are trained and hired. A carpenter should be framing, installing doors and frames, or installing millwork. An ironworker should be installing reinforcing or structural steel. Part of the laborers' work, however, should be handling materials and equipment.

Example

Journeyman Carpenter:

Wages	$ 37.36
Fringe benefits	$ 16.00
Taxes	$ 10.46
Total hourly cost to contractor	$ 63.82

(Total cost per minute [$63.82/hour/60 minutes/hour] = $ 1.06/minute.)

These are direct costs for the carpenter's wages. Tools, equipment, support facilities, and supervision are not included.

Current labor costs are quite high. The following example illustrates the cost of a carpenter to a contractor (labor rates will vary widely depending on the region and type of work performed).

At $1.06 per minute, the carpenter's time is very valuable. The contractor's goal is to be as labor efficient as possible, utilizing the labor for the actual work task.

A major concern is travel time within the jobsite. The worker travels around the jobsite during the shift, possibly from the job shack to the location of the work task, from the work task to the restroom, or from the work task to lunch. Time spent traveling means work is not being accomplished. If it takes a carpenter 15 minutes to travel from the entry gate to the work site, it will cost the contractor $15.90, without any production associated with that cost. The contractor does not expect the carpenter to run to his work, of course. Nonproductive time *is* expected during the day; however, the jobsite facility should be arranged to keep nonproductive times to a minimum.

Example

The site's sanitary facility (portable toilet) is located next to the job shack, which is convenient for the superintendent and visitors but not for the carpenters. Four carpenters are working on the site. A trip to the sanitary facility takes 15 minutes. Each crew member uses the sanitary facility four times during the shift. The labor cost for the trips to the facility is $255.28 per shift. If a sanitary facility is located near the work site, the average trip would be 5 minutes, with a cost of $84.80 per shift in labor cost. Assume that this work site would be active for the four carpenters for a month, or 20 working days. The cost of providing an additional sanitary facility near the work site would be $100 per month. By providing a sanitary facility near the work site, the contractor would save $3,309.60. This translates into 52 carpenter hours that could be applied to the work task.

When establishing the jobsite layout plan, the contractor should look at the areas of travel and nonproductive time for the crews and arrange the jobsite and facilities to minimize this time. The contractor must consider alternatives that will decrease labor time, economically and within reason for the size and configuration of the project, in the following nonproductive time elements.

1. *Travel time from gate to work site*
   - Gate and parking should be close to work site (may possibly move as job progresses)
   - Provide transportation to work site: truck, bus, vertical man lift
   - In high-rise buildings, it may be possible to increase the speed of the man lift, with different equipment

2. *Travel time to sanitary facilities*
   - Provide sanitary facilities close to work site
   - Relocate sanitary facilities as job progresses

3. *Travel time to coffee break*
   - Provide tables and chairs in safe area near work site
   - Provide dry shack near work site
   - Discourage coffee break (may not be possible if in union agreement)

4. *Travel time to lunch*
   - Provide tables and chairs in safe area near work site
   - Provide dry shack near work site

5. *Travel time moving material*
   - Have material located close to work site
   - Discourage craftspeople from moving material

6. *Travel time to ask superintendent questions*
   - Project office should be near work site
   - Walkie-talkies for crew to communicate with office

Selective time studies can be made on alternatives, comparing the cost and cost savings of each. Care should be taken to include the extra costs, along with the savings in labor. For instance, the contractor may have to provide an extra dry shack, at an additional cost, near the work site. Some of the facility improvements, such as a man lift with increased speed, will benefit the subcontractors as well as the contractor, and such savings, if possible, to realize, should also be included in the equation.

When optimizing transporting labor, particularly in high-rise buildings, delays need to be considered as well as the transportation from point A to point B. Vertical lifts rarely carry one person directly from the ground to the destination on an upper floor. Usually there are many stops for different people at different floors. The contractor must consider the average, quickest way to transport labor for the minimum amount of time. The following suggestions may optimize transportation.

- *Separate people and material.* Because moving material on vertical lifts takes much more time, particularly in loading and unloading, it is best to separate human transportation from material transportation. Material transportation can be limited to tower cranes or Chicago booms, with vertical transportation limited to human transportation. Certain parts of each hour could be divided for each for a vertical lift. For instance, worker transportation could be scheduled for 10 minutes at the hour and 10 minutes at the half hour, with the rest of the time (40 minutes of each hour) devoted to material transportation. Some high-rise buildings have two vertical lifts, one for workers and one for material transportation.

- *Schedule floor stops.* On taller high-rise buildings, the vertical lift for worker transportation may stop only on every other floor to limit the number of stops and to optimize the cycle time of the lift. If two lifts are used for worker transportation, one may stop more frequently than the other. The second lift might be the "express" lift.

Equipment Constraints

The jobsite layout can depend on the lifting and moving equipment that is used for the project. Once the equipment is determined, depending on its capabilities, cost, and other characteristics, the equipment puts some constraints on the site layout. Location of delivery points, site access for people and equipment, sequencing of events, and location of temporary facilities all affect what equipment is planned for the jobsite.

- *Point of delivery.* Once the equipment is decided upon, the point of delivery for material will relate to the location and capacity of the equipment. A tower crane, commonly used in building construction, has considerably more capacity for lifting near the mast than toward the end of the boom. Heavier loads, then, must be delivered fairly close to the mast and limited to a horizontal lift by the crane. If a forklift is used to transport the material within the jobsite, the point of delivery should have solid road access from the point of delivery to the installation location. If lifting equipment is located some distance from the public road access, sufficient jobsite haul roads must be made and maintained to accommodate typical delivery trucks. If a permanent concrete pumping arrangement is established, whether a permanent concrete pump or permanent (during construction) pipeline, a location for concrete trucks during delivery, staging, and access also should be established, with a firm, solid roadway, such as rolled gravel or asphalt paving.

- *Site access for people and material.* The gates and access into the site should be oriented to access the work site. Personnel entrance gates should be near personnel lifts if they are selected for the project. Temporary facilities, such as field offices and storage sheds, should be accessible to the work site via the site equipment.

- *Sequence of events.* The sequence of construction activities, particularly short term, will be determined by the amount of equipment used on the project and equipment scheduling. The type of equipment used and designated traffic patterns on the jobsite are factors used when determining the schedule of underground utility lines.

- *Location of temporary facilities.* The location and properties of the equipment used on the jobsite will influence the location of temporary facilities. Material storage should have easy access as well as the necessary equipment to facilitate its movement. If a tower crane is used for vertical transportation of material, movement would be facilitated by locating the storage within the reach and capacity of the tower crane. If this is not possible, as is often the case, additional equipment would be necessary for horizontal movement of the material on the site, such as a forklift or a small mobile crane. Personnel facilities, such as tool storage, dry shacks, jobsite office, and sanitary facilities, should be close to personnel movement equipment.

Site Constraints

The site itself controls the layout and the equipment that is used probably more than any other factor. An urban site may consist of the property being the same size as the building footprint. In an extremely tight site such as an urban office building, the contractor needs a great deal of creativity to provide adequate storage, temporary facilities, and equipment. Additional property may have to be obtained on a temporary basis. Full or partial street vacation may be necessary to provide delivery and access to the site. In a very cramped site, the point of delivery becomes the focus of site layout. Some considerations for the point of delivery include the following:

- Traffic patterns—easy flow onto and off the site, avoiding congestion of traffic on city streets

- Large enough space for all delivery vehicles—consider length; turning radius; height of truck, load, and onboard loading boom; and weight

- Accessible for loading equipment

- Queuing area for waiting trucks that will not disturb street traffic patterns—a concern particularly with concrete ready-mix trucks, where trucks need to follow each other closely to avoid interrupting the concrete pour

When constructing on a tight site, different arrangements should be made for material storage. After the building is sufficiently constructed, the building can serve as a storage area for some material. An off-site storage yard, usually close to the construction site, can be used for this purpose. When an off-site yard is used, extra equipment, such as lifts and trucks, is necessary to provide efficient movement of material. In some urban areas, such as New York City, marshaling yards outside of the dense urban area are used for the receipt, storage, and disbursement of material to the jobsite on an as-needed basis. On the cramped site, material may have to be delivered daily rather than stored on the jobsite. In dense urban areas, delivery of the material during the night may be the only feasible approach. When a large amount of material is needed, for instance, for a large concrete pour, the construction activity may need to be scheduled on a Sunday or at night to avoid the congestion of city traffic. Large fabrications also may have to be transported at night or during the weekend. Large mobile cranes for a short duration lift that need full street access normally have to be set up, the pick accomplished, and broken down in off hours to avoid disrupting the normal traffic flow.

Large sites also have constraints that must be considered in the jobsite layout. A too-large site may be inefficient and costly. The following factors should be analyzed when laying out a large site:

- Temporary fencing—The cost of fencing can be a factor.

- Haul roads—The cost of constructing and maintaining haul roads on the site. Consider the climatic conditions during the project in relation to the soil, gravel, or other material used on the haul road. Mud, dust, irregular frozen ground, and snow are factors that prevent normal truck transportation from using haul roads. The haul roads need to be constructed and maintained to be passable when needed.

- Extra equipment needed—Distant storage areas may require additional lifting and transportation equipment.

Elements of the Jobsite Layout Plan

The jobsite layout plan has a number of elements, many of which have been discussed to some extent. The next section will describe the necessary elements the contractor should consider when making the jobsite layout plan.

Material Storage or Laydown Areas

Material storage was discussed quite extensively in the previous section. The following guidelines can be used as a checklist for establishing adequate storage areas:

- Estimate the amount of storage needed. Use the construction schedule to help determine the amount of materials stored at different intervals, so the storage area can be used for several different materials.

Figure 6–4 Jobsite Material Storage

- Make sure adequate access is provided to the storage area for delivery and removal.

- Be sure the surface of the storage area is compact and solid. If using an open air storage area, provide adequate drainage. Paved areas allow for good storage, as they are stable and easily accessed. Parking lots paved early in the project may provide good storage areas; however, some repair or a seal coat on the paving may be needed after use.

- Make sure all material is on skids or pallets to prevent moisture from wicking the material from the ground surface.

- Protect weather-sensitive material from the elements. Tarps, temporary shelters, and other means may be necessary to protect the material from rain, snow, ice, wind, and sun.

- Parts of the structure may be used for storage of material. Storage within the structure is always limited; thus, the material stored in the building should be that which will be used in the particular area, that which is weather sensitive, and that which requires higher security.

- Temporary storage units are often used on the jobsite. These include mobile home-type trailers designed for storage, 40-foot transit vans, containerized storage units, and job-built storage buildings.

- When determining material storage on the jobsite, always consider the needs of the subcontractors, as the majority of material is supplied by them.

Temporary Facilities

Jobsite Offices

The jobsite office or "job shack" is essential for most commercial building projects. The jobsite office is the superintendent's headquarters, even when the superintendent is in the midst of the construction activities for most of the day. The jobsite office ranges from a clipboard in a pickup truck to multistory office facilities, depending upon the scope of the project. The jobsite office is often required in the General Requirements (Division 1) of the construction documents.

Figure 6–5 Jobsite Laydown Area

Functions of the Jobsite Office   A list of the functions of the jobsite office includes the following:

- The superintendent's headquarters and office. This is where the superintendent and field management personnel, such as field engineers, offices are located.

- The place of business for the contractor. This is where visitors, salespeople, architects, owner's representatives, subcontractors, and direct labor enter the jobsite to establish contact with the appropriate management personnel.

- The location of telephone and fax facilities. The contractor's telephone and fax machine are usually in the jobsite office.

- The location of the full and current set of construction documents, including addenda and changes. Most contract documents require that the contractor keep a complete and updated set of documents at the jobsite. This set of documents is used as a reference for architects, owner's representatives, building inspectors, and subcontractors as well as for the contractor's personnel.

- The location of the "record drawings" or "as-built" drawings, which show the actual dimensions and locations of the project as constructed. These record drawings are meant to be updated as the job progresses.

- The location of posters and information for employees. All employee information, such as safety posters, posters from state and federal agencies informing the employee of certain rights and obligations, and statements of company policy should be posted on a special bulletin board.

- The location of first-aid information and equipment. Emergency phone numbers must be posted in a prominent location, with the jobsite address or location. First-aid kits should be available at all work locations but should also be available at the jobsite office. Major first-aid equipment, such as stretchers, should be in the jobsite office, easily accessible.

Attributes of the Jobsite Office   A list of the attributes and equipment commonly found in the jobsite office includes the following:

- It must be lockable and secure off-hours. Today's jobsite office contains valuable equipment, such as computers, printers, plotters, copiers, and fax machines. Other valuable equipment used on the jobsite, such as surveying equipment and construction lasers, are often stored in the jobsite office as well. Many contractors install security systems in the jobsite office, as this is a frequent target for burglaries.

- It must have adequate desk space for the permanent jobsite management staff. Considerations that might be made when determining the size of the jobsite office include the following:

Superintendent: Lockable desk; location for computer, including power outlets and telephone and data line; lockable file cabinet; plan table; and telephone. If possible, the superintendent's office should be away from the public entrance to the jobsite office. It also should be out of sight of noncontractor personnel.

Jobsite clerk, office manager, or secretary: This person, when used on the jobsite, is the first point of contact at the jobsite and the office should be located at the entrance of the building. The desk should have a telephone, usually with a fax machine nearby. File cabinets also are necessary.

Field engineers: Each field engineer needs a desk. A common plan table can be used for more than one engineer. A great deal of time may be spent on the telephone with suppliers and subcontractors, so each engineer should have a telephone, if possible. Much of the field and office engineer's work is done on computers, so a space should be provided for a desktop model or laptop. A copy machine also is essential.

Foremen: Some jobsite facilities have a space that is jointly used by foremen for filling out time cards and reports.

- *Internet connection*: Appropriate Internet connection needs to be provided. If the site is using mobile devices, WiFi needs to be provided throughout the site. If BIM is active at the jobsite, facilities for the necessary computer hardware needs to be provided.

- *Space for a plan table with access for architects, owner's representatives, and subcontractors*: A rack also should be included, with all of the pertinent contract and shop drawings. An area should be provided for the project manual and current approved submittals. Additional facilities for the architect or construction manager may be specified in Section 01500, Temporary Facilities, in the project manual.

- *A window or windows with a direct view of the jobsite*: This is not always possible, but field management personnel need to be in touch, even if only visually, with the project.

- *Wall space for the project schedule*: A schedule that is used by the contractor usually is very visible and accessible in the jobsite office. Updates and changes normally are posted on the schedule. The more readable and accessible the schedule is in the jobsite office, the more it is used as a tool to manage the project.

- *Conference space, if necessary*: The jobsite is often away from the owner's, architect's, and contractor's facilities; thus, conference space should be available for project, safety, and foremen meetings and all other gatherings at the jobsite. A conference room or another area that can be used as such often is included in the jobsite office facility.

- *Storage space*: Secure storage space often is included in the jobsite office for equipment, tools, and small, valuable material. The jobsite office normally will have lockable storage cabinets. It also may have rooms designated for storage of tools, equipment, and material.

- *Adequate environmental features*: Most jobsite offices need heat or air conditioning, depending on the climate of the jobsite locations.

Types of Jobsite Offices

There are as many types of jobsite offices as there are projects and contractors. Each jobsite office facility must fit the project and management of the project. In addition, several factors enter into the selection of the jobsite office, including the following:

- Cost—The cost of the jobsite facility must be within the budget established by the estimate. The project's needs are considered in the estimate when establishing a budget. The monthly cost of the office facility and the anticipated duration of the project are used to establish the budget amount. The contractor may use a trailer or portable building for minimal cost or may rent or lease temporary facilities.

- Space at the jobsite—The space available at the jobsite will substantially affect the type of jobsite office. Tight space at the jobsite may force the contractor to find nearby offices. A small trailer may be the most acceptable office because of jobsite limitations despite the fact that more office space would be desirable.

- Availability—The availability of adequate jobsite office facilities in the locality also will help determine the type of office facility used. If jobsite space is tight or unavailable, the contractor may wish to rent a nearby building, warehouse, or office facility. If these are not available, the contractor must consider using the structure itself in the same way as the jobsite office. When a contractor uses a fleet of trailers or portable buildings as jobsites, the best ones that are available at the start of the project are generally used. This may not be the optimum jobsite facility for the project, but the price is usually right. Hauling costs also may limit rental facilities.

Common types of jobsite office facilities include the following:

- Existing buildings—Buildings near the jobsite can make good jobsite offices. Warehouses, office buildings, houses, and other types of structures can be used. These off-site offices must be adjacent or very close to the jobsite to avoid wasted travel time. Usually these facilities are rented on a short-term basis. Normally some cost is involved in remodeling the facilities for jobsite offices, which also needs to be considered when comparing rates.

- Modular office units—Numerous modular, portable units that are manufactured specifically for the temporary office are available in every size, configuration, and feature. There is, of course, a wide quality range also available. These modular units can be used as single units or several combined units. The contractor can purchase or lease them. When considering modular units, the following items must be added into the cost calculation:

  Hauling costs to and from the jobsite. The larger modular units have to be transported like a mobile home, which requires special transportation beyond the contractor's normal equipment. When renting or leasing units, this expense may be part of the quoted cost. Because transportation can be costly, confirm that this price is covered in the quoted rental costs.

  Setup and takedown of the temporary assembly, as necessary.

  Additional facilities to be constructed on the jobsite for modular units. These items could include stairs and ramps, wood decks between units, and floor and roof structures between the units.

  Wiring and plumbing of the modular units. Additional exterior security lighting is necessary.

  Additional furniture. Plan tables, plan racks, chairs, desks, file cabinets, and storage cabinets, beyond those furnished with modular units.

  Monthly utility costs for heat, electricity, water, and power for the jobsite office facility.

  Security system or special security provisions for the jobsite office.

- Trailers—Many contractors use trailer-mounted jobsite offices, which can be towed by a contractor's vehicle. These are usually smaller units, used on small to medium-sized projects. The obvious advantage is the cost savings in hauling to and from the jobsite. These smaller, more mobile units can be accommodated on the small site more easily than mobile home types of units. Contractors use different types of trailers: manufactured temporary office trailers, converted travel trailers, and custom-built trailers. Another relatively mobile small office unit is the wood-framed building on skids, normally transported on a flatbed truck or low-boy trailer. Examples of some common office trailer configurations are shown in Figures 6–6A and B.

Figure 6–6A illustrates some office configurations available in prefabricated mobile offices. The first unit shown is a small office to be used only with the superintendent on the project. An additional storage cabinet can be added for survey equipment. This office can accommodate about four people. The second unit shown is a small office with storage space for tools, equipment, and some materials. A double door provides access to the storage area. Most contractors build bins on each side of the storage room to hold tools. The third unit shown is an office trailer, which utilizes the 32-foot-long module. This office can accommodate a superintendent and field engineer.

Figure 6–6B illustrates larger units that are available in both the 48-foot and 60-foot lengths. These units have provisions for internal rest rooms. Some sites may have water and sewer hookups. The first unit shown is the 48 foot, the second the 60 foot. These larger units have a great deal of flexibility and can accommodate a staff of several individuals. For larger projects, a series of prefabricated units can be arranged to provide office space for the entire on-site management team. Decks can be built between the units to avoid unnecessary stair climbing.

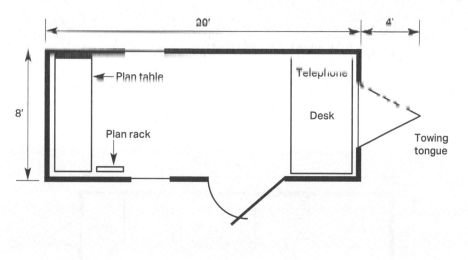

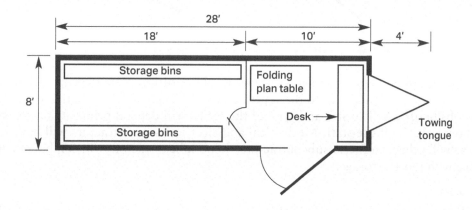

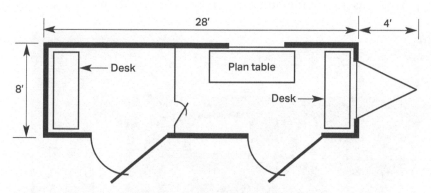

Figure 6–6A   **Example Office Trailer Configurations**

• Site-built jobsite offices—Some contractors will build the jobsite office on the actual work site. They may use a prefabricated system, with panels and roof sections, hauled flat on a truck and erected on the jobsite. The contractor also may opt to build a wood-frame structure on the jobsite. When using a warehouse or the underground parking floors of a building, the contractor can build a wood-frame structure and finish it like an office, with carpeting and suspended acoustical ceilings.

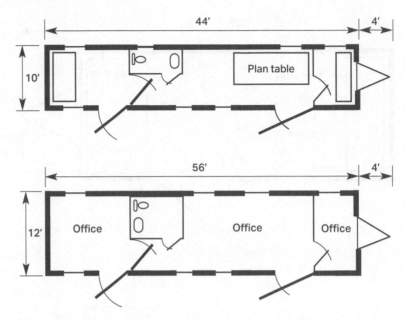

Figure 6–6B   Example Office Trailer Configurations

The photograph in Figure 6–7 shows a typical jobsite office. Note the copy machine, fax machine, and computer adjacent to the superintendent's desk. Some subcontractors may also furnish jobsite offices. The size and type of the office will depend primarily on the size of the subcontractor's jobsite staff. Mechanical and electrical subcontractors will have jobsite offices, as will other long-term subcontractors. Some subcontractors will combine their jobsite office with jobsite storage.

Dry Shacks

Traditionally, the contractor provides a dry place for construction workers to eat their lunch and a place to change their clothes. This is commonly called a **dry shack**. Union agreements often have a provision that requires a dry shack to be furnished. The dry shack, like all other facilities on the jobsite, has an infinite number of types and variations. A few types include a

Figure 6–7   Jobsite Office Interior

Jetta Productions/Stocksy/Adobe Stock Photo

small wood framed building, with a table and a place to store lunches, a modular unit with one room, a room in the job trailer, or an area in the building, near the work activities. Although dry shacks do not need to be elaborate, they should be clean, have adequate light, and be relatively comfortable for employees.

Tool Storage

The contractor normally furnishes power tools and larger tools for the work to be accomplished. These tools can include circular saws, drill motors, hammer drills, demolition hammers, laser levels, ladders, scaffolding, concrete vibrators, pumps, surveying equipment, and many others to facilitate construction activities. However, these tools are subject to theft because of their mobility and high value. Tool storage, then, must be extremely secure. Because many individuals on the jobsite use the tools, they should be in bins and organized so they can be quickly accessed.

A separate tool shed also could be used on the jobsite, preferably close to the work site. It often is located near the jobsite office for security reasons. The tool storage area needs to be secure as well, with strong locks and impenetrable window openings. This area often is combined with the jobsite office.

Sanitary Facilities

The contractor needs to provide sanitary facilities for its employees on the jobsite. Normally, the general contractor provides these facilities for all individuals on the work site, including subcontractors. The contractor will want to provide drinking water, washing water, and toilet facilities for jobsite employees, because these are necessities. Further, current safety requirements specifically outline what facilities must be provided on the jobsite.

Drinking Water   Fresh, potable drinking water must be available on the jobsite. To avoid wasted time, the water should be available at the crew's work site. Most contractors use 5-gallon insulated containers, equipped with a tap. Paper cups are provided with the container, usually attached to it. Safety regulations prohibit the use of a common cup for drinking water. A receptacle adjacent to the water container should be provided to prevent paper cups from being littered over the entire site. If potable water is not available on the jobsite, containers must be filled elsewhere and transported to the site. The containers should be rinsed and refilled daily and must be thoroughly washed weekly. Some union agreements may have additional requirements for drinking water, such as availability and adding ice to the water. During hot weather, adding ice to the containers maintains a cooler water temperature throughout the shift, preventing warm water in the afternoon.

Washing Water   Safety standards require that clean, tepid wash water between 70 and 100 degrees be provided at the construction jobsite. The standards also require that individual hand towels, such as paper towels, be provided with an appropriate receptacle. Until permanent toilet room facilities are established in the building, this requirement may be difficult to meet. A container of warmer water, marked "For Hand Washing Only," could be provided, preferably near the toilet facility or dry shack.

Number of Employees	Toilets Required
1 through 10	1
11 through 25	2
26 through 40	3
41 through 60	4
61 through 80	5
Over 80	One additional toilet for each additional 20 employees

Figure 6–8   Quantity of Toilets Required for Number of Employees

Toilets   Obviously, toilets are a necessity on the jobsite. They should be placed adjacent to the work area to avoid unnecessary travel time. Safety regulations require that toilets be provided at the work site. An example of the minimum requirement for toilets on the jobsite from a state safety standard is shown in Figure 6–8.

These requirements apply to *all* employees on the jobsite, including subcontractors. The toilet facilities may be located as per the work site, which may have fewer employees, but better facilitates work. The safety requirements also address the location of the toilet facility:

1. At all sites, toilet facilities shall be located within 200 feet, horizontally, of all employees.

2. On multistory structures, toilet facilities shall be furnished on every third floor.

Depending on the diversity of the workforce on the jobsite, company policy, and local, state, and federal regulations, the contractor may wish to provide additional and separate toilet facilities for each gender.

Prior to the installation of permanent sewer and water facilities, most contractors use portable chemical toilets. In most localities, these are rented and/or leased to the contractor by a business that also services them, usually on a weekly basis. The service includes emptying the tank and washing and disinfecting the unit. There is some variation in the size of these units, but usually they are about 4' × 4', with adequate ventilation.

When plumbing facilities are available, the contractor must also clean and disinfect the toilet rooms weekly.

Construction Waste Facilities   For new construction or remodeling, a considerable amount of waste needs to be collected, transported within the site, sorted, and transported off of the site. Vertical chutes often are used to transport the waste from upper stories to ground-level sorting areas or collection points. Separate bins are necessary for different types of waste to facilitate recycling. These locations, along with the general garbage collection "dumpster," should have good access for loading and transporting off-site.

Temporary Utilities

Because building utilities, such as power, water, and heat, are not available until the building is about two-thirds complete, temporary utilities are needed for construction operations. The contractor must arrange for the installation of these utilities, their locations, and their cost until the owner assumes beneficial occupancy. A discussion of temporary utilities to be considered in jobsite layout follows.

Temporary Power   The contractor will normally contract with the local power authority for a temporary electrical service for the jobsite. In many areas of the country, connection of this temporary service may have to be scheduled as much as 3 to 6 months in advance. Some companies can facilitate the connection 2 to 3 weeks from the order date. If construction activities need to commence prior to the connection of the temporary power, temporary generators normally are used. These usually are not a desirable alternative because of the cost of the generator rental and the cost of fuel. Several small generators normally are needed for several pieces of electrical-powered equipment.

The temporary power service must be placed using the following parameters:

• Locate as centrally as possible to avoid long power cords.

• Locate where service will not be moved until disconnected, when permanent power is installed.

• Ensure that power lines will not interfere with the structure or any delivery equipment.

• Locate lines, if underground power lines are being used, where they will not be dug up by construction operations.

The utility company and municipality have codes for the safe installation of a temporary power service. The temporary panel should be installed on an approved mast or pole, with breakers, and should be grounded. Both the utility company and the municipality must inspect the panel, mast, and grounding prior to allowing the utility company to connect power to the temporary service.

Most construction tools run on 110 volts. Some, such as the masonry saw and electric-powered compressors (for pneumatic tools), run on 220 volt power. The contractor must provide a temporary panel that will meet the needs of the construction activities and will often subcontract the installation of the temporary service and panel to an electrical contractor. It should be noted that the electrical subcontractor on the project will not usually include this temporary service in the project bid unless it is included specifically in the price quotation. Some contractors already have several temporary panels and masts and can furnish the service themselves.

The contractor must provide safe and code-compliant distribution of power from the panel. Distribution boxes should have ground-fault protection. All electrical power cords must be grounded and have a three-prong configuration. All extension cords must be in good repair and properly sized for their use.

Temporary Water   The permanent water connection may not be made until several weeks after the project has started. Pipes and fittings have to be approved, ordered, and delivered before the connection can be made. The tap into the water utility's main line must be scheduled, similar to the power connection. The contractor may have to investigate other means for temporary water, such as a temporary line or making arrangements for water delivery to the site.

Water is used in several construction activities. It is used in earthwork operations for compaction purposes and dust control; in concrete operations, in wetting the surfaces and cleaning the tools; in masonry operations, as it is added to the mortar on the jobsite; and in fire protection, as a temporary fire hydrant may be necessary during the construction activities.

The temporary water connection, like the temporary power connection, has several parameters that should be considered:

- Provide water to the most central point possible. Consider the effect of hoses to access routes.

- Avoid water distribution in an area that will be susceptible to breakage by construction equipment and delivery trucks.

- Coordinate the location of the underground temporary water line to avoid breakage during future excavation.

- Install the temporary line according to local codes. Provide adequate cover over underground water lines to avoid freezing.

Careful coordination with the water utility company is necessary. Unfortunately, the company furnishing the water will probably be a different firm than the one providing the electric service, depending on the locality. Some water utilities are owned and operated by the municipality, some are private utility companies, and some are water districts, separate from the municipal organization.

Temporary Weather Protection and Heat   Although temporary weather protection and heat are not necessarily jobsite layout considerations, they should be discussed briefly, as they are important elements during the construction process.

Weather protection may need to be installed during the winter weather to allow the construction process to continue. A variety of methods of covering the work are available, usually depending upon the severity of the weather and the type of work that remains to be done under the protection. A temporary frame structure can be erected, with a reinforced polyethylene fabric installed on the surface. Heat can be added with the temporary structure. Caution must be used in these types of structures because there is a great deal of heat loss, resulting in extremely expensive heating fuel costs. Caution also must be exercised to use heating equipment that will not cause fire damage. Ventilation of fumes from the heating equipment is a consideration as well.

Temporary heat within the structure under construction also needs to be planned. Many contractors use electric heat because of fire and ventilation considerations. This, however, consumes a large amount of power, and the temporary service should be sized for what heat is needed. All temporary heat is expensive, and each method has its advantages and disadvantages.

Jobsite Security

The jobsite needs to be secured, both for public safety and for the security of the installation and equipment. A jobsite, whether it is an excavated hole in the ground or a steel-framed high-rise building in construction, is considered an attractive nuisance. It is the contractor's responsibility to prevent the general public from entering the jobsite. If an individual is injured while entering an unsecured site, the contractor is generally held liable for that injury. The construction jobsite, while safe for trained and equipped construction workers, is not necessarily safe for the general public.

Vandalism and theft at the jobsite are major concerns for the contractor. Any construction site, in any geographical area of the country, is subject to vandalism and theft. Theft of materials, tools, and equipment is a frequent occurrence. Even theft of large pieces of equipment, such as backhoes and bulldozers, happens throughout the country.

The jobsite must prevent non-authorized personnel from entering its active areas. Further provisions also are needed on the site to secure materials, tools, and equipment from theft. The following list of provisions will help maintain a secure jobsite:

- A secure perimeter fence; secure and lock gates at night

- Bright yard lights at night

- Notify local police of the existing jobsite

- Secure or lock any equipment in concealed storage, if possible

- Do not leave keys in vehicles or on the jobsite at night

- If necessary, provide additional security at night, such as a watchman, security patrol, and so on

Perimeter Fencing

Construction documents may require a specific location for perimeter fencing. Usually the contractor is left to determine the amount and type of security fencing necessary around the project. Several options are available to the contractor:

- Rental fence—In most localities, businesses rent temporary fencing, usually by the month or year. The fence rental includes delivery, installation, and removal. A rental fence consists of galvanized chain link fabric, with temporary vertical pipes, usually at 10-foot centers. A rental fence usually does not have horizontal top or bottom pipe rails. This type of fence is economical, however, because it provides a mostly visual barrier and is fairly easy to purposely penetrate. This fence is popular for large sites because it is relatively inexpensive.

- Permanent fencing—Permanent fencing, depending upon the specification, usually is more secure than temporary fencing. Many contractors will install permanent fencing early in the project, using it both for temporary and permanent fencing. Permanent fencing, however, may not cover the extent of the area necessary during the construction phase. In these cases, the contractor might use a combination of the two. Often, security fencing is used at the very start of the project. Permanent fencing may be not as immediately available, as the product submittal needs to be processed and the material needs to be ordered.

- Wood-frame and panel fencing—Solid material, such as plywood, can provide a good barrier around the site while providing a visual barrier as well. This can be combined with sidewalk protection on urban sites. The municipality will have strict guidelines for the protection of pedestrians and sidewalks around the site, including overhead protection.

It is important to consider the size, type, amount, and location of the gates in the perimeter fencing. Most construction gates are swinging gates, but there may be site restrictions requiring sliding gates. The size of the delivery gates should be adequate for all delivery vehicles entering the site. Personnel gates also will be needed for access between employee parking lots and the worksite. In cases where both union and nonunion employees are working on the same site, separate, marked gates are required for both. Separate delivery gates also may be necessary in these situations. Adequate, secure locks are a must for all access gates. Strict key control should be maintained, with only necessary parties receiving keys.

Additional Security Measures

Many jobsites require more general security than perimeter fencing. Some of these measures might include the following:

- Night watchman—A permanent night watchman might be employed at the jobsite. The night watchman would need access to telephone and other communications devices. The night watchman might also be combined with a guard dog.

- Guard dog—A guard dog might be used in the construction area to prevent intruders from coming into the area. Notice of a guard dog may need to be posted, depending on local regulations. The contractor should always consult with local law enforcement authorities when establishing a jobsite security plan.

- Security patrol—Private security patrols can be contracted to provide periodic patrol of the jobsite.

- Intrusion alarms—Gates, job shacks, tool sheds, and storage buildings can be attached to security alarms that will notify a security service of intrusion. The security service, in turn, will call the police. Alarm bells at the jobsite also can be hooked to an intrusion detection system.

- Video surveillance—Internet connected video surveillance can provide 24-hour observance of the jobsite.

The general layout of the jobsite should consider security aspects. Exterior lighting should be provided, particularly at gates and other vulnerable points. The site should be observable from adjacent streets and roads, with occasional police patrols. The contractor might consult with local law enforcement authorities when formulating the jobsite layout and obtain their advice on security measures for the site regarding local and neighborhood conditions.

Access Roads

Proper planning of access roads to the site and within the site is essential to the efficiency of the project. The following goals should be achieved by all of the access roads involved in the project:

- The roads must provide direct access to all points needing access. Such points would include storage areas, installation areas, and entries to the work sites.

- The access roads must be built solidly to withstand the loads, the traffic, and the weather conditions during the period of use.

- The access roads must be built to accommodate the type of vehicle and load that will use it, which relates to the width of the roadway, the radius at the corners, and the slope or grade of the roadway. When constructing haul roads for excavation work, using trucks or scrapers, the contractor should always remember that the strength of the road surface, equated by "rolling resistance," and the slope of the roadway, or "grade resistance," affect the duration of the hauling operation and thus the cost of the hauling operation.

- Access roads must be placed during a time and in a location where they will not be moved or replaced. Underground utilities can disrupt the traffic on haul roads. Timing the underground utility construction prior to the construction of the haul road can avoid disruption of the traffic pattern. If the haul road does need to be disrupted during its use by the construction of underground utilities, then plans should be made for alternate temporary routes. Timing of these disruptions should be carefully coordinated with the construction schedule.

- Access roads should be appropriately constructed to the type of traffic that will be using them. A roadway for public vehicle traffic has different requirements than that for a haul road for scrapers.

- Haul roads should cause a minimal amount of dust. If roads are constructed of earth materials, a plan of dust control, such as periodic watering, should be made.

Two basic types of construction roads exist: access to and access within the construction site. Both road types affect the jobsite's operation. Both types of roads also have some distinctions, as discussed next.

Access to the Site

The construction site is not always immediately accessible by public roads and streets. Roads often need to be constructed from the nearest public roads to the new facility. Usually the construction of these roads will be included in the construction contract. Roads need to be constructed according to the construction documents. As most access roads become public streets and roads, they must meet the road standards for the local municipality. If new access roads are in the contract, their construction should take priority, if possible. Ideally, construction of the new permanent access roads should be done prior to the project, but this is not always possible. Many times, construction of the roadways is done by a separate contract, with a schedule totally unrelated to the project construction schedule. Temporary access roads often are needed until permanent access roads are available for use. In these cases, the access road should be built to accommodate the necessary traffic during its use and should be maintained to that condition.

The access road to the site should be as direct as possible from the existing public roads. Because the construction project will require numerous deliveries, access should be identified and easy to describe to delivery companies. The access road should be constructed directly to the delivery area of the project, as the majority of construction traffic relates to deliveries. Adequate parking areas for construction employees need to be established and need to be close to access roads.

Access within the Site

The access roads within the site are rarely designed or defined by the construction documents because they are the contractor's responsibility. Some occasions allow permanent internal roadways to be used during the construction phase, but these usually are constructed after the buildings and structures on the site. The contractor should determine the location of these roads, how they will be used, and what type of roadway will be necessary. Compacted natural earth roadways can be good construction roads if the soil is gravelly, with good drainage. If the natural soil is clay or fine silt, the material drastically changes form upon the introduction of water and probably is not appropriate for an access roadway. Occasionally, the use of a geotextile material that provides stability to the soil is necessary, with the addition of gravel or crushed stone for the roadway surface.

Site Drainage and Water Control

The contractor needs to control site drainage within the area to prevent disruption of work. Drainage and possible pumping should be used to keep excavated areas clear of water while work is being done there. The contractor also will be responsible for controlling all site drainage to avoid environmental damage or influence. Many states and municipalities require the contractor to submit a plan on site storm water drainage and containment. For construction sites that are one acre or larger, a Storm Water Pollution Prevention Plan (SWPPP) must be prepared and submitted to the Environmental Protection Agency (EPA). This plan must be followed and monitored for compliance to avoid polluting the waterways or groundwater. Noncompliance to the SWPPP regulations can result in substantial fines from the EPA.

Signs and Barricades

Signs and barricades are part of the entire jobsite layout plan. They are part of the safety plan of a jobsite but also can identify correct routes to and within the area.

Signs

Signs can be used to direct traffic to and from the jobsite. Some of the signs that can be used in jobsite organization include the following:

- Project sign—Normally a specified sign listing information about the project, such as owner, architect, contractor, and major subcontractors

- Location signs—Miscellaneous signage on roads to indicate the route to the jobsite for delivery trucks

- Gate signs—Some gates are restrictive regarding which company's personnel can enter. The gate signs normally list the firms that are required to use the gate. This provision is used when both union and nonunion contractors are working on the same project.

- Directional signs—Signs indicating location of deliveries, one-way roadways, and locations of contractors' offices

- Safety information signs—Danger signs, hard-hat area signs, and other signage indicating any safety precaution (See chapter 9 for a further discussion.)

Barricades

Barricades can be used for safety, security, and definition of traffic patterns. They are used in the following applications:

- In a safety situation, to prevent individuals from proceeding to an area

- In dealing with the public, the barricades need to be identifiable and substantial enough to physically prevent passage into the area

- To define the site area and protect the public, such as walkway protection

- To divert traffic into certain areas. This could be used to direct concrete trucks to different areas other than the previous delivery location.

Organizing Jobsite Layout

The process of laying out the jobsite takes into account all factors related to the project and uses all methods for efficiency. Jobsite layout is probably best done by an individual who completely understands the project and the construction plan for the project. Some references used for determining jobsite layout include the following:

1. Construction documents, specifically the following:
   - Division 1, General Requirements of the Project Manual—Information should be contained in this division concerning specific project instructions, such as parking facilities, use of the site, and required temporary facilities.
   - Site plan, architectural drawings—An existing site plan and the constructed site plan may be available, which will provide a base for the layout. Layout of the site plan can be facilitated by using a computer-aided drawing (CAD), perhaps from the architect.
   - Mechanical and electrical site plans—These site plans often are separate from the architectural site plan. Location of underground utilities and mechanical and electrical site work is needed in jobsite layout for planning access roads and planning the location of temporary facilities.

- Elevations and building sections—These drawings help determine the reach and length of lifting equipment.

2. Construction schedule—This schedule will help determine the length of certain construction operations and the time needed for use of the equipment.

3. Capacity charts and technical data concerning cranes, lifting, and conveyance equipment

4. Local codes for use of public roads, temporary vacation, and safety provisions required to protect the public

5. Safety standards for safety-related requirements, with temporary facilities and lifting

6. Data on the size of the larger lifting loads that will be encountered

7. Information from subcontractors on storage needs for their materials

8. Budgets established by the estimate that determine maximum cost for the elements of the jobsite layout

A drawing should be made of the site, including all items that add a constraint to the jobsite layout. Some of these items include:

1. The existing building and structure location

2. The new building and structure location

3. The existing roadways and streets adjacent to the jobsite

4. The underground and overhead utility locations—both existing and new

- Sewer, both sanitary and storm, including drywells
- Water
- Natural gas
- Electrical power
- Steam, if provided by a central steam plant
- Telephone/data

5. The paved surfaces, both existing and new

All of this information probably is not on a single sheet of the construction drawings. Additional information could be drawn onto the site plan, but usually there is more information than is needed on the site plan. A tracing could be made of the site plan, for additional information. A computer-aided design (CAD) system can be useful in these situations. The utility lines can be added in "layers," with designated colors. A CAD can be used without the original drawings, using outlines for structures and buildings.

The constructor, after having all of the constraining factors on a drawing, can then start laying out the roadways, access, lifting facilities, and temporary facilities. A CAD system can provide several different scenarios, quickly and easily. Many different solutions are available, and the constructor will be looking for the solution that best optimizes time and cost in completing the work.

Figures 6–9 and 6–10 illustrate a jobsite layout drawing. Figure 6–9 indicates information shown on the site plan in the construction drawings. Figure 6–10 shows site access, site offices, and other information determined during jobsite layout planning.

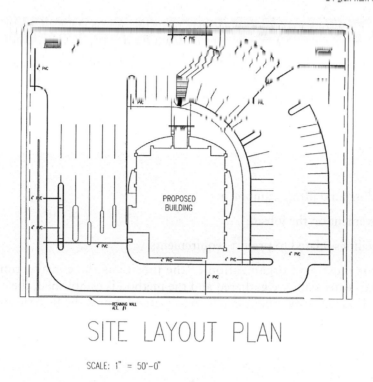

SITE LAYOUT PLAN

SCALE: 1" = 50'-0"

Figure 6–9   **Site Plan from Construction Drawings**

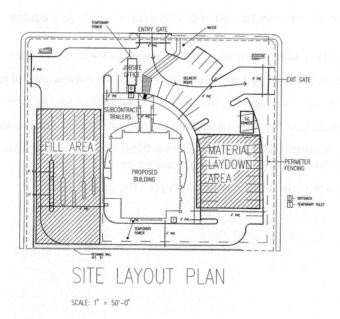

SITE LAYOUT PLAN

SCALE: 1" = 50'-0"

Figure 6–10   **Jobsite Layout**

Summary

Jobsite organization is a factor in the profitability of a construction project. It has a distinct impact on the productivity of every craftsperson on the site. The contractor should carefully consider all aspects of the project when laying out the jobsite, such as the following:

- Delivery access

- Material storage

- Access roads

- Material handling and lifting equipment

- Personnel movement on the jobsite

- Temporary facilities related to project requirements

The contractor must plan organization of the jobsite as the construction of the project would be planned. After data are gathered and the method is established, the contractor has to implement it, and, as with any other plan in construction, it must be flexible and accommodate changes in the construction process.

Review Questions

1. What are some aspects of the jobsite layout plan?

2. What factors would you consider to increase productivity by efficient material handling?

3. What factors would you consider when determining the optimum equipment for moving material?

4. What plans could you implement on a jobsite to reduce wasted time for the crew?

5. What are some factors that you would examine to determine the type of jobsite office?

6. What are some temporary facilities that you will need to plan for the jobsite?

7. What factors would you consider necessary for construction access roads?

8. Site drainage and storm water control can be critical items in jobsite layout. How would you determine the necessary requirements?

9. What are some useful references when laying out the jobsite plan?

Chapter 7

Meetings, Negotiations, and Dispute Resolution

Objectives

This chapter discusses the types of meetings held on construction projects and the exchange of ideas on negotiations and methods of dispute resolution. The objectives of this chapter are to:

- Introduce the basic format that construction meetings should follow
- Describe the different meetings, what they accomplish, and who should attend
- Discuss the agendas that should be used for the different meetings
- Review the different methods used to resolve disputes, such as mediation and arbitration
- Discuss the claim process from claim to arbitration using a flowchart
- Analyze why negotiations fail or succeed

Today's constructor must negotiate in one form or another, from signing the contract until the end of the project. Once a project has been sold to an owner, writing subcontracts, settling changes, applying for payments, and finishing the project punch list all require some form of negotiation with another party. Sometimes negotiations are with the owner, other times with the architect or subcontractor. Negotiations on the construction site occur at all levels and in all positions. Projects in construction are always complicated, individual trades are very specialized, and the potential for misunderstanding and confusion is ever present.

As complexity increases throughout the project, additional formal lines of communication are required. **Meetings** are a convenient means of facilitating communication. They should be formally scheduled and used to inform individuals of progress, to discuss problems, and to propose and seek solutions. Jobsite-related meetings can be classified as follows:

- Partnering meeting and workshop session (project team)
- Contractor's preconstruction planning and organization meeting
- Preconstruction meeting with subcontractors
- Preconstruction meeting (owner, architect, and contractor)
- Project meeting (weekly or biweekly)
- Subcontractor coordination meetings (contractor and subcontractors)
- Schedule meetings
- Safety meetings (discussed in chapter 9)
- Staff meetings
- Specialized meetings
- Project closeout meeting
- Postproject review and evaluation

Construction meetings should follow the basic format as in other industries.

Agendas should be developed for all meetings. Meetings are held to inform people and to find solutions to problems, not to socialize. Time is precious for all of the professionals who are active in a construction project. When possible, the agenda and list of attendees should be distributed before the meeting. Agendas for some meetings can be somewhat standardized, even though the details of all meetings differ from week to week and job to job. Specific tasks and ideas parties will be expected to discuss are placed on the agenda. Meetings should be held at a scheduled time during the project, using minutes or other types of logs and letters so that individuals or companies can receive clarification when needed.

Not all meetings must be formal, but written details of the discussions that occur must be kept. Meeting minutes are an effective way to record the intent of meetings and to hold individuals accountable for their statements. Meeting minutes should be a fair depiction of what actually transpires during the meeting. Many times the note taker will slant the minutes toward his or her company's favor. This form of deception should be avoided, as it breaks down any trust that might exist. After distribution, the minutes will be reviewed by all attendees. At the next meeting, the previous minutes will be approved and, if not accepted, corrections made. The question of who should take the notes and who should receive copies is important. Construction team minutes should be distributed to all attendees as early as possible, allowing enough time for review before the next scheduled meeting. Several applications for mobile devices are available. These applications can facilitate quick distribution of minutes via email. Some applications have a recording function as well. Minutes can help clarify pending problems, place responsibility for solutions on individuals, and act as reminders before the next meeting. A list of action items leads to further discussion. Items are added, and other areas are deleted. Any active project that has good communication will utilize an ongoing list, much like a "to-do" list that some people use to organize their day. It generally is preferred by the general contractor that minutes be taken by contractor personnel to maintain control of the meeting and the project. Though recording, formalizing, and distributing the minutes takes considerable effort, they are an important means of project communication. Many architects and owner's representatives do not have the additional manpower to produce and distribute timely minutes.

Figure 7–1 is an example of one form of meeting minutes. A more detailed discussion about the elements of meeting minutes is contained in chapter 5.

Note that in Figure 7–1 areas exist for listing attendees and their companies. Discussion topics are itemized and numbered to facilitate later referral to a specific item or question. Note that on the right side of the form, on the same line as the item number, the column "responsibility" is given.

Team Relationships and Cooperation

Several years ago, the construction industry went through a period of distrust and adversarial relationships on construction projects. Many participants in the process were more interested in obtaining additional compensation than cooperating to provide projects that met cost expectations, were completed on time, and satisfied the customer with the quality of the work. The concept of "partnering" was developed to enhance the relationships within the construction team, promoting a compatible atmosphere on construction projects.

The partnering process used sessions with all of the project participants to create an informed and cooperative team to successfully formulate, design, and construct a viable construction project. Partnering early in the project can create relationships between participants that eliminates problems and provides a forum for solving problems.

Some of the topics discussed in the partnering sessions are:

- Introduction of team members. Typically, the actual team members will vary from previous projects.

- A discussion about changing the "work-as-usual" attitude.

- A discussion about the roles and positions for individuals involved with the project and their importance.

- A discussion about how problems could be solved at the lowest level.

- Agreement of understanding between team members.

FGH construction company

MEETING MINUTES

FGH Construction Company, Inc.

Date : _____

Sheet _____ of _____

Minutes of Minutes: _____

On : _____

Subject : _____

Project Name: _____

Project Number : _____

Location: _____

ATTENDEE:

Name	Company
_____	_____
_____	_____
_____	_____
_____	_____
_____	_____

Item No.	Description	Status	Due Date	Responsibility
1.	Discussed outstanding paint color submittal	New	6/6/2026	Jlrn R.—FGH
2.				

_____

Meeting Notes Taken By: _____

P.O. Box 3888
New City, CA 93478
(805) 444-9900
FAX: (805) 444-9901

Figure 7–1   Example Meeting Minutes

Partnering sessions usually have agreements between team members to maintain a collaborative environment on the project. On many projects, partnering has evolved to less formal agreements but the attitude on the projects has become much more cooperative. Team members concentrate on the success of their segments of the project and the total success of the project.

The Contractor's Preconstruction Planning and Organization Meeting

The contractor's preconstruction planning and organization meeting is necessary to accomplish a successful project. A well-planned project from its inception has positive long-term returns. Prior planning solves problems before the project starts, enabling the management team to concentrate on project start-up. After the Notice to Proceed, the project management team focuses on implementing rather than planning the project. Time is not unlimited, and with each extra day the contractor incurs indirect jobsite costs. The prejob planning session can be broken into five or more distinct parts. Some firms have developed checklists for each of the phases to expedite the planning and organization of the project. Prejob planning involves the following five organizational sections:

1. Review of staffing requirements based on project manual requirements and any special project requirements, that is, environmental, training, hazardous waste, and so on. The complexity of the project also should be discussed. Organizational charts that list the names and responsibilities of each person should be developed. Descriptions of each position should accompany the organization chart.

2. A review of the estimate and estimator's intent should be made. A review of the subcontractors, long-lead items, areas of risks, and special equipment needs also would be done by the estimator. The estimate must be revised into a project budget, which may require a major change in the estimate items to ensure that they are compatible with the cost control system. The contractor should begin writing major equipment purchase orders and any subcontract agreements.

3. Development of the construction plan and preliminary schedule. Decisions about how this particular project will be built are made. This schedule is the basis for the final construction schedule and should have a great deal of input and thought behind it. A detailed 90-day schedule also should be completed.

4. Project safety, fire protection, environmental considerations, and other specification regulations requiring specific plans should be outlined, and tasks should be assigned to complete them.

5. Review the external and internal administrative requirements of procuring required bonds, insurance, permits, minority/woman-owned business enterprises requirements, and other miscellaneous items.

Figure 7–2 presents an example of a preconstruction planning and organization checklist, which can be used to set the agenda for a preconstruction planning meeting.

Preconstruction Meeting with Subcontractors

A preconstruction meeting with subcontractors is not always held but has some merit for more complicated projects. A meeting of all subcontractors is not possible until subcontractor scope, Disadvantaged Business Enterprises selections, subcontractor negotiations, and other issues are resolved. Many problems can slow the selection of subcontractors, thus making it impossible to hold a prejob meeting with all of the subcontractors involved. If relatively few problems are anticipated with subcontractor selection, this meeting is helpful in completing project preplanning. Material problems, work sequence, access and subcontractor storage, and hoisting arrangements are among the issues that can be discussed. The meeting also provides time for the contractor to discuss the contractor's administrative processes for submittals, payment, and jobsite safety. Figure 7–3 illustrates a sample agenda for a preconstruction meeting with subcontractors.

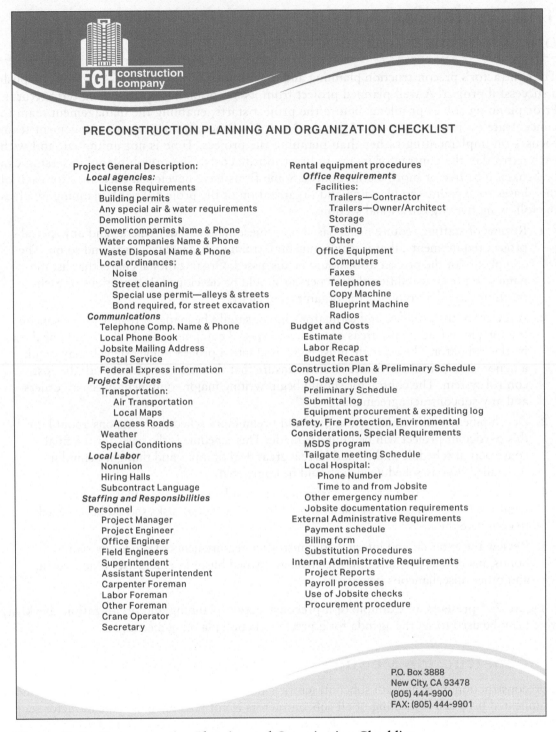

Figure 7–2   Preconstruction Planning and Organization Checklist

Project Preconstruction Meeting

The project preconstruction meeting is the meeting that "kicks off" the project. It is the meeting that first establishes the relationships that will continue to develop as the project is built. The preconstruction meeting's agenda will discuss and clarify critical areas that impact on project personnel's ability to work and solve problems. A suggested minimum agenda for the preconstruction meeting should contain the following elements:

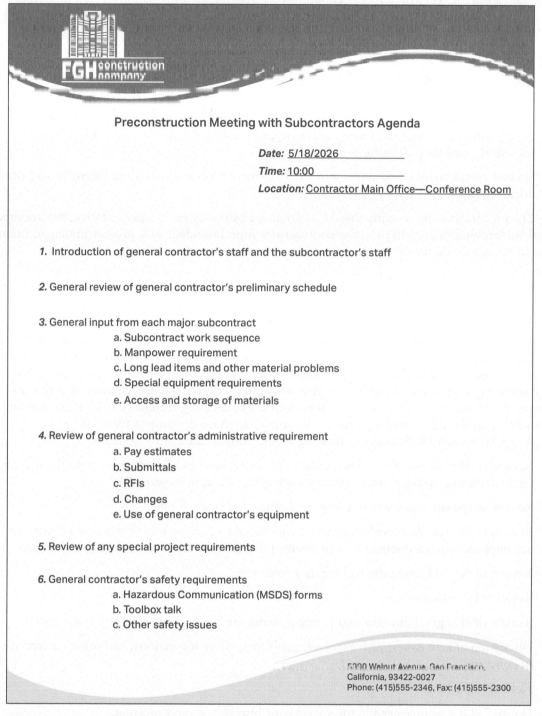

Figure 7–3   Agenda, Preconstruction Meeting with Subcontractors

- Introduction of all of the project team members and their responsibilities
- Review of the contract
- Discussion and agreement to a Notice to Proceed date
- Layout and field control issues
- Review of preliminary schedule and sequence of work
- Owner's site restrictions (for example, traffic, noise, hour of work, and so on)

- Temporary facilities to be placed on site, field offices for the owner's representative, and other facilities to be occupied by testing and other inspectors

- Quality control and other areas of coordination and cooperation

- A general discussion on the weekly or biweekly project meeting to be held when work commences

- Administrative procedures and processes to be used on the project, that is, payment requests, change orders, change directives, authority, requests for information (RFIs), field orders, submittals, and shop drawing process

- Special certifications and paperwork requirements, such as certified payrolls and other documentation

The preconstruction meeting should be attended by the owner's representative, the architect and the architect's consultants, the contractor's superintendent and project manager, major subcontractors, and major equipment suppliers.

Project Meetings

Project meetings are generally scheduled on a weekly or biweekly basis. These meetings are where questions are asked and answered and provide a forum for owner's representatives, architects, contractors, and subcontractors to discuss their concerns. It also is an opportunity for the contractor to keep the designer and owner up to date on progress, any changes affecting work, future problems that may arise, and other issues. The meeting should be held at the jobsite, if possible, and should present a positive opportunity to move the project forward.

A typical agenda for this type of meeting would contain the following items:

- Review of the last meeting minutes (As minutes are sent to all parties prior to the meeting, only changes or additions to the minutes are discussed at this meeting.)

- Review of the submittal status, using a submittal log as a reference

- Review of the schedule, including work completed to date, a 3-week preview of work to be accomplished, and a discussion of problems related to the schedule and project duration

- Review of the RFI, using the RFI log as a reference

- Review of substitutions

- Review of changes, both new and pending, using the change order log as a reference

- Discussion of new issues, such as jobsite problems, safety inspections, and other current areas of concern

- Field observations

Figure 7–4 is a sample agenda for a weekly or biweekly project meeting.

Construction Phase Subcontractor Meetings

Many general contractors schedule a weekly subcontractor meeting the day before weekly project meetings. This coordination meeting's goals are similar to the project meeting's. Current problems are verbalized and an opportunity is provided to discuss and solve anticipated problems. Coordination among subcontractors is one of the major responsibilities of the construction's project team. If done properly, the owner and designer are unaware of the process. The agenda for this meeting should be as formal as the other types of meetings previously discussed. Without a written agenda, no organization will exist, resulting in little or no clarification or accountability of existing problems to complete the meeting. The attendees will range from the subcontractors'

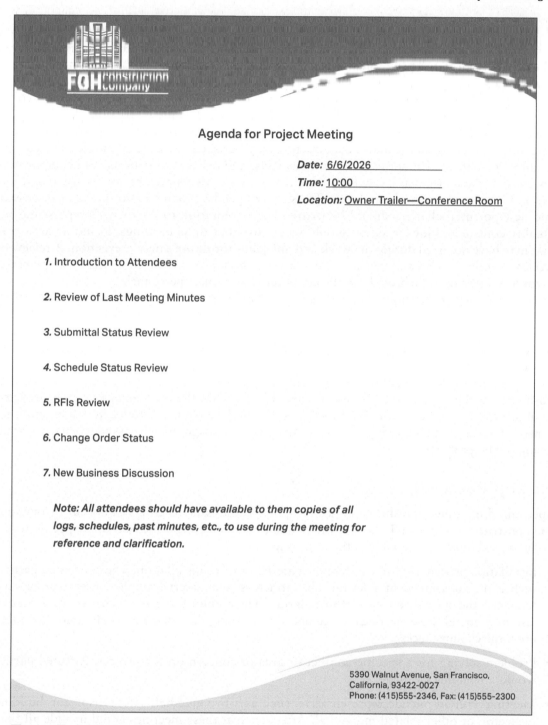

Figure 7–4 Project Meeting Agenda

office people to the on-site foremen of different subcontractors. It is important that the superintendent be well informed of the activities scheduled for the next period, so this information can be used to set the agenda and arrange for the appropriate subcontractors to attend the meetings. This may take some coordination and management skill on the superintendent's part. Quite often, if the work scheduled does not relate to a particular subcontractor, the subcontractor probably will not attend, even if requested. If these meetings do not solve coordination problems among subcontractors, the superintendent will be involved in a number of individual meetings with subcontractors, which makes coordination more complicated, not to mention disrupting the flow of the project.

Construction Staff Meetings

Construction staff meetings are held for larger projects to coordinate different areas of work. The superintendent and project manager will provide the leadership for these meetings, with all project staff present, to discuss problems and find solutions for any existing or future problems that may arise. The superintendent, assistant superintendents, area superintendents, project manager, field engineers, office engineers, project engineer, foreman, and other key craftspersons, such as the crane operator, should attend. Staff meetings are held strictly for contractor's personnel, but major individual subcontractors may be asked to attend if a topic of discussion might involve them. The status of submittals, RFIs, and delivery of material and equipment is reviewed at these meetings. New RFIs from the superintendents present are discussed and formalized for transmittal to the architect. The status of pending changes also should be discussed, and new potential changes should be written for presentation to the owner's representative. Quality control and jobsite safety should be discussed at these meetings, including accidents that may have occurred during the week and any plans for future safety prevention. A review of weekly "toolbox" talks and jobsite safety meetings should be performed as well. Any potential hazardous areas must be brought to the attention of all project personnel.

A three-week construction schedule is a good planning tool for proposed work. The schedule normally would examine in detail the previous week and two weeks in advance. This schedule provides direction for all project construction staff for a 2-week period. A 90-day summary schedule also is helpful for determining longer-lead items that may be delayed in the submittal process or that may have RFIs attached to them. This meeting differs from other meetings discussed in that it is an internal management meeting. Specific tasks will be assigned, and accomplishments will be expected by project leaders. For instance, the field engineer may be directed to implement a specific layout, the project engineer may be requested to locate a submittal that is needed to start the purchasing process, or the project manager may be asked to solve a certain change order problem.

Specialized Meetings

Specialized meetings, coordination meetings, or specific-issue meetings can occur throughout the construction process. These are often single-issue meetings, focused on a specific topic. Some typical topics would include the following:

- Installation procedures for a system or material prior to installation. The concerned parties, such as the superintendent, relevant subcontractors, and material supplier, meet to discuss the sequence and special concerns of installation. The architect and the owner's representative also may attend these meetings for guidance concerning the intended installation, depending upon the circumstances.

- Problem solving for a specific conflict or area of concern on the project. Affected parties would attend this meeting.

- Meeting with an outside representative, such as a fire marshal, safety inspector, building inspector, or other related individual. Attendance at these meetings could include all field management and active subcontractors or only specific parties, depending upon the issue.

- Payment processing, if not included in the project meeting.

Because these meetings can be time consuming, they should be limited regarding topic and attendance. They also should promptly address the topic, come to a resolution, and adjourn.

Project Closeout Meetings

The project closeout meeting also is based on an ongoing process. This meeting provides the opportunity to define closeout procedures and for the owner to further specify any additional items needed in the operation of the facility. This meeting should be held early enough to discuss the completion of the pending punch list and to review the status of substantial completion for the project. Discussion can concern the record drawings and operating and maintenance manuals, relating primarily to schedule, content, and presentation. Project closeout meetings can help the facilities management team assume the responsibility for maintenance and operation of the building. Another topic of importance, depending upon when the meeting is held, is the keys and keying schedule. The keying requirement usually is spelled out clearly in the specifications, but facilities management personnel usually are the recipients of the keys.

A project closeout meeting can be a last chance to adjust outstanding changes, review allowances not completely used, and discuss procedures for final billings. A list of final cleanup, window cleaning, and a demobilization schedule should be given to the architect, owner, and the owner's facilities management group.

A project closeout checklist should be developed for use by the project manager. The list should include items discussed in chapter 16. This checklist also can be used as the agenda for the project closeout meeting.

Postproject Review and Evaluation

The final act of the field management team should be an in-house project review. This review should include a formal presentation of the project from start to finish. It is the last chance to save, for historical purposes, the positive and negative attributes from the project. A review of the cost reports, productivity charts, and other important estimating data should be examined with the estimating staff. In addition to the data, a description of all of the items that might have impacted on or influenced productivity is considered. The type and size of equipment used, how the concrete was placed, the quality of the craftspeople, the weather, and the management of the process all help explain the actual unit prices developed for historical estimating data.

Part of the postproject review should contain a formal review of the subcontractor's performance. This should be in the form of a written report, detailing how the subcontractor performed, who the foreman was, what problems occurred, and how these problems were resolved. Both the quality of the subcontractor's work and the safety practices of the crews should be included on the form and in the discussion. The subcontractor's evaluations can be used for selecting subcontractors for future projects.

Negotiations

A construction project is a fluid process, requiring negotiation and compromise by most parties. Often, areas of disagreement arise that are not completely defined in the contract documents. The team represented by the owner, architect, and contractor must be in constant communication with one another to accomplish the common goal of producing a facility that meets the owner's needs, the owner's budget and time frame, and the level of quality specified by the documents. The three major contractual participants in a construction project must learn to apply effective methods for problem solving. The solution to most problems will require some compromise by all involved parties. The goal is not to "win" every situation but to solve each problem with minimal impact to all parties. Solving the problem quickly and effectively should be the goal in all negotiations.

The process of negotiating is meant to resolve an issue, not to position one party against another party for possible financial gain. This process may be influenced by a stronger position by one of the parties. Position strength, however, changes throughout the project and changes with different issues. At times, the architect may be in a stronger position, while other times the contractor may. All negotiations should be done in good faith, with each party remaining honest. Since negotiations continue throughout the project, a continuous honesty and directness is required by all parties.

Negotiations can commence at the onset of the project, including negotiations for project price, terms, and contract duration, and can continue throughout the project. Honest and complete negotiations should be handled fairly by all parties at each point.

When the negotiating process breaks down, all parties involved move to other forms of dispute settlement. Many owners are adding formal nonbinding mediation clauses in their contracts along with the standard arbitration clauses. Most contractors will not sign contracts without the standard arbitration clause but have no problem when an additional form of dispute resolution is introduced. Arbitration has played a key role in construction dispute resolution. The American Arbitration Association (AAA) is the leading dispute resolution group in the country. Many contracts state this organization's name in the contract's arbitration clause. Section 15.4 of Form A201 2007, General Conditions of the Contract from the American Institute of Architects (AIA), is shown in Figure 7–5.

The notification times and the specific flow of a dispute or claim is fairly concise. A flowchart of the project can act as a reminder of what needs to be done if arbitration occurs. The flowchart in Figure 7–6 shows the claims process from the AIA A201 2007 General Conditions of the Contract.

Mediation is the process of bringing together disputing parties with the aid of a trained mediator (facilitator) to discuss the problems and find a middle ground or solution to which both parties can agree. Mediation is a nonbinding process, so problems are not always resolved, but this should still be the first form of alternate dispute resolution used. The AAA's contract language for mediation that follows can be used in conjunction with a standard arbitration provision:

> If a dispute arises out of or relates to this contract, or the breach thereof, and if the dispute cannot be settled through negotiation, the parties agree first to try in good faith to settle the dispute by mediation administered by the American Arbitration Association under its Construction Industry Mediation Rules before resorting to arbitration, litigation, or some other dispute-resolution procedure.

Mediation is first used when negotiations fail to resolve a particular dispute. An outside neutral player is used as a facilitator and adviser for each party trying to resolve the dispute. The facilitator, who does not impose solutions, will make suggestions in an attempt to move the parties closer to a resolution, guiding all members involved to resolve the dispute among themselves. Arbitration, another form of dispute resolution, provides an outside neutral party who not only hears the problem but also will make a binding ruling. In contrast to mediations and arbitrations, negotiations do not need a neutral party to achieve an acceptable outcome. Other contractors have used the idea of dispute avoidance and resolution to include partnering strategies in their job contracts to make project members aware of and anticipate where sources of future disputes may arise. The key element to all alternate dispute avoidance or resolution strategies is to keep project members communicating and participating in the daily process of resolving the problems at hand.

Arbitration, as stated earlier, can be and generally is binding. Both parties select and agree upon an arbitrator or arbitrators from a list of professionals. Arbitration was developed to save time by eliminating the court litigation process. Generally, at this stage both parties will have an attorney present but will not be represented by the attorneys during arbitration, because this process is not conducted like a court of law. Depositions will be taken before the arbitration, and attorneys' fees will not be considered part of the settlement, which makes arbitration costly for both parties.

Under the AAA's Construction Industry Arbitration Rules, three tracks are available. "Fast Track" rules involve claims of less than $50,000, "Regular Track" for those between $50,000 and $1,000,000, and "Large, Complex Construction Case Track" for those over $1,000,000. Highlights for these three tracks, according to the AAA, include the following:

15.4 Arbitration

15.4.1 If the parties have selected arbitration as the method for binding dispute resolution in the Agreement, any Claim subject to, but not resolved by, mediation shall be subject to arbitration which, unless the parties mutually agree otherwise, shall be administered by the American Arbitration Association in accordance with its Construction Industry Arbitration Rules in effect on the date of the Agreement. A demand for arbitration shall be made in writing, delivered to the other party to the Contract, and filed with the person or entity administering the arbitration. The party filing a notice of demand for arbitration must assert in the demand all Claims then known to that party on which arbitration is permitted to be demanded.

15.4.1.1 A demand for arbitration shall be made no earlier than concurrently with the filing of a request for mediation, but in no event shall it be made after the date when the institution of legal or equitable proceedings based on the Claim would be barred by the applicable statute of limitations. For statute of limitations purposes, receipt of a written demand for arbitration by the person or entity administering the arbitration shall constitute the institution of legal or equitable proceedings based on the Claim.

15.4.2 The award rendered by the arbitrator or arbitrators shall be final, and judgment may be entered upon it in accordance with applicable law in any court having jurisdiction thereof.

15.4.3 The foregoing agreement to arbitrate and other agreements to arbitrate with an additional person or entity duly consented to by parties to the Agreement shall be specifically enforceable under applicable law in any court having jurisdiction thereof.

15.4.4 CONSOLIDATION OR JOINDER

15.4.4.1 Either party, at its sole discretion, may consolidate an arbitration conducted under this Agreement with any other arbitration to which it is a party provided that (1) the arbitration agreement governing the other arbitration permits consolidation, (2) the arbitrations to be consolidated substantially involve common questions of law or fact, and (3) the arbitrations employ materially similar procedural rules and methods for selecting arbitrator(s).

15.4.4.2 Either party, at its sole discretion, may include by joinder persons or entities substantially involved in a common question of law or fact whose presence is required if complete relief is to be accorded in arbitration, provided that the party sought to be joined consents in writing to such joinder. Consent to arbitration involving an additional person or entity shall not constitute consent to arbitration of any claim, dispute or other matter in question not described in the written consent.

15.4.4.3 The Owner and Contractor grant to any person or entity made a party to an arbitration conducted under this Section 15.4, whether by joinder or consolidation, the same rights of joinder and consolidation as the Owner and Contractor under this Agreement.

Figure 7–5   Arbitration Section, AIA Document A201 2007, General Conditions of the Contract
(Reprinted with permission)

"Fast Track"

- A 60-day "time standard" for case completion

- Establishment of a special pool of arbitrators who are prequalified to serve on an expedited basis

- An expedited arbitrator appointment process, with party input

- Presumption that cases involving less than $10,000 will be heard on documents only

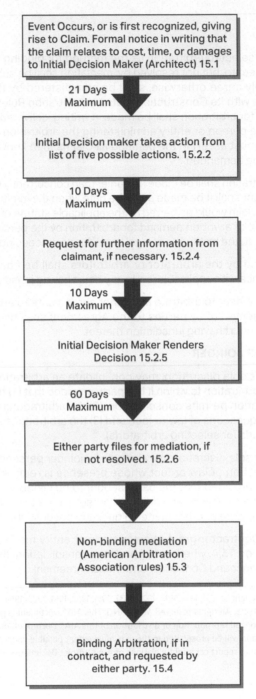

Figure 7–6   Flow Chart, Dispute Notification Procedure, Adapted with permission from AIA Document A201 2007, General Conditions of the Contract

- Requirement of a hearing within 30 days of the arbitrator's appointment

- A single-day hearing, in most cases

- An award no more than seven days after the hearing

"Regular Track"

- More party input into the AAA's preparation of lists of proposed arbitrators

- Express arbitrator authority to control the discovery process

- Broad arbitrator authority to control the hearing

- Written breakdowns of the award and, if requested in a timely manner by all parties or in the discretion of the arbitrator, a written explanation of the award

- Arbitrator compensation starting with the first day of service (with the AAA to provide the arbitrator's compensation policy with the biographical information sent to the parties)

- A revised demand form and a new answer form, both of which seek more information from the parties to assist the AAA in better serving the parties

"Large, Complex Construction Case Track"

- Mandatory use of the procedures in cases involving claims of more than $1 million

- A highly qualified, trained Roster of Neutrals, compensated at their customary rate

- A mandatory preliminary hearing with the arbitrators, which may be conducted by teleconference

- Broad arbitrator authority to order and control discovery, including depositions

- Presumption that hearings will proceed on a consecutive or block basis

Arbitration can result in a compromised solution for all parties, but most often this is not the case, and, unfortunately, this can take a long time to complete. The wise contractor, architect, engineer, owner, and subcontractor will fairly and, with sensible compromise, solve and implement solutions to problems before, during, and after the completion of a project.

If all members of the construction team are professional and informed participants, all changes and claims can be negotiated without mediation, arbitration, and litigation. Most problems that arise in construction are not black-and-white, but if all parties are looking for solutions, results are much easier to accomplish.

Summary

Meetings are a major form of communication during the construction project. Some types of meetings held for a construction project include the following:

- Contractor's preconstruction planning and organization meeting

- Preconstruction meeting with subcontractors

- Project preconstruction meeting

- Project meetings

- Subcontractor meetings

- Partnering meetings

- Contractor staff meetings

- Project closeout meetings

- Postproject evaluation meeting

Agendas prepared prior to the meetings are essential to meeting organization. Minutes of all meetings are necessary to provide a record for reference of the meeting and discussions.

Negotiations are an important part of the construction project, from start to finish. Negotiations need to be made in good faith, with all parties expecting compromises. When negotiations fail, mediation and arbitration can settle project disputes.

Review Questions

1. Why would an owner wish to have a partnering meeting and workshop on their project? Which party of the project teams should attend?

2. Name five different types of meetings and list the primary goal or objective for having each meeting listed.

3. Who should attend the project preconstruction meeting?

4. Write a typical agenda for a project meeting.

5. Why does the construction industry use the process of negotiating?

6. Are there any trends in contract language in the area of dispute resolution, and, if so, what are they?

7. If your contract included AIA Document A201, what section determines when arbitration may be demanded and what is the time frame required by this clause?

8. According to the AAA Construction Industry Arbitration Rules, how many tracks are available? What are their names and what is the main determining factor as to which track is used?

9. Using Figure 7–6, after an event occurs or is first recognized, giving rise to a claim, when can arbitration occur if a mechanic's lien has been filed?

10. Meeting minutes are an effective way to record the content of meetings. What other major reason is there to have meeting minutes?

Chapter 8

Jobsite Labor Relations and Control

Objectives

This chapter discusses the organization of the jobsite labor, labor productivity, and supervision and control of construction labor. The objectives of this chapter are to introduce the following:

- Most common factors that affect labor productivity
- Hidden factors that are often not as obvious as other factors
- Typical hierarchy of labor and management on a construction project
- Use of labor agreements
- Importance of the superintendent's role in the supervision and control of labor
- Use of a reporting system for cost control, historical job cost, and productivity control

The term **labor** describes craftspeople who actually perform construction work, from the foreman to the individual tradesperson. The term "labor" indicates direct labor, or craftspeople employed by the contractor at the jobsite. The contractor pays the wages, fringe benefits, taxes, and workers' compensation for these employees and is responsible for managing the direct labor on the jobsite through the superintendent and through field management. The contractor provides supervision, task direction, material, and equipment for direct-labor employees. Because of this responsibility, the contractor also controls the labor and has flexibility in moving employees from task to task, an effect on employees' productivity, control of duration of activities, and control in fluctuating the crew size, as necessary. The contractor does not have direct control of subcontractor's labor, as these employees are controlled by the subcontractor's management. The contractor's use of direct labor depends on project requirements, labor force available, subcontractors available, local customs, company policy, and the expertise of the contractor's field management.

The contractor employs a variety of different craftspeople, including laborers, carpenters, operating engineers, and ironworkers. These employees are assumed to possess the knowledge and skill necessary for their crafts. Some contractors require that employees perform a variety of craft-related tasks; however, it is assumed that they are skilled in each task. The contractor must depend on a certain level of productivity of employee labor for each craft so that reliable cost estimates, crew compositions, crew assignments, and schedules can be prepared.

This chapter concerns the management of jobsite labor. An assumption is made that if the employee is classified in a certain craft, such as, carpentry, then that employee is skilled in that craft and is fairly equal in productivity potential. Differences exist in crafts, productivity rates, and customs in various geographical areas.

Labor Productivity

Labor productivity can be defined as the rate at which tasks are produced, especially the output per unit of labor. Other definitions include "work performed per unit of time" or "time to perform unit of work." The goal in managing construction tasks is to produce the optimum output per labor hour. The output desired naturally complies with project requirements for materials, construction techniques, appearance, performance, and workmanship. Productivity rates should be established in the estimate regarding perception of conditions and project requirements. The productivity rates used in the estimate are generated from historical data, both from the contractor's own records and from a variety of available references.

Many different factors can affect labor productivity on a project. Project supervisors should be familiar with the most common factors affecting labor productivity, which include the following:

- Lack of supervision or poor supervision
- Lack of coordination of subcontractors with work activities

- Improper or insufficient material available for tasks
- Poor jobsite layout
- Lack of proper tools for work activities
- Congested work areas
- Poor housekeeping
- Accidents and unsafe conditions on the jobsite
- Excessive moving of craftspeople from project to project
- Adverse weather conditions
- Poor lighting in the work area
- Inadequate heat or ventilation in the work area
- Tardiness of excessive absenteeism
- Uncontrolled starting time, quitting time, coffee breaks, and lunch breaks
- Shortage and location of close parking, changing rooms, restrooms, and drinking water
- High employee turnover
- Use of improperly or poorly trained craftspeople
- Supervisors not making timely decisions
- Poor attitude among employees
- Poor use of multiple shifts
- Working overtime
- Construction mistakes caused by complexity, poor drawings, or lack of communication
- Impact of changes on production work

Most superintendents and foremen would admit that these are not revelations. Unfortunately, supervisors are aware of these problem areas in a broad sense but sometimes are not cognizant of them on specific projects with their particular crews. The most serious problems are the ones that impact upon productivity without the superintendent's knowledge. Solutions are available for all productivity problems, but problems must be communicated to the superintendent with sufficient time to successfully alter conditions. Serious problems arise for many reasons. A discussion of these reasons follows.

Impact of Changes

Momentum or flow of work can be disrupted by changes in the work. If an error occurs in the construction drawings or if a latent condition is discovered during a work activity, a delay will occur. Changes will often consume field personnel, resulting in neglect in continuing other areas of work. Frequent changes produce confusion in crews, which reduces productivity. Crews often have a different attitude to work changes, consequently working without the same motivation to complete activities quickly and efficiently. The removal of recently completed installations can demoralize crews and slow productivity.

Although changes during construction are often beyond the control of the contractor, the field staff can minimize the impact of changes to construction productivity. Knowledgeable examination of the construction documents can reveal problems prior to crew assignments. It is desirable to solve problems before tasks are assigned. When changes are implemented, crew directions should indicate these changes. Construction documents must be notated to show changes accurately. The field management staff should work carefully with the crew to keep the momentum going, both in the area of change and in other areas of work.

Poor Weather

Bad weather often is not adequately anticipated, forcing changes in schedules, production, and damage to completed work. Productivity decreases in poor weather to varying degrees, depending upon the severity of the weather and the work tasks. Weather can affect some construction materials, such as concrete and mortar, as well as the efficiency of the labor. When protective clothing, such as rain gear or cold-weather gear, is necessary, labor is impeded.

Initial project planning should consider seasonal weather conditions. Anticipating bad weather and planning weather-sensitive activities around it can reduce some of the impact. Flexibility should be built into the work schedule to allow for downtime during inclement weather. When cold or rainy weather is predicted during construction activities, an analysis is necessary to compare the productivity loss with the cost of temporary weather protection, such as a tent and temporary heat. It often is desirable to protect the work area and continue with activities during these periods.

Special considerations are necessary for crews working in nonideal weather conditions. During hot weather, enough cold drinking water must be furnished at the installation location. Coordination of work activities during cooler times of the day may be advisable. Shaded areas are often needed for work areas, as are windbreaks to control wind and dust effects on the construction installation.

Rainy weather requires protection of the work area, maintenance of haul roads and jobsite access, and dry shack provisions for changing clothes and eating lunch. In fine-grained soils, rain will produce mud, which slows work considerably. Preparation for these conditions can be made, with provisions such as preparing haul roads and jobsite access with a gravel surface and adequate drainage.

Material Problems

Late deliveries require crews to move to other work areas, halting the production at one area and requiring startup of new work activities. Also, shortages can stop crews from working, forcing workers to be laid off for short periods of time. If crews are required to carry materials long distances before work can occur, productivity is affected. Double handling of materials will result in damage to materials, increased waste, and lost time.

Jobsite management is responsible for ensuring that the correct amount of material is available for installation and for appropriate jobsite storage of material. Careful attention to the construction documents, site conditions, work assignment packages, and progress of the project is necessary to order and schedule delivery of materials. Coordination of the procurement schedule, as discussed in chapter 4, is extremely helpful when material is being delivered to the jobsite to coincide with construction activities.

The material supplier may be responsible for incomplete deliveries, improper material delivered, defective material, and late delivery of material. Confirmation with the supplier prior to delivery is helpful in receiving the proper material for the project. Some material contracts and purchase orders have provisions for back charging the supplier for damages; however, this is often not feasible.

High Labor Turnover

High labor turnover may be an indication of poor planning, general unrest, and lack of leadership by the foreman and/or superintendent. New training may be required each time this situation occurs, and high levels of unrest or low morale can lead to a slowdown of work.

Construction labor is fairly mobile from contractor to contractor. The contractor may be using employees who are not familiar with the type of installation needed or the methods. Training may not be consistent in the available labor force.

Jobsite management must employ the correct labor for the project. It is important that jobsite management be experienced in the type of construction on the project. Many contractors have teams consisting of a superintendent, field engineers, and foremen, and a few craftspeople who will remain from project to project. This consistency helps screen appropriate labor for the project. Despite the fact that foremen are technically considered labor rather than management, they are an important bridge between management and labor, leading the crew in techniques, methods, and productivity. Trained foremen in labor techniques, safety procedures, crew management, productivity control, and cost control are essential for effective labor management. Every project has a selection period for its labor crews, which involves hiring and firing, but astute labor managers will keep this period to a minimum, selecting the proper crews quickly. The size and quality of the labor force in the community at the time of the project have a major effect on this type of labor problem, but active management can optimize each situation.

Accidents and Unsafe Conditions

All work will quickly come to a halt when an accident occurs on a jobsite. Employees who do not feel safe tend to be overly cautious when performing their work tasks, thus noticeably slowing production. A clean and safe jobsite is conducive to obtaining maximum productivity from labor crews.

Many construction companies realize the importance of safety on jobsite production. Contractors are required by state and federal regulations to have in place an active construction safety program, but the degree of implementation on the jobsite is a matter of commitment by the construction company. The impact of a safe and clean jobsite on productivity cannot be understated. The cost of keeping a clean jobsite is considerably less than the cost of lost productivity, accidents, and safety fines associated with poor housekeeping.

Working Overtime

Working longer days or adding additional days of work on a prolonged basis will result in increased injuries and safety problems. As workers become tired from longer periods of work, they begin to adjust their pace or slow their productivity to avoid fatigue. When forced to work overtime, an employee may become disgruntled, causing low morale among other employees. In the same respect, if overtime is offered to one employee and not another, jealousy may become a problem among employees.

Overtime is expensive to the contractor in terms of both additional wages and lost productivity. Although conditions exist when overtime is necessary, this can usually be avoided by proper project planning and crew size. Careful analysis of work tasks can reveal opportunities to use multiple or larger crews to facilitate work during regular shifts. Using the construction schedule to determine the time frame available for the tasks related to crew output should help determine the number and type of crews. Particular job conditions must be considered in this determination. Labor supply largely controls these strategies. Care must be taken to maintain effective leadership of added crews, with capable foremen and field management personnel.

When increased production is required for a long period of time, more shifts may be added. In conditions where extra crews are not efficient, the second shift can add production. Although there are additional costs associated with a second shift, such as a labor premium and additional supervision, the costs of a double shift are usually much less than overtime premiums. The double shift is efficient when all applicable trades participate.

Projects in Existing Facilities or Congested Areas

Areas where finishes are in place or where the client's employees are working will cause a slowdown in construction productivity. Either the craftspeople will damage completed finishes, requiring replacement or touch ups, or work will slow to protect work already in place. When areas become too congested, with more than one trade working in the same area, productivity is greatly affected. None of the trades can accomplish their tasks as efficiently as they can in an area where they may be the only trade. When working around the client's employees, special precautions may have to be implemented, again slowing productivity.

In remodeling, addition, or renovation projects, the productivity rates in the estimate normally reflect the project conditions. As congested and occupied conditions can significantly impact productivity rates, careful planning and crew supervision is necessary. Even when work is required in occupied spaces, planning can isolate construction work from other functions in the space. Isolation of construction activities from occupant functions is important in achieving the necessary productivity. Thorough planning is necessary to maintain productivity rates under these conditions, such as having the appropriate amount of materials transported to the work location, having the proper construction equipment for conditions, isolation of the workforce from distraction, having the proper environmental conditions (light, heat, and ventilation), control of dust and noise from occupied areas, and timely cleanup of congested work areas.

The occurrence of any of these factors that affect productivity often is beyond the control of the superintendent and foreman, but understanding their potential impact on productivity may help mitigate the problem. Also, in discussing these troublesome situations beforehand, any problems outside the scope of the contract can be discussed as possible adjustments to the contract. Awareness of these factors by jobsite management can help eliminate their negative impact.

Jobsite Labor Organization

An understanding of the typical hierarchy of labor and management on a construction project is necessary when building teams to construct the project. Each of the major work activities of the project are packaged into smaller tasks, with assignments of specific trades or a mixture of trades to accomplish these tasks. The superintendent manages jobsite activities. Some projects with distinct project elements, such as separate buildings or structures, will have more than one superintendent. On large projects, assistant superintendents, project engineers, or area superintendents may be used to control segments of the work. These assistants may even have some specific specialties themselves, such as mechanical or electrical skills. Field engineers assist other jobsite management with layout, shop drawings, and miscellaneous project activities. They usually are salaried employees at the bottom tier of the management level.

Labor consists of four tiers: foreman, lead craftsperson, journeyman craftspeople, and apprentice. All of these positions are hourly, and when the crew is unionized, all belong to the same union. Foremen and lead craftspeople normally receive a premium, per hour, for their responsibilities, such as one or two dollars per hour above the craftsperson's wage level. The craftspeople are broken into skill and training levels, the highest being a journeyman, the next being an apprentice (first-year, second-year, and so on), and the last being a helper. Where there is no formal training, the term **apprentice** is not applied. The definition of an apprentice is one who is in training under the supervision and mentoring of a person skilled in one's trade. Most apprenticeship programs include regular training off of the jobsite. The term **helper** is used for an unskilled person who has no training and is not enrolled in a training program for a specific trade. Not all trades recognize the helper classification. Figure 8–1 indicates a typical jobsite labor hierarchy.

Labor Agreements

Commercial building construction is accomplished by both union and open shop (nonunion) construction trades. Union affiliation is a decision made by the employees. Many areas of the country have both union contractors and nonunion contractors competing for the same construction work. Different mixes of union and open shop contractors exist throughout the country, varying from all union to all nonunion construction workers.

When a contractor employs union labor, a **labor agreement** exists between the contractor and the union. This agreement is a contract between the contractor and union, requiring certain

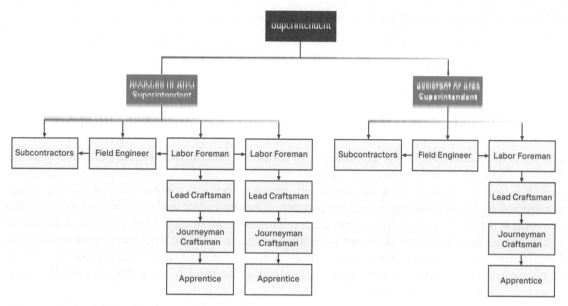

Figure 8–1 Typical Labor Organization

responsibilities of both parties. The contractor and union, upon signing a labor agreement, are contractually bound to each other. The union agrees to provide trained craftspeople, and the contractor agrees to provide specific wage rates, fringe benefits, and working conditions. The union maintains a trained hiring pool of journeymen and apprentices who are furnished to the contractor.

The agreement specifies procedures for hiring; work rules, such as hours and working conditions; and compensation to the employee, such as wages, fringe benefits, travel pay, and subsistence reimbursement. The agreement between the union and the contractor may be individually negotiated between separate contractors and the union or between a management group and the union. A management organization, such as the Associated General Contractors of America, Inc., can represent its member contractors, who assign their bargaining rights to the management organization.

The labor union utilizes business agents who represent union members, ensuring that contractors live up to their agreement. Shop stewards are union members who are employed on the jobsite and who represent union employees on the jobsite. Union leadership can provide an adversarial role or a facilitator role. With increased competition by open shop contractors, union leadership can soften its role and actually help the contractor by furnishing highly trained and qualified labor.

The typical labor agreement covers work, conditions, and wage rates. The following articles are contained in the agreement between the Inland Northwest Chapter of the Associated General Contractors of America and the Washington State Council of Carpenters:

- A statement of purposes—promote cooperation between the contractor and local union organization

- The parties' and management's rights under the labor agreement

- Rules governing strikes, lockouts, and slowdowns

- The agreement's area of jurisdiction

- The issue of using only subcontractors that also are signatory

- Definition of payday, holidays, workweek, workday, shifts, when overtime is defined

- Agreement on how grievances and jurisdictional disputes will be settled

- Employee substance abuse, safety, and accident prevention issues

- Wage rates for different classifications of carpenters

- Hiring hall procedure, work rules (tools, transportation, appointment of foreman)

- Apprenticeship training and classification

A general contractor typically will have labor agreements only with a few unions, which will be hired directly. A general contractor might have labor agreements with the following unions: carpenters, laborers, cement masons, ironworkers, operating engineers, and teamsters. A contractor may only have agreements with carpenters and laborers, subcontracting out tasks that involve other trades. The labor agreement will contain a **subcontractor clause** that will prohibit the contractor from subcontracting work to nonunion firms for a particular labor classification. For instance, if the contractor has an agreement with the carpenters' union, the contractor is required to accomplish tasks such as concrete forming either with its own forces or with a subcontractor that employs union carpenters. This contractor can, however, hire a nonunion excavator, as the contractor does not have an agreement with the operating engineers' union. Despite having agreements with one or more unions, the contractor can subcontract work to either union or nonunion contractors who do not accomplish work listed under the work description in the union agreements.

Dual gates may be necessary on projects using both union and nonunion workers. These are used to separate potential union and nonunion workforces, pursuant to National Labor Relations Board procedures, to avoid secondary boycotts by one group over another nonparticipating firm. Dual gates apply to admission of the general contractor's craftspeople as well as subcontractors' employees and the delivery of materials to the project. Merit shop and nonunion construction firms will plan into the job the use of dual gates, which includes security fencing, location of entrances, parking, deliveries, job trailer locations, and other pertinent site layout. One gate is set up for the entrance and exit of union firms and employees, the other for nonunion firms and its employees. Laws and rules governing picketing of a project require that picketing cannot occur at the gate reserved for the neutral employer, the nonunion firms not involved in the labor dispute. Picketing can target only the specific or primary firm engaged in the labor dispute. The use of dual gates should be discussed with all contractors and subcontractors at the beginning of the project, or as subcontractors move onto the site. Gates can be adjacent to each other, but by placing them apart, potential picketing conflicts are eliminated. See Figure 8–2 for a sample gate sign.

Supervision and Control of Labor

The Superintendent

The superintendent is the contractor's jobsite representative and quite often the only person who can truly control costs, time, and quality. The superintendent is responsible for timely productivity within the company and for coordinating subcontractors on the job, which requires subcontractors' work to be completed on time and within the specifications and subcontracts.

A superintendent's typical day, if there is such a thing, starts with a walk on the jobsite, but the superintendent is the last person on the site to leave. The superintendent's first concern is to lay out the day's schedule for his own forces, who usually begin work at 7:00 A.M. If the work is not ready and preplanned, worker productivity is at a standstill. Foremen must be informed and ready to direct craftspeople to the area where they will be working and to the particular tasks they will be expected to accomplish. Most work activities utilize a combination of trades and take multiple days to complete. The superintendent must possess both the understanding and the visualization of what work needs to be done, the ability to plan the progression and completion of work activities, and the ability to tie each work activity to the next. All employees who are in supervisory roles must have an overall vision of the project as well as an understanding of the thousands of individual tasks and work items that must be accomplished to complete a project. Work items for

TIIIS GATE TO BE USED ONLY BY THE FOLLOWING
EMPLOYEES, MATERIAL PEOPLE AND SUPPLIERS
OF THE STATED FIRMS!

FGH Construction Company, Inc.

RANDOM Electric Company

JOY SHEETMETAL SUPPLY COMPANY

**ALL FIRMS NOT LISTED ABOVE MUST USE
OTHER DESIGNATED GATES.**

Specifications:

Dimensions: 4' by 6'
2" Lettering
Bold typeface in red
Firms in black
Background, white

Figure 8–2   Gate Sign

the general contractor and subcontractor must all be coordinated because of their interrelationship. For instance, the electrical conduit may pass through the concrete floor done by the general contractor into a metal stud wall done by another subcontractor or into a ceiling space occupied with HVAC ductwork, water lines, drain and vent line, sprinkler lines, conduit for cabling, lighting, and a number of other items. This coordination and completion of work is the main responsibility of the superintendent, jobsite management personnel, and foremen.

What follows is a description of a superintendent's ordinary day on the construction site:

On this particular day, the weekly toolbox safety talk is scheduled to start. The superintendent leads the discussion on the topic of confined spaces. He will then describe where and how this is applicable to the project the craftspeople are working on. It takes about fifteen minutes. The crafts then break up for direction on work activities of the day. The superintendent has prepared formwork detail drawings for one of his foremen and has given it to him. In passing, the superintendent mentions that he is expecting a delivery of miscellaneous metals later in the day and will need the rough terrain crane for unloading. Later on a job walk, a short discussion will occur between the subcontractor's foreman and the superintendent, as he observes the subcontractor's work, the number of craftspeople the subcontractor employs, the location of the project where they are working, and other coordination problems that may occur. On the way back to the trailer, the field engineer stops the superintendent with a layout question about a wall that the carpenters will be starting in two days and questions the arrival status of the inserts from the miscellaneous metals fabricator. Back at the trailer, the superintendent checks the scope of work and looks for an approved shop drawing from the fabricator. A call to the fabricator indicates that some inserts will arrive today but they are not sure if they are the correct ones. The project engineer asks for verification of shop drawing approval and checks the truck's delivery slips for the proper inserts. A call then comes over the radio from the carpenter foreman concerning a location question on mechanical sleeves that will be installed by the subcontractor in the concrete wall the next morning. Finally, the superintendent sits down for his first cup of coffee when low and behold, the owner, construction manager, and inspector all want to have a meeting. The day will continue at this hectic pace until the crafts leave at 3:30 P.M. Then, and only then, can the superintendent start his planning for the next day, week, and month. Prior to leaving for home, the superintendent will record his day's activities in reports and in his daily diary.

The *superintendent* is the principal manager of the work, oversees the subcontractor as the work is being accomplished, supervises the general contractor's own labor forces, and correlates all of the functions of the site construction staff. Along with the foreman on the project, the superintendent provides the leadership and motivation to accomplish assignments. Individuals who aspire to become superintendents will display the following characteristics:

- Visualization and planning skills
- The ability to organize and motivate people
- Understanding of technical and mechanical subjects
- Ability to make decisions
- Innovative and resourceful
- Ability to adapt to changes
- Along with leadership, the ability to instruct, teach, and train
- Strong work ethic
- The capability to work with other team members as an equal partner

The Foreman

The foreman is the critical link to the craftsperson. The foreman is in a unique position—on one job the foreman and on the next job with a different company perhaps one of the crew members.

The construction industry and the companies within the industry hope to keep all of their trained craftspeople and key foremen working year-round and year to year, but, realistically, only some firms maintain a steady workload. The job of the foreman is to "push" the work. **Pushing the work** can be defined as evaluating the workman, making sure that one's skills fit the work and that one aggressively completes the work at hand. A good foreman will know how to efficiently use the labor, equipment, and materials to accomplish day-to-day tasks. The foreman is the individual who understands the technical part of the work. The foreman should develop loyalty and responsibility to the company. Companies have found that when the foreman is isolated or not considered part of the company, theft and poor workmanship from other trades increases, friction or polarization of trades starts to occur, and material waste increases. All of this points to the important role of the foreman. The foreman is the eyes, ears, and often the spokesperson for the superintendent. On smaller projects, the superintendent can be a "working" superintendent. The term **working** refers to the superintendent who is actually performing work with one's tools. In many instances, the foreman is elevated to part-time superintendent. In that case, the foreman also can be called a working superintendent.

Overtime

One key decision made by the superintendent is the use or authorization of overtime. The reason for overtime is project, task, and time specific. There is no set of rules to govern when to use overtime. The following list provides guidelines to help the superintendent make this decision:

- If the equipment used is very costly, compared to the labor expended, overtime may be appropriate.

- If bad weather will greatly affect the time to complete an activity and the cost to stop and start the activity is costly, overtime may be appropriate to complete the activity.

- Only truly critical activities should be viewed for overtime.

- Overtime should be used selectively to bonus a foreman or specific craftsperson. (Special care should be taken when used in this manner.)

- On some tasks, labor shortages can be anticipated, such as finish carpenters; thus, overtime may be used.

- Some tasks cannot be done during poor weather, or specific equipment will not function; thus, overtime should be considered.

Employee Relations

The superintendent has the responsibility of hiring and firing employees. Generally it is the superintendent's direct responsibility to determine whether an employee has the skills to perform the required task, whether the employee is working up to a normal productivity level, or whether the employee is performing to the required level of quality workmanship. A major time when employees are laid off is when work is nearing completion. The superintendent will determine, with the help of the foreman, which workers are to be kept and which will be terminated for "lack of work." Termination for lack of work is not viewed as a negative discharge.

Employee Training

Formal craft training has typically been done in the union sector of the industry. Most states allow only one approved active apprentice training program. Most apprentice training will be done by the appropriate union with which the apprentice is affiliated. Today, this is being challenged by the merit shop organizations. Associated Builders and Contractors is the leading organization to develop training programs outside of the unions. An example of the type of training that occurs is represented by the carpenters' union. An individual is an apprentice for four years prior to becoming a journeyman carpenter. The apprentice will take classes while working in the trade, giving the individual the dual "real-world" work and the "hands-on" lab and classroom training. Many firms prefer to have some apprentices on the job because they are generally eager to learn and work hard, and they have a sliding pay scale based on the number of years of apprentice training they have accomplished. This scale is negotiated in the master agreement, discussed earlier.

Historically, some vocational training has occurred at community colleges, and in some states, special vocational training centers and schools are active in craft training. Generally these programs do not have a mandatory work rule, so training occurs only in the lab and classroom. Many studies have noted that the construction industry critically needs skilled tradespeople.

Tools

The use of tools is another area of concern to the superintendent and foreman, who must ensure that the proper tools are available to the craftsperson. In many areas, trade practices or labor agreements establish what tools the craftsperson will provide and what tools the construction company is responsible for providing. In most commercial projects, all power tools will be provided by the company, along with cords and ladders. The craftsperson may be required to have a specific selection of hand tools, which varies from craft to craft and from residential to commercial work. Tools are almost never provided or even loaned to subcontractors and their craftspeople. A typical list of hand tools a carpenter would provide includes the following:

- Handheld hammers
- Hand saws: ripping, finish, hacksaw, coping saw
- Screwdrivers, chisels
- Wrenches, pliers
- Hand levels
- Miscellaneous hand tools

Smaller tools typically furnished by the contractor include the following:

- Hand shovels, picks, sledgehammers
- Circular saws, drill motors
- Electrical cords
- Pneumatic tools and compressors
- Powder-actuated tools

The foreman also is responsible for tool security. Two levels of security need to be established: (1) to prevent loss of tools when the project is shut down after work hours and weekends and (2) to minimize minor theft of small items during the business day. Most large losses occur from theft after hours and on weekends. Project sites are often isolated and dark and lack security personnel. Tool security generally is accomplished with the use of lockable toolboxes, which must be left in secure places but left close enough to the work area to provide reasonable tool distribution in the morning and easy access to putting away tools at the end of the shift. If the toolbox is near the area where crafts are leaving the jobsite through uncontrolled exits, theft may occur. All tools should be marked with company identification. A company should not allow workers to take tools home for personal use, as they may be forgotten and cannot be used the next day.

Labor Records

In conjunction with the processes of leading, directing, organizing, and planning work to be accomplished, all firms must implement a labor reporting system that will provide information to accounting for payroll, information for historical reporting of labor productivity, and information pertaining to cost and production control during the job. This system and the information generated must be simple to use and must provide for the level of data needed for future estimating. Because activities can be quickly completed and productivity influenced by so many factors, the system must also provide timely information for the control of the labor or cost items involved. Most direct labor on projects today are paid weekly from information generated by time cards. Additionally, the time card will show the labor distribution or project cost account that the labor is applied against. The report generated from the time card is called a weekly labor report, which shows weekly and cumulative labor costs versus budgeted hours and dollars. An additional report used in combination with the weekly labor report is a weekly quantity report, also based or collected on a project cost account basis, which allows a comparison to be made of man-hours or the cost of labor to the quantities. The list of project cost codes is carefully assembled and is unique to each project. Similar work from project to project will have the same cost distribution code or project cost account code, making the historical comparisons somewhat easier. This comparison is a difficult task, as jobsite conditions vary from project to project. If one project is done in the rain while another is completed during a dry time of year, increased productivity would be expected from the craftsperson doing the work in the dry weather conditions. Labor cost accounts concern "self-work" or work that will be performed by the firm's own personnel. These craftspeople will then be on payroll and will be subject to direct control of the field personnel, as most work activity has additional costs associated with it. A separate code must be developed for differentiating between labor costs (-01), material costs (-02), equipment costs (-03), subcontractor costs (-04), and other costs (-05). The following list illustrates the cost codes for project elements on a particular project.

Typical Master List of Project Cost
Accounts for Concrete Only

03.00	CONCRETE WORK	03.170	Concrete Stairs
03.010	Continuous Footing	03.180	Precast Concrete Stairs
03.020	Grade Beams	03.190	Apron Slabs
03.030	Column Footings	03.200	Sidewalks
03.040	Pilaster Footings	03.210	Concrete Driveways
03.050	Piers	03.220	Mechanical Bases/Pads
03.060	Pilecaps	03.230	Transformer (Electrical) Pads
03.070	Thickened Slab @ Bearing Partition	03.240	C. I. P. Curbs
03.080	C. I. P. Walls	03.250	Pilasters
03.090	C. I. P. Columns	03.260	Tiltup Walls
03.100	C. I. P. Beams	03.270	Other Precast Work
03.110	C. I. P. Spandrels		Open for Additional Codes
03.120	Interior S. O. G.	03.400	Spandeck
03.130	Floor Hardener/Sealer @ S. O. G.	03.600	Inspection and Testing of Concrete
03.140	Structural Slabs	03.750	Reinforcing Steel
03.150	Lightweight Concrete Fills/ Topping	03.760	Reinforcing Accessories
		03.770	Slab Dowels
03.160	Grout Column Bases	03.780	Wire Mesh

It should be noted that the type of work this contractor may be performing is defined by the codes chosen to track costs. Also note the lack of codes in the area of formwork, finishing, and rubbing and curing.

The originating document for labor information is the employee's time card. Time cards can be individual, grouped on a daily labor time card by trade, or all crafts may appear on one time card. If multiple trades are involved and each trade has its own foreman, grouping by trades works well. If the project size is very small, the other two forms work equally as well. It is important that the distribution of time, as applied to the various codes, be accurate. This means that the person in charge of supervision who is closest to the work should fill out the distribution. Typically, this is done at the foreman level. Figure 8–3 is a typical sample daily labor time card that mixes carpenters and laborers, with their hours worked, spread to multiple codes.

The time card is used in two ways by supervisors assigned to the project. First, management or office personnel use the time card to verify accurate hours worked by employees. If time is being shown by employees who are absent from the project, theft of company money is occurring. This is a serious crime on the employee's part and may result in the company requesting law enforcement. Second, the information is used to set productivity standards for future estimates in the bidding process. These labor unit costs become one of the most important pieces of information the field can supply the company when matched with weekly quantities. The weekly quantity report, shown in Figure 8–4, compares work activities with cost codes and the amount of work accomplished last week, this week, to date, and amount to complete.

No.	Name	Craft	Time Classif.	Hourly Rate	Cost Code					Total Hours	Gross Amount
					3.010	3.020	3.030	3.120	3.801		
24	Ramsey	CF	RT	$25.00	8					8	200.00
			OT								
13	Hojas	C	RT	$22.00	2	6				8	176.00
			OT								
55	Gin	C	RT	$22.00			5	3		8	176.00
			OT								
122	Drew	L	RT	$15.00		1		2	5	8	120.00
			OT								
145	Elliot	L	RT	$15.00		2	2		4	8	120.00
			OT								
			RT								
			OT								
			RT								
			OT								

Project **Creston Water Treatment Plant**
Date **5/6/2026**
Weather **Sunny**
Prepared by **T. Bono**

Figure 8–3   Time Card

The weekly quantity report and time card are two pieces of information combined by the accounting office and returned to the field in the form of a weekly labor cost report, shown in Figure 8–5. This is one of the main tools used by the field staff to analyze the progress and to project the final cost and schedule for the different work activities that are occurring.

Figure 8–6 illustrates the paper flow for labor control and the results—a payroll check to the employee and a labor cost report to the field and office staff.

Weekly Quantity Report

Project **Creston Water Treatment Plant**
Week Ending **5/8/2026**
Prepared by **K. Franklin**

Cost Code	Work Activity	Unit	Total Last Week	Total This Week	Total To Date	Total To Complete
3.010	Continuous Footing	Cyd.	60	20	120	0
3.020	Grade Beams	Cyd.	85	10	95	0
3.030	Columns	Cyd.	0	0	0	125
3.120	S.O.G.	Cyd.	150	60	280	340
3.801	Finishing-Trowel	Sft.	2200	1250	4400	6550

Figure 8–4   Weekly Quantity Report

Weekly Labor Cost Report

Project   Creston Water Treatment Plant
Date   5/6/2026
Week Ending 5/6/2026   Prepared by   K. Franklin

Cost Code	Description	Unit	Quantity			Labor Costs			To Date		Projected	
			Budget	This Week	To date	Budget	This Week	To date	1	( )	1	( )
3.010	Concrete Foot	Cyd	400	20	200	4000	200	2200	200		200	
3.020	Gr. Beams	Cyd	100	10	100	2000	176	1656		344		344
3.030	Columns	Cyd	57	0	0	1710	176	176		176	176	
3.120	SOG	Cyd	257	60	60	5140	1200	1200				
3.801	Finishing	Sft	7000	810	810	7000	700	700		200		200

Figure 8–5   Weekly Labor Cost Report

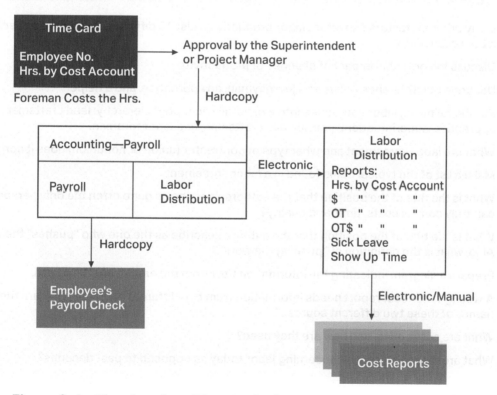

Figure 8–6   Flowchart from Time Card Information

Because of the potential for abuse, the project must have a system in place to prevent misuse, to solve problems of timekeeping, to check employees in and out each day, to verify and confirm an employee's time if mistakes are made on a payroll check, and to establish an audit procedure for accurate recording of quantities and cost codes. Toward this end, some companies use a system of brass tags for checking individuals in and out of jobsites. Tags sit on a numbered board; as the employee removes the numbered tags, an empty spot is left. The tags are individually assigned, and often the number represents a craft as well. This craft numbering system makes it easier to determine the number of different craftspeople on the project for daily job reports and for the foreman's use. The foreman will know instantly who is missing, along with the timekeeper, if the project warrants such a position.

Summary

The major issues concerning labor during the past decades have been maintaining an adequate number of skilled craftspeople on projects, creating a productive workforce, employing a trained workforce, and employing trained supervisors. All of these concerns still apply to today's workforce, which will be more diverse and not as mobile, with supervisors who may have less technical knowledge and craftspersons who are not motivated by the same techniques used in the past. Projects have become more complex. Company management is beginning to rely on more information generated at the job level for competitiveness in the marketplace. Supervisors must be able to lead and motivate employees as well as satisfy the owner and architect. Companies are becoming more client based, requiring the project management team to become more responsive to the owner's needs and at the same time remain as competitive and productive as possible. The craftsperson is increasingly becoming a more important member of the contractor's team.

Review Questions

1. Many different factors can affect labor productivity. List 10 different factors that affect labor productivity.

2. Discuss the potential impact of changes of productivity.

3. Describe the difference between a journeyman, an apprentice, and a helper.

4. Put the following labor categories into a generally accepted hierarchy: lead craftsman, apprentice, superintendent, journeyman craftsman, and labor foreman.

5. What is a labor agreement and what type of contractor (union or nonunion) does it apply to?

6. Make a list of the typical items found in a labor agreement.

7. What is the title of the position that the authors describe as quite often the only person who can truly control costs, time, and quality?

8. What is the title of the position that the authors describe as the one who "pushes" the work? Also, what is the definition of "pushing the work"?

9. Prepare a diagram indicating the information flow from the employee's time card.

10. A weekly labor cost report needs information from two different sources. What are the names of these two different sources?

11. What are cost codes, and how are they used?

12. What are the major issues concerning labor today as opposed to past decades?

Chapter 9

Personnel and Safety Management

This chapter is a discussion of the importance of personnel and safety management as well as methods to accomplish better construction site safety. The objectives of this chapter are to:

- Discuss the causes of injuries, illnesses, and fatalities on the construction site
- Explain the reasons for and how to start a safety and health plan
- List the typical corporate safety policies
- Review the use of Occupational Safety and Health Act (OSHA) regulation for construction and explanation of how OSHA administers its regulations
- Explain safety awareness and accident prevention
- Prepare the various forms used in the day-to-day administration of a safety program on the Jobsite
- Categorize the major areas found in the code of safe practices
- Illustrate the material Safety Data Sheet process, its forms, and procedures needed
- Create the flowchart of what and when to report and record the different injuries, illnesses, and fatalities

Introduction to Construction Safety

The construction industry is one of the most dangerous industries in the United States. In 2021, there were over 5,000 construction workers killed on the job, accounting for nearly 20% of all workplace fatalities; thus, personnel and safety management is a *must* for the construction industry—an industry with a notoriously high accident and fatality rate. Accidents that result in injuries, illnesses, and fatalities occur because of many factors:

- The inherent hazardous nature of construction work.

- The many methods and types of operations needed by construction companies to meet and complete assignments, resulting in confusion about safe methods to accomplish work activities.

- Each construction project is unique and thus poses separate circumstances and safety hazards; work is not confined to a single workplace but occurs at multiple jobsites.

- Each construction activity has a relatively short duration; thus, safety procedures are normally not well established; the "learning curve" for safe and productive work often is not optimized because of this short duration.

- Because construction is a very mobile industry, the workforce changes frequently, with varied levels of competence and expertise among employees; these employees may not be trained in safe work methods prior to arriving on the jobsite.

Construction safety management is a systematic approach to identifying, assessing, and controlling hazards in the construction workplace. It is a proactive approach to safety that seeks to prevent accidents and injuries.

The construction employer is responsible for providing a safe working environment as well as safety training for the work activities. Through the federal Occupational Safety and Health Act (OSHA), construction industry firms have become aware of the need for highly visible and proactive safety programs. These firms also have developed the attitude that all employees, from the president to the carpenter, are responsible for safety.

Studies show that fatal accidents do not discriminate against a worker based on age, experience, union versus nonunion, day of the week, craft, or position in the company. Figure 9–1 illustrates the relationship of construction fatalities with the numbers of employees from different age groups.

The lack of safety guidelines and awareness affects all aspects of a construction company, from overall profits to employee and family morale. OSHA was passed in 1970 — it was the first time the federal government began imposing national safety regulations on all industries and businesses. This act permits states to pass and implement their own state OSHA bills, using the federal act as a minimum standard. The following are states that have opted for their own method of regulation: Alaska, Arizona, California, Connecticut, Hawaii, Indiana, Iowa, Kentucky, Maryland, Michigan, Minnesota, Nevada, New Jersey, New Mexico, New York, North Carolina, Oregon, Puerto Rico, South Carolina, Tennessee, Utah, Vermont, Virgin Islands, Virginia, Washington, and Wyoming. Note that Connecticut, New Jersey, and New York do not cover all employees, only state and local government employees. There are many issues that fall into the area of environmental concerns or hazardous materials use and handling and/or disposing of materials regarding safety. Many of these regulations are rooted in the Williams-Steiger Occupational Safety and Health Act (1970) and the Environmental Protection Act (EPA). An example of the combined agencies working together is the asbestos issue. OSHA is the body that protects workers who are using asbestos, while the EPA sets the compliance codes for the removal and disposal of the material.

OSHA and each state affiliate require construction firms to create and implement a safety and health program, following OSHA guidelines. To comply, this program must be a written plan containing the following key elements:

- Management commitment

- Hazard assessment and control

- Safety planning, rules, and work procedures

- Safety and health training

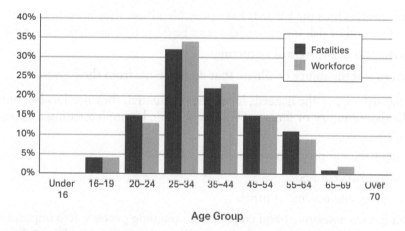

Figure 9–1   Analysis of Fatalities by Age Group and Percentage of Workforce

Courtesy of OSHA

A suggested outline for a safety and health plan that incorporates the key elements and important subcategories has been developed for the contractor's use by the California Occupational and Health Administration (CAL/OSHA) Consultation Service. The following company safety policy outline is adapted from CAL/OSHA:

I. Corporate and Management Commitment
    A. Policy Statement
        May include safety and health goal
        Illustrates management involvement in workplace safety and health
    B. Objectives for the Safety and Health Program
        Based on the priorities of your workplace
        Should be measurable with time frames for completion
    C. Assignment of Responsibility for S and H
        Descriptions of duties
        Policy on accountability

II. Hazard Assessment and Control
    A. Hazard Assessment and Correction

Construction hazard assessment and control is the process of identifying, evaluating, and controlling hazards on a construction site. It is an important part of ensuring the safety of workers and the environment.

The hazard assessment process typically includes the following steps:

1. *Identify hazards:* The first step is to identify all potential hazards on the construction site. This can be done by conducting a walk-through of the site and looking for potential hazards, such as:
   - Falls
   - Electrical hazards
   - Hazardous materials
   - Confined spaces
   - Machinery hazards

2. *Evaluate hazards:* Once the hazards have been identified, they need to be evaluated to determine the level of risk they pose. This can be done by considering the following factors:
   - The likelihood of the hazard occurring
   - The severity of the injury or illness that could result from the hazard

3. Control hazards: Once the hazards have been evaluated, they need to be controlled to reduce the risk of injury or illness. This can be done by implementing a variety of control measures, such as:
   - Providing personal protective equipment (PPE)
   - Using safety procedures
   - Implementing engineering controls

Construction hazard assessment and control is an ongoing process. It is important to regularly review the hazard assessment and control plan to ensure that it is up-to-date and that the controls are effective.

Here are some of the benefits of construction hazard assessment and control:
   - Reduced risk of injuries and illnesses
   - Increased productivity

- Improved morale
- Reduced liability
- Improved public image

By conducting regular hazard assessments and implementing effective control measures, construction companies can help to create a safer workplace for their workers and protect the environment.

Additional tips for conducting a construction hazard assessment:

- Get input from all stakeholders, including workers, supervisors, and managers.
- Use a variety of methods to identify hazards, such as walk-throughs, interviews, and accident reports.
- Consider the potential for hazards to change over time.
- Develop a plan to control hazards that is specific to the construction site.
- Train workers on the hazards and control measures.
- Monitor the effectiveness of the control measures and make changes as needed.

B. Accident Investigation

After a construction accident, the following should be done:

1. Assess the situation and provide medical attention to any injured workers. If the accident is serious, call 911.
2. Secure the accident scene and prevent anyone else from being injured. This may involve cordoning off the area with caution tape or using barricades.
3. Investigate the cause of the accident. This may involve interviewing witnesses, reviewing safety records, and inspecting the accident scene.
4. Take steps to prevent similar accidents from happening in the future. This may involve implementing new safety procedures, training workers on new safety protocols, or making changes to the worksite.

It is important to remember that the goal of a construction accident investigation is to prevent future accidents, not to assign blame. The investigation should be conducted in a fair and impartial manner, and all relevant information should be gathered. Once the investigation is complete, the findings should be used to make changes to the worksite and safety procedures to prevent similar accidents from happening in the future.

Here are some additional tips for conducting a construction accident investigation:

- Gather as much information as possible about the accident, including the following:
  - The date, time, and location of the accident
  - The names of the people involved in the accident
  - The extent of any injuries
  - The condition of the worksite at the time of the accident
  - The weather conditions at the time of the accident
  - Any safety procedures that were in place at the time of the accident
- Interview witnesses to the accident. Witnesses can provide valuable information about what happened and how the accident could have been prevented.
- Review safety records. Safety records can help identify any potential hazards that may have contributed to the accident.
- Inspect the accident scene. Inspecting the accident scene can help identify any physical evidence that may help explain how the accident happened.

- Develop a plan to prevent similar accidents from happening in the future. Once the investigation is complete, the findings should be used to develop a plan to prevent similar accidents from happening in the future. This may involve implementing new safety procedures, training workers on new safety protocols, or making changes to the worksite.

    C. Record Keeping

        Log and Summary of Occupational Injuries and Illnesses

        Material Safety Data Sheets

        Employee access to personal medical and exposure records

        Other required or appropriate records

    D. Equipment Monitoring and Maintenance Program

        Production equipment

        Personal protection equipment

III. Safety Planning, Rules, and Work Procedure

    A. Control of Potential Hazard

        Regarding equipment design, purchasing, engineering, maintenance, and use

    B. Safety Rules

        General

        Specific to tasks, based on safe work procedures

        System for informing employees

    C. Work Procedures

        Analysis of tasks to develop safe work procedures

        Implementation

    D. Employee Involvement

        Reporting hazards

        Enforcement of rules

        Disciplinary procedures and reorientation

    E. Emergency Procedures

        First Aid

        Emergency Medical

        Fire, egress

IV. Safety and Health Training, Initial and Refresher

    A. Supervisor

        Safety and Health policy, rules, and procedures

        Hazards of the workplace and how they are best controlled.

        Accident Investigation

    B. Employees

        New employee safety orientation

        General and specific rules

        Use of personal protective equipment

        Preparation for emergencies

        Training required by OSHA requirement

        Safe work procedures

Specific language of many health and safety laws states that the employer will instruct employees in general safe work practices, provide specific instruction with regard to hazards unique to any job assignment, and schedule periodic inspections.

Construction accidents are expensive; thus, the losses associated with these injuries must be controlled.

In addition to the previous key elements of the safety and health program required by OSHA and individual states, a company's in-house personnel and safety management plan should consist of the following additional subcategories:

Corporate Policy on Safety

The corporate policy on safety should be a clear and concise statement of the company's commitment to safety. It should outline the company's expectations for employee safety and the consequences for violating those expectations. The policy should also establish a safety committee or other structure for overseeing the company's safety program.

Safe Practice and Operations Code

The safe practice and operations code should be a detailed document that outlines the specific safety procedures that employees must follow. The code should cover all aspects of worksite safety, including personal protective equipment, hazard recognition, and emergency procedures. The code should be easy to understand and should be readily available to employees.

First Aid

The company should provide first aid training to all employees. This training should cover the basics of first aid, including how to stop bleeding, how to treat shock, and how to perform CPR. The company should also have a first aid kit on site at all times.

Fire Protection

The company should have a fire protection plan in place. This plan should include procedures for fire prevention, fire detection, and fire suppression. The company should also have fire extinguishers and other fire suppression equipment on site.

Substance Abuse

The company should have a substance abuse policy in place. This policy should prohibit the use of alcohol and drugs on the job. The policy should also establish procedures for dealing with employees who violate the policy.

Personal Protective Equipment Requirements

The company should provide personal protective equipment (PPE) to all employees who need it. PPE can help protect employees from injuries caused by hazards such as falls, electrical shock, and exposure to hazardous materials. The company should have a system in place for ensuring that employees use PPE correctly.

Protection of the General Public

The company should take steps to protect the general public from hazards on the jobsite. This may include fencing off the jobsite, posting warning signs, and using noise controls.

Hazardous Materials Communication

The company should have a system in place for communicating information about hazardous materials to employees. This information should include the hazards associated with the materials, the proper procedures for handling and storing the materials, and the emergency procedures in the event of a spill or release.

Safety Communication

The company should communicate safety information to employees on a regular basis. This communication can be done through toolbox talks, safety meetings, and safety posters. The company should also encourage employees to report any safety concerns they have.

Project Surveys

The company should conduct regular surveys of its projects to identify potential safety hazards. These surveys should be conducted by a qualified person and should include a review of the project plans, the worksite, and the equipment being used. The results of the surveys should be used to develop and implement corrective actions.

Accident Reporting and Investigation

The company should have a system in place for reporting and investigating accidents. All accidents should be reported to a designated person or committee. The investigation should be conducted in a timely manner and should be thorough and objective. The findings of the investigation should be used to develop and implement corrective actions.

OSHA Records and Regulations

The company is required to keep certain records related to safety. These records may include accident reports, injury and illness logs, and training records. The company is also required to comply with all applicable OSHA regulations.

Corporate Safety Policy

Safety is a company-wide issue. Creating a safety program and safety manual is only the beginning of developing safe jobsites to encourage employees to think "safety" as they start and complete project tasks. Corporate safety policy begins with a company declaration, stated objectives, and both accountability and authority for the implementation of safety regulations for a safe site.

The safety program manual generally provides written guidelines for a comprehensive safety program. A typical policy declaration from the president of the firm might include the following information:

1. The idea that safety is the highest priority in the workplace. Employees should not expect to work in an unsafe manner or environment. The company will not fire an employee for bringing to the attention of his supervisors unsafe conditions or actions.

2. The company should state who is accountable for providing a safe environment. This authority and accountability generally is directed to the superintendents and foremen, as they are the ones in charge of day-to-day activities. Some firms also will designate an on-site safety engineer or safety manager who has specific duties.

3. The preface of all company manuals should include an open letter from the president to all employees addressing their responsibilities and their mandated use of the safety manual and information about the company's safety program. The following statements should be included as a way of encouraging employee participation to help provide a safe working environment:

- A safety policy and manual are provided to the employee so he will have a complete understanding of the companies' efforts to create a safe workplace. It also is the employee's responsibility to oneself, one's family, the company, and one's fellow workers to be aware of and practice safety procedures.

- Poor planning, lack of awareness, or failure to adhere to safety standards while an employee is performing their job or visiting the jobsite or an overall indifference to safety procedures can cause jobsite accidents.

- Safe practices, use of safety equipment, following safety rules, pointing out unsafe acts by others or unsafe conditions on the jobsite, and being a full participating member of the company's safety team are necessary for all employees.

Safe Practice and Operations Code

The section on safe practice and operations details safety rules and guidelines concerning the individual jobsite. Accidents can be classified into two major categories: 1) unsafe actions by people and 2) unsafe conditions left uncorrected. The following list includes some of the most common causes of accidents.

Unsafe actions by people:

- Failing to correct and tell others about existing unsafe conditions

- Using tools in a manner not intended

- Using tools that have not been maintained or serviced properly

- Removing safety guards or other safety equipment

- Working at heights without proper safety equipment

- Using a ladder in an unsafe manner

- Being unaware of other working conditions in the area where working

- Ignoring posted safety warnings or notices

- Working with people under the influence or being under the influence of a controlled substance

- Leaving exposed live electrical connections

- Leaving unsafe conditions uncorrected

- Having jobsites without adequate fire protection equipment

- Leaving jobsites without readily available personal protection equipment

- Having inadequate or poor project housekeeping

- Leaving open or unprotected openings

- Leaving live and accessible electrical wiring

- Not providing first aid equipment or training

- Allowing employees who are substance abusers to be on the jobsite

- Moving materials without the ability to control their movement or final placement

To encourage smart safety practices among their employees, some firms will distribute OSHA guides. Employees carry the guides with them as a handy reference about OSHA safety issues while on the job. Figure 9–2 shows three such books.

Figure 9–2   OSHA Handbook Guides

Designer491/Dreamstime.com

Accident Prevention

As part of the creation of a safe workplace, safety awareness has become an integral part of the construction jobsite.

One of the ongoing safety training and awareness exercises is the "tailgate" or "toolbox" safety meetings, which are on-site meetings held with all workers and their supervisors in an attempt to reinforce to each individual the many jobsite hazards that may exist and the consequences of unsafe actions for individual workers. In California, CAL/OSHA regulates the industry and requires weekly tailgate safety meetings (Sections 8406 and 1509 of Title 8 of the California Administrative Code). These meetings usually run between 10 and 15 minutes long. Areas that should be discussed include work practices, tools and equipment and their correct usage, attitudes, and/or other relevant activities. Topics should be current and relate to the tasks the workers now perform and will perform in the near future. The meetings also should provide individual workers the opportunity to discuss or relay needed safety corrections to all other workers. Only major issues should be discussed at these meetings, avoiding unnecessary exchanges and complaints.

The meeting should be led by supervisors. The toolbox meeting is intended to increase communication about safety issues so that future accidents can be prevented. Each meeting should follow a set agenda. The following items can be used as an outline:

1. Points to remember regarding when and where to hold the meeting:
   - Limit to 10 to 15 minutes
   - Preschedule for both date and time
   - Hold meeting at the beginning of the shift
   - Meet in a place where everyone can hear
   - Take the time to show examples of problems being discussed

2. Topics to be discussed:
   - Topics should relate to the craft and the work being performed at the time of the meeting
   - Topics should be specific in nature and be the most critical in a list of topics

- Topics need to be completely discussed before employees begin to interact

3. Preparation of subject matter:
   - Prepare to discuss the why, what, and how of the topic
   - Use terminology the employee or craftsperson will understand in his daily work

4. Record of meeting:
   - Record the people present
   - Record the topics discussed
   - Record the date and time
   - Use a standard form and format (see Figures 9–3 through 9–6)

Here are some tips for conducting effective tailgate meetings:

- Keep the meetings short and to the point.

- Use visuals to help illustrate your points.

- Get workers involved in the discussion.

- Make sure the meetings are relevant to the work that will be done that day.

- Follow up on any safety concerns that are raised.

Fact sheets provided by the agency that has jurisdiction over the construction site should be made available to employees. Fact sheets are a good place to start when building safety discussions, safety training, and toolbox talks. They make good handouts for OSHA 10-hour and OSHA 30-hour training sessions. CAL/OSHA provides fact sheets about specific requirements, for instance, on compression gas cylinders, describing their proper handling and usage regarding hazard control (see Figure 9–7).

Pocket-sized safety rule books are available from state agencies or commercial publishers. Employees can be required to read and carry these pocket references on the jobsite. Any tool or reference that will help the employee follow safety regulations, whether on the job or in safety meetings, will help reduce jobsite accidents.

Here are some additional benefits of tailgate or toolbox safety meetings:

- They can help to identify and correct potential hazards before they cause an accident.

- They can help to improve worker awareness of safety hazards.

- They can help to build a culture of safety on the jobsite.

- They can help to reduce the number of accidents and injuries.

Tailgate or toolbox safety meetings are an important part of any comprehensive safety program. By conducting regular meetings and following the tips above, you can help to create a safer work environment for your employees.

Medical and First-Aid Facilities and Services

As projects become larger and more complex, an emergency services plan must be completed. This plan must address how an injury will be treated and, if transportation of an injured individual is required, how that will occur. OSHA requires the contractor to meet certain requirements for applying first aid, for the availability and amount of first-aid kits, and for the amount of supplies in each kit. It is important that specific injuries be treated only by physicians, such as eye injuries or removal of foreign objects from the eye. OSHA also provides first-aid training and certification of trained workers in first aid. First-aid courses are available in most communities, either through a contractor's association or through the Red Cross. Most jurisdictions require one person on each crew to have full, updated first-aid training, and most contractors require all field management personnel to have current first-aid cards.

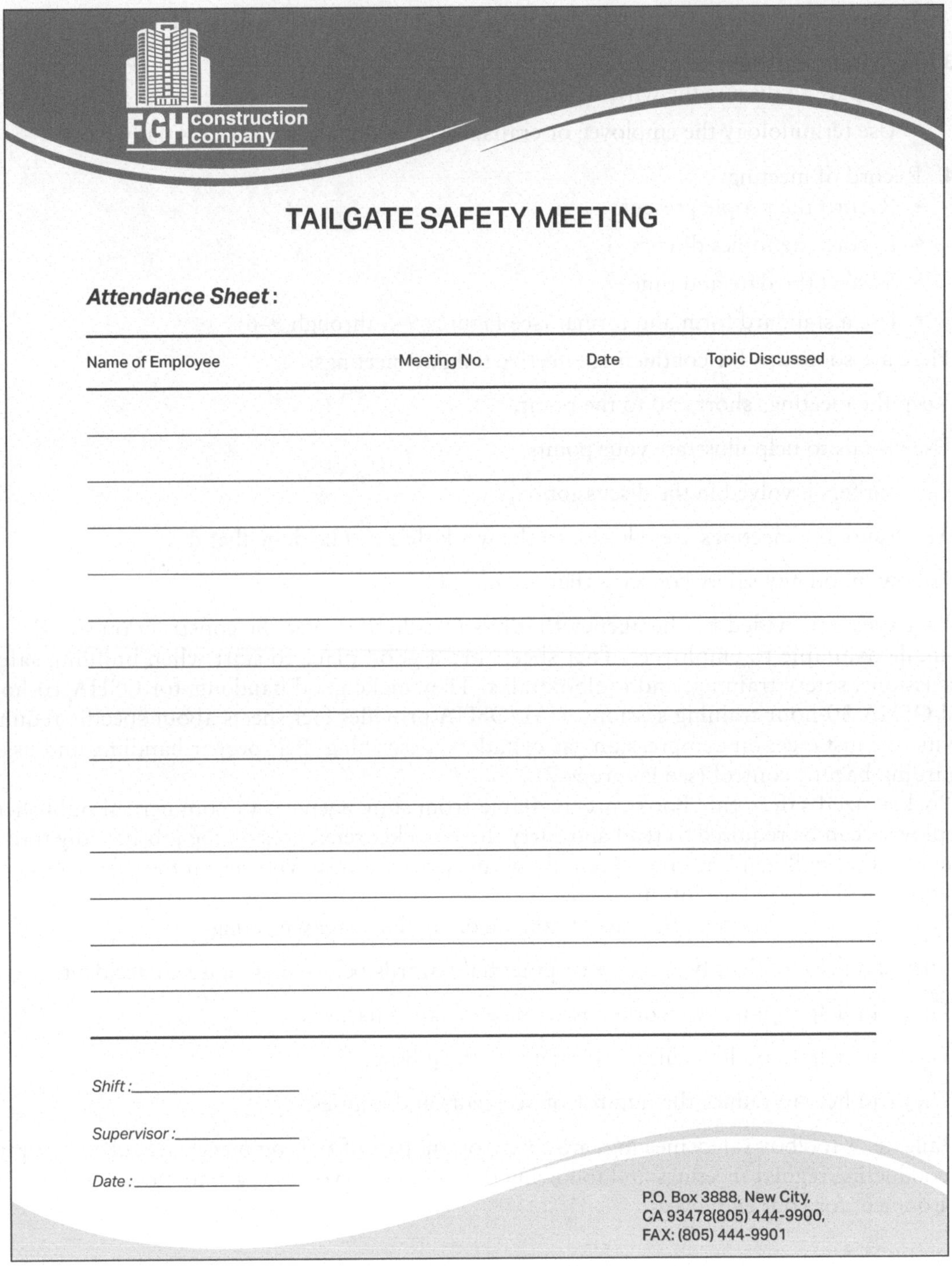

Figure 9–3   Tailgate Safety Meeting Attendees Form

Protection of the General Public

Most construction activities occur where the general public has some form of access to them. The nature of construction work attracts people of all ages to jobsites. Often people will comment, "I wonder what they are building there." It is the contractor's responsibility to make sure the general public is warned of all hazards on the construction site as well as to isolate the site from casual passersby. At all times, signs, barricades, and public protection devices

SAFETY MEETING REPORT FORM

FGH construction company

Date of Meeting : _____

Supervisor : _____

Project Number : _____

Topic or Area of Discussion :

_____
_____
_____

Summary of Specific Items Discussed :

_____
_____
_____

Conclusion or changes to the jobsite to create a safer workplace :

_____
_____
_____

Action Items needing immediate abatement :

_____
_____
_____

Remarks or comments :

_____
_____
_____

P.O. Box 3888, New City,
CA 93478(805) 444-9900,
FAX: (805) 444-9901

Figure 9–4   Safety Meeting Report Form

must be visible and in place. Most urban areas have regulations about sidewalk protection walkways and vehicle access into and out of the site. A good reference for pedestrian safety and protection is offered by Caltrans called *Temporary Pedestrian Facilities Handbook* (http://www.dot.ca.gov/hq/construc/safety/Temporary_Pedestrian_Facilities_Handbook.pdf). It should be noted that when providing this temporary pedestrian protection, it must comply with all the Americans with Disabilities Act Accessibility Guidelines (ADAAG). The Caltrans reference gives a good ADA checklist for temporary pedestrian protection.

FGH construction company

EMPLOYEE SAFETY RECORD CARD
(Employee is to sign and return this card)

Name (Please Print) _____

Address _____

Home Phone _____

Social Security Number _____

Person to Be Contacted in Case of Emergency _____

_____

Phone _____

I agree to report any injury received during the course of work to my supervisor. I have received a copy of the safety Manual for Maintenance and General Construction and agree to follow the rules.

Employee's Signature _____

Employee Safety Courses List
The Safety Courses Received : _____

First Aid _____

OSHA 10-Hour Course_____ Yes _____ No_____

Other_____

Employee safety contacts list the toolbox talks, job safety analysis, on-the-job safety training, and other safety training. The employee notes that they have received the training and the date received.
On-the-job safety training is also to be listed.

Date	Subject	Date	Subject

P.O. Box 3888, New City,
CA 93478(805) 444-9900,
FAX: (805) 444-9901

Figure 9–5   Employee Safety Record Card

Some basic safeguards to protect the general public include the following:

- Using noise controls. This will help to reduce the noise levels from construction activities, which can be a nuisance to the general public.

- Keeping the worksite clean and free of debris. This will help to prevent people from tripping and falling.

- Communicating with the public. This will help to keep people informed about the construction project and the safety measures that are in place.

- Barriers in the form of fences and gates

FGH construction company

EMPLOYEE SAFETY DISCUSSION ATTENDANCE

Project Start Date : _____

Project Manager : _____

Project Number : _____

Name of Employee	Safety Discussion Code Number								
	1	2	3	4	5	6	7	8	9

Each Employee Should Be Contacted at Least Once During the Month.

Place Subject Code Numbers Listed Below in Proper Square Above as Each Employee Is Contacted.

1. Housekeeping	2. Prompt reporting of accidents	3. Eye protection	4. Hearing protection
5. Horseplay	6. Bypassing safety devices	7. First aid	8. Safe lifting procedures
9. Past accidents	10. Using unsafe equipment	11. New employee safety orientation	

Note : Add more items here and more item numbers across.

P.O. Box 3888, New City,
CA 93478(805) 444-9900,
FAX: (805) 444-9901

Figure 9–6   Employee Summary Safety Discussion Attendance

- Overhead protection from falling objects
- Signage—both hazard and directional (Figure 9–8)
- Traffic controls
- Security and surveillance
- Walkway protection
- Solid walls for protection from flying objects

CAL/OSHA FACT SHEET NO.15

Compressed Gas Cylinders

Overfilling is a major cause of occupational injuries associated with the handling of compressed gas cylinders. If the specified filling density is exceeded, the cylinder becomes "liquid filled" and too little vapor space is left in the cylinder preventing expansion of the gas at higher temperatures. This hydrostatic pressure can increase to the point where the cylinder ruptures.

Overfilling is caused by failure to determine the capacity of the cylinder (expressed in cubic inches or water weight) or failure to properly determine the tare weight of the empty cylinder.

To avoid overfilling, know what the various markings stamped on the compressed gas cylinder mean, especially the specification number and the service pressure number. (See illustration A for the location of these marks on the cylinder.) Both marks provide information which is essential for the safe handling of compressed gas cylinders.

SPECIFICATION NUMBER

The specification number refers to the specific regulations under which the cylinder was manufactured. The regulations detail what inspections are required, whether the cylinder may be refilled or must be disposed of after a single use, how it is to be shipped, and for what gases it is authorized. The regulations also state the authorized service pressure of the cylinder.

Although cylinders are now manufactured according to specifications set by the Department of Transportation (DOT), in the past specifications have been set by both the Interstate Commerce Commission (ICC) and by the Bureau of Explosives (BE).

The specification number is preceded by the letters of the agency which established the specification. On Canadian cylinders the specification number is preceded by either CRC (Canadian Regulatory Commission) or BTC (Board of Transport Commissioners).

SERVICE PRESSURE

When a cylinder is authorized for use at only one service pressure, no pressure is marked. In order to determine the authorized service pressure, consult the appropriate specification. Some specifications may authorize cylinder use at various pressures. In this case the design service pressure is marked on the cylinder immediately following the specification number. For example, in illustration A the number DOT 3E1800 indicates Department of Transportation specification 3E with a service pressure of 1800 psig. Certain cylinders (3A and 3AA) may be filled to 110% of marked service pressure if they qualify by retest and are provided with frangible disc safety devices without fusible metal and are charged with non-liquid, non-flammable gas. These cylinders are marked with a plus sign following the hydrostatic retest date.

Charging the cylinder in excess of its service pressure rating is unsafe.

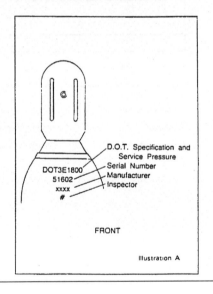

Illustration A

Figure 9–7   CAL/OSHA Safety Fact Sheet No. 15
Courtesy of CAL/OSHA

Fire Protection

Fire prevention and protection is a major loss prevention activity in the construction industry. Fires can cause extensive damage to property and equipment and can also result in serious injuries or death. By taking steps to prevent fires and to protect the workplace from fire, construction companies can help to keep their employees safe and their property secure.

As a major loss prevention activity, fire prevention and protection rank among one of the top areas in safety control. The project superintendent must assess the project for potential

Avalon/Construction Photography/Alamy Stock Photo

Figure 9–8   Examples of Safety Signage

Naleenmud/Shutterstock.com

fire hazards and scrutinize areas and activities that can cause fires to reduce property damage and possible burn injuries to workers. The key to fire prevention is early detection of potentially hazardous areas and conditions, such as plumbing, welding, smoking, and so on. When developing a loss prevention plan for fire protection, the first step involves posting emergency numbers and knowing the response time from local fire departments. Good housekeeping provides the basis for sound fire prevention. Storage of combustibles in an area away from and out of the building is important.

Fire extinguishers must be placed in the same approximate place throughout the project area, making sure these places are near areas or activities that may be prone to fires. Fire extinguishers are rated by the type of fires for which they are effective, and this information must be posted

istock.com/KaraGrubis

Figure 9–8   Examples of Safety Signage (*Continued*)

Naleenmud/Shutterstock.com

as well as understood by all craftspeople. These fire extinguishers are dated for current charge and must be maintained at all times. Random inspections by local fire officials often are made to construction sites. Charged fire extinguishers and other means of fire suppression normally are reviewed during these inspections.

Designated smoking and no-smoking areas should be part of a fire prevention plan. Hazardous areas with flammable chemicals should be marked as "no-smoking" areas.

Electricity is a major source of fires, as is combustible liquid; thus, both need to be properly handled. The correct storage and handling of combustible liquid should be reviewed on a weekly basis. Flammable liquids must be carefully stored on the jobsite, usually away from other materials. A complete inventory of flammable and hazardous materials must be kept on the jobsite.

Flame-cutting and welding areas are the major causes of site fires, so control of work areas for these activities is necessary. Flame cutting and welding should be isolated from combustible materials such as lumber. Many owners require the general contractor or subcontractor to obtain special mandatory cutting and burning permits before beginning any renovation or new construction projects.

Subcontractor activities must comply at all times with the general contractor's fire prevention plan and also must be policed by all of the general contractor's site management personnel.

During some months of the year and with specific types of work that require drying, heaters will be used, which have the potential to become fire hazards and so should be checked on a regular basis to ensure their safe operation. Some types of heaters are safer than others in construction areas. A variety of heaters that use fuel oil, propane, natural gas, or electricity are available, but some may be inappropriate for interior use. Ventilation of fumes also is necessary to provide a safe environment for temporary heaters.

Substance Abuse

Substance abuse is a serious problem in the construction industry. According to the Substance Abuse and Mental Health Services Administration (SAMHSA), construction workers are more likely to abuse alcohol and drugs than workers in other industries.

Substance abuse can have a number of negative consequences for construction workers. These include:

- Increased risk of accidents and injuries: Substance abuse can impair judgment and coordination, which can lead to accidents and injuries.

- Decreased productivity: Substance abuse can lead to decreased productivity, as workers may be less focused and less able to work safely.

- Increased absenteeism: Substance abuse can lead to increased absenteeism, as workers may miss work due to illness or injury.

- Increased turnover: Substance abuse can lead to increased turnover, as workers may leave their jobs due to the negative consequences of substance abuse.

There are several factors that contribute to substance abuse in the construction industry. These include:

- Long hours: Construction workers often work long hours, which can lead to fatigue and stress.

- Dangerous work environment: The construction industry is a dangerous workplace, and workers may use alcohol or drugs to cope with the stress of the job.

- Peer pressure: Construction workers may feel pressure from their peers to drink or use drugs.

- Access to alcohol and drugs: Alcohol and drugs are often readily available on construction sites.

Substance abuse usually is divided into three categories:

- Alcoholic beverages

- Legal drugs

- Illegal drugs

Quite often, habitual abuse and being "under the influence" of illegal drugs and/or alcohol is a sickness that requires outside treatment. The use of prescription drugs also can pose a hazard for the worker, causing side effects such as drowsiness, hyperactivity, or possible dependency. Supervisors on the job must always be aware of the physical and mental condition of employees. Too often a "problem" employee is ignored, resulting in a serious accident where an employee might injure themselves or others in the work area.

Substance abuse programs should contain three elements. The first element should address a **standard of conduct** that defines and creates a zero-tolerance level for the use of alcohol and drugs while on the job as well as coming to work under the influence. When the results of off-duty excessive use of alcohol or drugs cause absenteeism, tardiness, or the inability to perform one's work, a zero-tolerance level of acceptance also must be enforced. An employee must realize that one's actions can result in an injury or fatality to oneself or others. Illicit activities, such as selling, distributing, or possessing illegal drugs, should be grounds for dismissal and for referral to local law enforcement authorities. Many firms are developing drug testing requirements that are used prior to employment.

The second element should create an **employee awareness** of drug and alcohol abuse and establish a prevention program. Employees should be required to attend formal sessions that discuss the dangerous effects of using drugs and alcohol on the jobsite. As part of a company's educational program, employees should be provided with information concerning the availability of drug and alcohol counseling, the type of treatment available, and rehabilitation facilities.

The last element of a formal substance abuse program is an **assistance program** for employees who are addicted to either drugs or alcohol. This program must be affiliated with a licensed professional in alcohol and drug treatment. The program also should ensure that the employees learn to take responsibility for their actions, and it should clarify the written and stated company policy concerning second-time abuse of alcohol or drugs. This part of the program must be treated with strict confidentiality.

Random drug testing also is used in substance abuse programs to determine drug use. Drug testing is often used to determine suitability for employment. It also is used in random situations and usually includes *all* employees. Some legal issues exist when employing a drug testing and substance abuse program; thus, legal counsel is necessary when setting up this program. Only certified testing services should be used in drug testing programs. The applicable labor unions must be aware of these programs.

The conditions set forth in the standards of conduct and the need for mandatory employee awareness education must be a "condition of employment" by which all employees must abide. Many times key employees abuse one or more rules during a project, but the misuse of alcohol and drugs on the construction site must not be tolerated, as the consequences can be disastrous.

Personal Protective Equipment

As part of an overall safety plan, a supervisor must understand the importance of personal protective equipment. Individual protection equipment falls into eight categories:

- Eye and face protection

- Head protection

- Hand protection

- Foot protection

- Respiratory protection

- Protection from falls when working at heights (safety harnesses, lifelines, and lanyards)

- Hearing protection

- Body protection

The contractor is obligated to furnish special protective gear for employees, such as respirators, hearing protection, safety harnesses, and so on. The employee is expected to wear appropriate clothing, such as jeans, long sleeved shirts, boots, and even steel-toed boots. Employers will furnish rain gear when employees are working in rainy conditions. Regulations do not require eye protection to be worn 100 percent of the time while working, but regulations for construction are approaching that requirement. Many construction firms have become proactive by requiring employees to wear eye protection throughout the work day.

Proper use of protective equipment should be fully explained in the jobsite safety manual and reinforced in weekly toolbox safety meetings. Compliance with rules for proper use of protective equipment should be strictly enforced on the jobsite.

Hazardous Materials Communication

By law (29 CFR Sec. 1910.1200—The Federal Hazard Communication Standard), every project employee has the right to information concerning all chemicals being used on a project and any harmful effects they may cause. The construction process utilizes many different types of materials, all of which can cause potential harm to employees. An in-house system to document and post a Safety Data Sheet (SDS) on all materials that will be used on the site during the construction process and the permanent materials that will be incorporated into the building should be developed and maintained on the project site.

The responsibility for such a program generally falls on the project engineer, office engineer, or a designated safety administrator. One requirement for the program is employee accessibility to the SDS. A system must be devised to file this information, such as the Construction Specifications Institute format for filing materials, which is the most appropriate system to use in the building industry.

The necessary steps in a right-to-know SDS program are the following:

1. *Inventory all chemical products on the jobsite.* An up-to-date list of chemical products for each jobsite is necessary. Many construction chemicals fall within the hazardous categories. Some of the most common include acids and cleaning agents, adhesives, degreasing agents, detergents, gasoline, fuel oil, janitorial supplies, paints, shellacs, varnishes and lacquers, solvents, copy machine fluid, wood preservatives, and many others.

2. *Label hazardous chemical containers.* Each container must be labeled correctly. The warning must convey the specific hazard of the chemical; for example, if inhaled, this chemical will cause lung damage. In this case, lung damage is the hazard.

3. *SDS.* A detailed SDS is required for each chemical on the jobsite. Figure 9–9 provides a sample SSDS, used on a typical project. These sheets, which are available from the chemical manufacturer, must be kept on file on the site. Information contained in the SDS information includes the chemical makeup of the substance, fire and explosion hazard data, reactivity data, health hazard data, precautions for safe handling and use, and control measures.

4. *Inform all employees about the hazard communication program, then identify and train employees who may be exposed to hazardous chemicals.* The contractor is responsible for training employees in the proper use of chemicals. Management is responsible for the safe storage, use, and disposal of the chemicals and also must furnish all protective clothing and gear to protect employees from the hazards of the product. Management also is responsible for the proper ventilation of chemicals as well as for the environmental conditions in which chemicals are being used. Management should evaluate whether the product is appropriate for particular conditions of use.

5. *Develop and maintain at the jobsite a written program that explains how employees are informed and trained about hazardous chemicals in the workplace.* Sample programs are available from OSHA and state safety agencies.

MATERIAL SAFETY DATA SHEET
("ESSENTIALLY SIMILAR" TO FORM OSHA 20)
OSHA 29 CFR 1910.1200

SECTION 1 - MATERIAL OR PRODUCT IDENTIFICATION AND USE

MANUFACTURER'S NAME	EMERGENCY TELEPHONE NO.

ADDRESS (Number, Street, City, State, and ZIP Code)

CHEMICAL NAME AND SYNONYMS	TRADE NAME AND SYNONYMS
CHEMICAL FAMILY	FORMULA

SECTION II - CHEMICAL DATA AND COMPOSITION (HAZARDOUS INGREDIENTS)

CHEMICAL FAMILY

FORMULA

CHEMICAL SUBSTANCES	CAS NO.	TLV	OSHA PEL
HAZARDOUS MIXTURES OF OTHER LIQUIDS, SOLIDS, OR GASES	TLV		

SECTION III - PHYSICAL DATA

BOILING POINT(F.)	SPECIFIC GRAVITY (H$_2$O 5 1)
VAPOR PRESSURE (mm Hg.)	PERCENT, VOLATILE BY VOLUME (%)
VAPOR DENSITY (AIR11)	EVAPORATION RATE (_____ 5 1)
SOLUBILITY IN WATER	APPEARANCE AND ODOR

SECTION IV - FIRE AND EXPLOSION HAZARD DATA

FLASH POINT (Method used)	FLAMMABLE LIMITS

EXTINGUISHING MEDIA

SPECIAL FIRE FIGHTING PROCEDURES

UNUSUAL FIRE AND EXPLOSION HAZARDS

Page (1)   (Continued on reverse side)

Figure 9–9   Material Safety Data Sheet

Courtesy of OSHA

SECTION V - HEALTH HAZARD DATA

THRESHOLD LIMIT VALUE

EFFECTS OF OVEREXPOSURE

EMERGENCY AND FIRST AID PROCEDURES

SECTION VI - REACTIVITY DATA

STABILITY	UNSTABLE		CONDITIONS TO AVOID
	STABLE		

INCOMPARABILITY (Material to avoid)

HAZARDOUS DECOMPOSITION PRODUCTS

HAZARDOUS POLYMERIZATION	MAY OCCUR		CONDITIONS TO AVOID
	WILL NOT OCCUR		

SECTION VII - SPILL OR LEAK PROCEDURES

STEPS TO BE TAKEN IN CASE MATERIAL IS RELEASED OR SPILLED

WASTE DISPOSAL METHOD

SECTION VIII - SPECIAL PROTECTION INFORMATION

RESPIRATORY PROTECTION (Specify type)

VENTILATION	LOCAL EXHAUST	SPECIAL
	MECHANICAL (General)	OTHER

PROTECTIVE GLOVES	EYE PROTECTION

OTHER PROTECTIVE EQUIPMENT

SECTION IX - SPECIAL PRECAUTIONS

PRECAUTIONS TO BE TAKEN IN HANDLING AND STORING

OTHER PRECAUTIONS

PAGE (2)

Figure 9–9 Material Safety Data Sheet (*Continued*)

Courtesy of OSHA

Safety Communications

All states require that safety communications be conveyed to employees in a variety of ways. Previously, this was discussed in tailgate or toolbox meetings. The posting of federal- and state-required posters and forms on the jobsite concerning safety will be examined later in this section; however, employers can also develop their own safety awareness posters and announcements, which can be visible in company magazines, at company-sponsored events such as picnics, and at award banquets.

Some specific requirements for posted safety communications, illustrated in Figure 9–10, include the following:

- Safety and health protection on the job

- Emergency telephone numbers

- Exiting and exit routes

- No-smoking signs

- Traffic direction signs

- Industrial welfare commission orders/Davis Bacon requirements

- Discrimination in employment

- Notice to employees regarding unemployment and disability insurance

- Payday notice

Figure 9–10   Jobsite OSHA Bulletin Board

ZikG/Shutterstock.com

- Summary of occupational injuries and illnesses posted during the month of February

- Location of the SDS

- General safety awareness

- Crane and hand signals for controlling crane operations

- Fire protection and prevention

Another form of safety communications recently developed uses the Internet and computers. One such company is ClickSafety (http://www.clicksafety.com). ClickSafety states in one of their brochures that it is "an Internet-based safety training, incentive awards and risk management program that will help contractors deliver job-appropriate training in both English and Spanish from any Internet-connected PC." The service provides online safety courses, tracks which employees have taken what classes, and tests for comprehension. The construction company has the option to choose which employee takes which classes. Employees can receive an OSHA 10-hour certificate by completing ClickSafety's OSHA 10-hour course or OSHA 30-hour certificate online.

Accident Reporting and Investigation

Accident reports are specific accounts describing particular incidents or accidents and are part of a company's safety program. The governing safety organization, whether it is OSHA or the state, requires detailed periodic reports and the use of prescribed forms. In addition to the required forms, the contractor should develop a form to document accidents and use the information to prevent future mishaps. Note that reporting is required within 8 hours of the death of any employee as a result of a work-related incident. This reporting must be direct to the OSHA office. Reporting within 24 hours is required after one or more employees is hospitalized. Non-notification will result in very large fines.

The construction company's accident form must be completed within 24 hours of the occurrence. The superintendent or field engineer should prepare the report, obtaining information from the accident victim, the foreman of the crew, and witnesses. Photographs of the conditions surrounding the accident should be taken and attached to the report. The report should be kept in the project safety file, then distributed to the company safety officer or safety committee and the project manager.

The following information should be contained on an accident report form, as shown in Figure 9–11:

- Name of the individual: personal data, including address, Social Security number, employee number, and other related information

- Location of the accident: project and exact location in the project

- Description of the accident: description of the accident, first aid administered, and medical attention needed, if any

- Crew foreman: name and location of foreman at time of accident (include or attach foreman's statement to form)

- Witnesses: names of witnesses to accident (include or attach their statements to form)

- What caused the accident: It is essential in each accident investigation to determine what caused it. Although an accident occurs because of a combination of factors, there probably is an identifiable reason why it happened and how it can be avoided in the future. Accidents commonly happen because of incomplete knowledge about how to safely perform a particular task, faulty equipment, lack of safety equipment, negligence by the employee or another party, and failure of temporary or permanent construction.

ACCIDENT REPORT

Project: New City Plaza, New City, CA   **Proj. No.:** 2-98   **Date:** 5/26/2026

	Name	Address	Soc.Sec.No.
Injured Employee:	Harold A. Johnston	II, 5390 Dulzura, Atascadero CA	534-90-9078

Accident Location   :   Building A, forming tilt-up panels

Accident Description   :   Carpenter Johnston cut right hand with circular saw while cutting lumber for tilt-up forms. Guard jammed on saw. Cut on right side of hand, just skin, no bone.

First Aid Applied?   :   Wrapped immediately, pressure applied at wrist by J. Anderson.

Medical Treatment Required :   Taken by J. Anderson, in company pickup, to City Hospital Emergency room. Wound was cleaned, sewed, 6 stitches, bandaged. Johnston given tetanus shot. Returned to jobsite. (Hospital report attached.)

Lost Time Due To Accident
(Estimate)   :   None estimate, employee returned to work

Foreman: *J. Anderson*   **Witnesses:**   *W. Mincks*
             (statement attached).   (statement attached).

Cause Of Accident   :   Guard jammed on circular saw. Carpenter continued to work.

Action Taken   :   Circular saw #110 taken out of service: sent to Repair shop. Toolbox talk scheduled for 5/27/2026 - safety concerns when using saws and tools.

Report By: _____

Date: _____

P.O. Box 3888, New City,
CA 93478(805) 444-9900,
FAX: (805) 444-9901

Figure 9–11   Accident Report

- Action taken following the accident: After determining what caused the accident, certain steps need to be taken quickly and decisively. If a ladder fails and causes the accident, the ladder must be removed. If an employee appears negligent, further investigation may be necessary, followed by dismissal if the employee is found negligent.

- Time lost by the accident: Time lost is a determining factor regarding the severity of an accident to the contractor, as well as the amount of time an employee is off duty while recuperating from the accident. After minor medical attention, an employee may be able to return to work immediately, without any lost time, or an employee may also be able to continue on the job but perform a different work task until the injury has healed, which is not normally considered a "lost time" accident. If an employee cannot return to work for one week, the lost time would be 7 days, or 40 hours.

OSHA Records and Regulatory Requirements

Construction firms must keep detailed records for OSHA as well as report specific types of illnesses or injuries. If a firm employs 11 or more employees at any one time in the previous calendar year, it must file OSHA Form 300 and Form 300A. OSHA 300 is the Log of Work-Related Injuries and Illnesses, OSHA 300A is the summary, and OSHA 301 is a supporting document that is used to record additional information pertaining to each injury and illness logged on OSHA Form 300.

OSHA 300, shown in Figure 9–12, consists of three distinctive parts:

1. Identifying the employee
2. Describing the case
3. Classifying the case

The supplementary record form, OSHA 300A, shown in Figure 9–13, consists of the following three parts:

1. Description of how the accident or illness occurred
2. List of objects or substances involved
3. Nature of and location where the injury/illness occurred

OSHA now permits other forms to be used in lieu of OSHA 301, for example, workers' compensation and private insurance forms. To qualify and be in compliance, these forms must contain all of the items stated on the OSHA 301 Form. An example of an alternate report is Form 5020 from the State of California.

These forms must be kept at every physical location when the projects are designated fixed establishments. Records for employees of nonfixed establishments, such as electricians performing service work out of a van, can be kept at the field office or mobile base of operations or at the established central location. The address and telephone number recorded on the form are those of the nonfixed site. These records are to be kept for a period of five years in a safe and secure location, preferably by a designated person.

Recording Injuries and Illnesses

Not all injuries or illnesses must be recorded. When an illness or injury occurs on the jobsite, many factors must be considered before the case can be classified. The following questions must be analyzed to ensure the proper procedure in completing OSHA Form 301, shown in Figure 9–14, and OSHA Form 300/300A for compliance with state and federal regulations:

1. Who employs the injured person?
2. Was there a death, an illness, or an injury?
3. Was the case work related?
4. Was the case an injury or illness?
5. Was the injury recordable, based on medical treatment beyond first aid, loss of consciousness, restriction of work or motion, transfer to another job, or diagnosis of a significant injury or illness?

These questions, which have been placed in chart formation in Figure 9–15, will help determine recordable and non-recordable cases.

To aid in establishing a work relationship to an injury or illness, OSHA has developed the guidelines, shown in Figure 9–16.

OSHA's Form 300

Log of Work-Related Injuries and Illnesses

Year 20____

U.S. Department of Labor
Occupational Safety and Health Administration

Form approved OMB no. 1218-0176

Attention: This form contains information relating to employee health and must be used in a manner that protects the confidentiality of employees to the extent possible while the information is being used for occupational safety and health purposes.

You must record information about every work-related death and about every work-related injury or illness that involves loss of consciousness, restricted work activity or job transfer, days away from work, or medical treatment beyond first aid. You must also record significant work-related injuries and illnesses that are diagnosed by a physician or licensed health care professional. You must also record work-related injuries and illnesses that meet any of the specific recording criteria listed in 29 CFR Part 1904.8 through 1904.12. Feel free to use two lines for a single case if you need to. You must complete an Injury and Illness Incident Report (OSHA Form 301) or equivalent form for each injury or illness recorded on this form. If you're not sure whether a case is recordable, call your local OSHA office for help.

Establishment name _____

City _____   State _____

Identify the person

(A) Case no.

(B) Employee's name

(C) Job title (e.g., Welder)

Describe the case

(D) Date of injury or onset of illness

(E) Where the event occurred (e.g., Loading dock north end)

(F) Describe injury or illness, parts of body affected, and object/substance that directly injured or made person ill (e.g., Second degree burns on right forearm from acetylene torch)

Classify the case

Using these four categories, check ONLY the most serious result for each case:

(G) Death
(H) Days away from work
(I) Remained at work — Job transfer or restriction
(J) Remained at work — Other recordable cases

Enter the number of days the injured or ill worker was:

(K) On job transfer or restriction ____ days
(L) Away from work ____ days

Check the "Injury" column or choose one type of illness:

(M)
(1) Injury
(2) Skin disorder
(3) Respiratory condition
(4) Poisoning
(5) All other illnesses

Page totals ▶

Be sure to transfer these totals to the Summary page (Form 300A) before you post it.

(1) Injury (2) Skin disorder (3) Respiratory condition (4) Poisoning (5) All other illnesses

Page ____ of ____

Public reporting burden for this collection of information is estimated to average 14 minutes per response, including time to review the instructions, search and gather the data needed, and complete and review the collection of information. Persons are not required to respond to the collection of information unless it displays a currently valid OMB control number. If you have any comments about these estimates or any other aspects of this data collection, contact: US Department of Labor, OSHA Office of Statistics, Room N-3644, 200 Constitution Avenue, NW, Washington, DC 20210. Do not send the completed forms to this office.

Figure 9–12 OSHA Form 300

Courtesy of OSHA

OSHA's Form 300A

Summary of Work-Related Injuries and Illnesses

Year 20___

U.S. Department of Labor
Occupational Safety and Health Administration

Form approved OMB no. 1218-0176

All establishments covered by Part 1904 must complete this Summary page, even if no work-related injuries or illnesses occurred during the year. Remember to review the Log to verify that the entries are complete and accurate before completing this summary.

Using the Log, count the individual entries you made for each category. Then write the totals below, making sure you've added the entries from every page of the Log. If you had no cases, write "0."

Employees, former employees, and their representatives have the right to review the OSHA Form 300 in its entirety. They also have limited access to the OSHA Form 301 or its equivalent. See 29 CFR Part 1904.35, in OSHA's recordkeeping rule, for further details on the access provisions for these forms.

Number of Cases

Total number of deaths

_____
(G)

Total number of cases with days away from work

_____
(H)

Total number of cases with job transfer or restriction

_____
(I)

Total number of other recordable cases

_____
(J)

Number of Days

Total number of days of job transfer or restriction

_____
(K)

Total number of days away from work

_____
(L)

Injury and Illness Types

Total number of . . .
(M)

(1) Injuries _____

(2) Skin disorders _____

(3) Respiratory conditions _____

(4) Poisonings _____

(5) All other illnesses _____

Post this Summary page from February 1 to April 30 of the year following the year covered by the form.

Establishment information

Your establishment name _____

Street _____

City _____ State _____ ZIP _____

Industry description (e.g., *Manufacture of motor truck trailers*) _____

Standard Industrial Classification (SIC), if known (e.g., *SIC 3715*) _____

Employment information *(If you don't have these figures, see the Worksheet on the back of this page to estimate.)*

Annual average number of employees _____

Total hours worked by all employees last year _____

Sign here

Knowingly falsifying this document may result in a fine.

I certify that I have examined this document and that to the best of my knowledge the entries are true, accurate, and complete.

_____ Title _____
Company executive

(___) _____ Date ___ / ___ / ___
Phone

Public reporting burden for this collection of information is estimated to average 50 minutes per response, including time to review the instructions, search and gather the data needed, and complete and review the collection of information. Persons are not required to respond to the collection of information unless it displays a currently valid OMB control number. If you have any comments about these estimates or any other aspects of this data collection, contact: US Department of Labor, OSHA Office of Statistics, Room N-3644, 200 Constitution Avenue, NW, Washington, DC 20210. Do not send the completed forms to this office.

Figure 9–13   OSHA Form 300A

Courtesy of OSHA

OSHA's Form 301
Injury and Illness Incident Report

U.S. Department of Labor
Occupational Safety and Health Administration

Form approved OMB no. 1218-0176

Attention: This form contains information relating to employee health and must be used in a manner that protects the confidentiality of employees to the extent possible while the information is being used for occupational safety and health purposes.

This *Injury and Illness Incident Report* is one of the first forms you must fill out when a recordable work-related injury or illness has occurred. Together with the *Log of Work-Related Injuries and Illnesses* and the accompanying *Summary*, these forms help the employer and OSHA develop a picture of the extent and severity of work-related incidents.

Within 7 calendar days after you receive information that a recordable work-related injury or illness has occurred, you must fill out this form or an equivalent. Some state workers' compensation, insurance, or other reports may be acceptable substitutes. To be considered an equivalent form, any substitute must contain all the information asked for on this form.

According to Public Law 91-596 and 29 CFR 1904, OSHA's recordkeeping rule, you must keep this form on file for 5 years following the year to which it pertains.

If you need additional copies of this form, you may photocopy and use as many as you need.

Information about the employee

1) Full name _____

2) Street _____
   City _____ State _____ ZIP _____

3) Date of birth ___ / ___ / ___

4) Date hired ___ / ___ / ___

5) ☐ Male
   ☐ Female

Information about the physician or other health care professional

6) Name of physician or other health care professional _____

7) If treatment was given away from the worksite, where was it given?
   Facility _____
   Street _____
   City _____ State _____ ZIP _____

8) Was employee treated in an emergency room?
   ☐ Yes
   ☐ No

9) Was employee hospitalized overnight as an in-patient?
   ☐ Yes
   ☐ No

Completed by _____

Title _____

Phone (___) ___ - ___   Date ___ / ___ / ___

Information about the case

10) Case number from the Log _____ (Transfer the case number from the Log after you record the case.)

11) Date of injury or illness ___ / ___ / ___

12) Time employee began work _____ AM / PM

13) Time of event _____ AM / PM ☐ Check if time cannot be determined

14) *What was the employee doing just before the incident occurred?* Describe the activity, as well as the tools, equipment, or material the employee was using. Be specific. *Examples:* "climbing a ladder while carrying roofing materials"; "spraying chlorine from hand sprayer"; "daily computer key-entry."

15) *What happened?* Tell us how the injury occurred. *Examples:* "When ladder slipped on wet floor, worker fell 20 feet"; "Worker was sprayed with chlorine when gasket broke during replacement"; "Worker developed soreness in wrist over time."

16) *What was the injury or illness?* Tell us the part of the body that was affected and how it was affected; be more specific than "hurt," "pain," or sore." *Examples:* "strained back"; "chemical burn, hand"; "carpal tunnel syndrome."

17) *What object or substance directly harmed the employee? Examples:* "concrete floor"; "chlorine"; "radial arm saw." *If this question does not apply to the incident, leave it blank.*

18) *If the employee died, when did death occur?* Date of death ___ / ___ / ___

Public reporting burden for this collection of information is estimated to average 22 minutes per response, including time for reviewing instructions, searching existing data sources, gathering and maintaining the data needed, and completing and reviewing the collection of information. Persons are not required to respond to the collection of information unless it displays a current valid OMB control number. If you have any comments about this estimate or any other aspects of this data collection, including suggestions for reducing this burden, contact: US Department of Labor, OSHA Office of Statistics, Room N-3644, 200 Constitution Avenue, NW, Washington, DC 20210. Do not send the completed forms to this office.

Figure 9–14 OSHA Form 301

Courtesy of OSHA

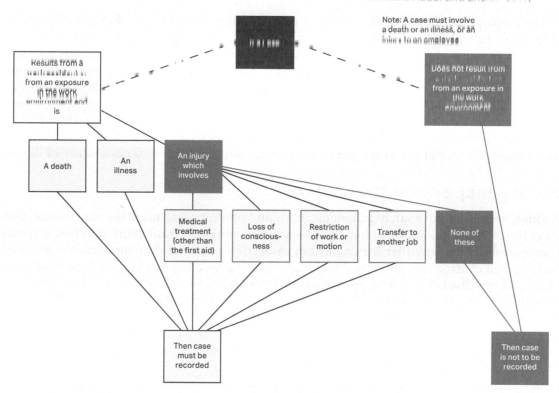

Figure 9–15   Guide to Recordability of Cases Under the OSHA Act

Courtesy of OSHA

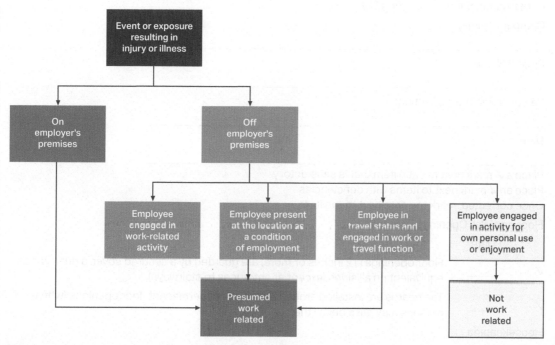

Figure 9–16   Guidelines for Establishing Work Relationship

Courtesy of OSHA

The employer has certain obligations to report injuries and illnesses, but not all must be reported to federal or state authorities. Two categories exist in which recorded cases must be reported: 1) audits of recorded injuries or illnesses for a certain time frame, requested by federal or state health and safety organizations, and 2) all accidents resulting in one or more fatalities or hospitalization of three or more employees. Some states have more stringent reporting requirements. The employer must orally report within 8 hours work-related fatalities and incidents involving the hospitalization of three or more employees to the nearest OSHA office or the OSHA Hotline at 1-800-321-OSHA. Again, some states have more stringent requirements; for example, CAL/OSHA requires immediate notification of a death or serious injury or illness.

Safety Inspection Checklists

Another way to improve safety communications and prevent accidents is the use of inspection checklists. Construction inspection checklists can be obtained from many different Internet sources, but a company that uses a custom inspection checklist that supports the areas of building and construction performed will find that the inspection checklists will be used more often and not discarded. There are several different ways to use inspection checklists on a construction site. They can be used by supervisors to conduct regular inspections of the site, or they can be used by employees to self-inspect their work areas. Inspection checklists can also be used by contractors to ensure that their subcontractors are meeting safety standards.

It is highly recommended to review both the information and safety help from OSHA.gov. This site has the full regulations and requirements for the construction industry, but also has training materials and forms to help change a company into a safety-first company.

Figure 9–17 provides a shortened version of a safety checklist. Take time to review and complete this checklist.

Construction Safety Inspection Checklist

Company Name:

_____

Project Name:

_____

Person doing the inspection:

_____

Date: Time:

_____

Place a ✓ mark next to each item that is satisfactory.
Place an ✗ mark next to items with deficiencies.
Once corrected, mark the date next to the item.

Floor and Wall Openings
        Date

✓   _____   Floor openings (12 inches or more) are guarded by a secured cover, a guardrail or equivalent on all sides (except at entrances to stairways).

✓   _____   Toe boards are installed around the edges of permanent floor openings (where persons may pass below the opening).

Housekeeping
        Date

✓   _____   Exits and access ways: maintained/unobstructed

✓   _____   Trash Receptacles: Adequate Number/Maintained

✓   _____   Material Storage

✓   _____   Toilet facilities (Adequate Number)

Figure 9–17   Construction Safety Inspection Checklist

Environmental Protection and Safety

Often some of the most important safety issues are not included, primarily the ones that come from the Environmental Protection Agency (EPA). The tendency is to worry about OSHA regulations when discussing safety. This text has a chapter on many of the issues associated with waste management and sustainable construction practices, which overlap the EPA policies. It is important that we look at safety very holistically and include a discussion of the key environmental requirements for construction, which can be considered part of a safety program.

During the construction process we often start with demolition and some removal of past construction. When demolition is part of the process of building a new structure or building, not only are we generating solid wastes but often hazardous wastes that promote major safety concerns. Note that a list of hazardous wastes and their allowed concentration can be found in the Regulations, Resource Conservation and Recovery Act (RCRA). In the chapter on waste management, the text discusses generators of hazardous waste, storage of these wastes, and disposal.

When discussing employee safety, the following questions should be considered: Have all the harmful substances been considered? Having a checklist will be helpful. The materials on the list could include asbestos, lead (mostly paints), solvents, paints, silica, etc. Note that most of these materials can become airborne or are liquids that can cause skin problems, or if ingested, sickness or death. As with asbestos, long-term negative effects, including cancer, can happen.

The construction team should also ask about the risk of exposure for all working on the project. If exposure risks are not carefully discussed, groups of employees, subcontractors, or others may come in contact with these hazardous materials or processes. Precautions should be made and identified for everyone on the project, along with documented notification of where these materials are, how they will be removed, transported, and disposed of.

An area that most construction sites should review is the use of masks and which types of masks are needed on the project. Often there is not a reliable process in place to ensure that the proper personal protective equipment is on the job and accessible for use by the employee(s) working within the area(s) that contain hazardous material. As is the case with asbestos and lead abatement, very specific procedures are required throughout the removal and disposal process. These rules are very specific and come with large fines for not adhering to these prescribed processes. Individuals doing the work must be certified. Understanding what materials the project is dealing with and how to safely address the materials are important parts of overall planning and implementation.

When planning and discussing demolition, other items must also be considered and handled safely. PCB waste can be found in fluorescent light ballasts, and fluorescent lamps could contain mercury. PCB falls under the Toxic Substances Control Act (TSCA), while fluorescent lamps are considered universal waste and have different rules that are less stringent.

Lastly, there will be a short discussion in this chapter on air quality and safety, the Clean Air Act, the effects of trucks and equipment on the site, and standards for dust emissions. Enclosed spaces must be investigated and safety considerations for employee health and safety, especially when dealing with hazardous emissions and by-products due to the construction process, drywall dust for example, must be implemented. Using gas engines in these spaces can cause health issues and even death in extreme cases. The procedures for concealed spaces and their rules, processes, and use of a competent person should be noted.

Summary

Construction is a high-risk industry, and workers are exposed to a variety of hazards, including falls, electrical shocks, and injuries from machinery. To protect workers, construction companies must implement a comprehensive safety program.

A comprehensive safety program should include the following elements:

- Hazard identification and assessment: The first step in any safety program is to identify and assess the hazards present in the workplace. This can be done by conducting a job hazard analysis (JHA). A JHA is a systematic process for identifying and evaluating the hazards associated with a particular job.

- Safe work procedures: Once the hazards have been identified, safe work procedures must be developed to control them. Safe work procedures should be specific, detailed, and easy to understand. They should also be written in a way that is consistent with the hazards identified in the JHA.

- Training: All workers must be trained on the safe work procedures that apply to their job. Training should be conducted regularly and should be updated as necessary.

- Personal protective equipment (PPE): PPE can help to protect workers from hazards. All workers must be provided with the PPE that they need to do their job safely.

- Supervision: Supervisors must be responsible for ensuring that workers are following safe work procedures and using PPE. Supervisors should also be trained on how to identify and correct unsafe work practices.

- Incident investigation: When an accident occurs, it is important to investigate the incident to determine the cause. This information can then be used to develop corrective actions to prevent similar accidents from happening in the future.

By implementing a comprehensive safety program, construction companies can help to protect their workers from injury and death.

In addition to the above, here are some additional tips for improving construction safety:

- Create a culture of safety: A culture of safety is one where everyone is committed to safety and where employees feel comfortable reporting unsafe conditions.

- Encourage workers to speak up: Workers should be encouraged to speak up if they see something unsafe. They should not be afraid of retaliation.

- Provide regular safety training: Safety training should be provided to all workers on a regular basis. The training should be specific to the hazards that workers are exposed to.

- Use safety checklists: Safety checklists can help to ensure that all safety precautions are being taken.

- Inspect the worksite regularly: The worksite should be inspected regularly for hazards. Any hazards that are found should be corrected immediately.

- Maintain equipment properly: Equipment should be maintained properly. This will help to prevent equipment-related accidents.

- Adhere to safety regulations: All safety regulations must be adhered to. This includes federal, state, and local regulations.

By following these tips, construction companies can help to create a safe workplace for their employees.

In today's construction environment, the contractor can no longer passively promote safe work practices. With the passage of the Occupational Safety and Health Act of 1970, employers were mandated to follow and adhere to federal and state safety regulations. In addition, construction companies also realized the need to develop and implement their own in-house safety regulations. Whether safety requirements are federal-, state-, or self-imposed, employers must demonstrate a commitment to safety, must have in place hazard assessment and control programs, must develop and implement safety planning, must have rules and work procedures that are proactive and pertain to the job site, and must provide safety and health training that is thorough and applicable to the work performed by its employees. It is not enough to make one's project engineer, the safety manager at the site and expect to be in compliance with safety regulations and prevent accidents.

One of the most aggressive and proactive safety programs developed for the construction industry's use is DuPont's STOP safety program. The acronym stands for Safety, Training, Observation, and Prevention. What makes this program so effective is the added key ingredients to the already developed and implemented safety programs. The key ingredients include positive intervention into the unsafe act that caused the accident resulting in the illness or injury, education of the employee regarding why the act causing the accident is unsafe, and a method of tracking the occurrence and developing ways of ensuring positive improvement. Employers are realizing that the consistent and regulated monitoring of safety practices does pay. Construction firms that have poor safety records are becoming less competitive in the marketplace because of higher costs of insurance, lower morale of employees, increased costs of fines at the jobsite, and overall loss of job profits.

Review Questions

1. Why does construction have a high rate of injuries, illnesses, and fatalities?

2. What does OSHA stand for, when was it first passed, and does it permit states to pass and implement their own state bills?

3. Are construction firms required to create and implement a safety and health program, and what are the key elements?

4. Name six additional subcategories to the key elements.

5. What is the intent of a toolbox meeting?

6. Flame cutting and welding are major causes of site fires. Describe the ways to lower the risk of fire from these activities.

7. Which of the following is/are considered substance abuse, and which is/are considered a sickness requiring outside treatment?

   Alcoholic beverages

   Legal drugs

   Illegal drugs

8. What are the three elements of a substance abuse program?

9. Name the five necessary steps in a right-to-know program.

10. Draw a flowchart that could provide a guide for recordability of cases under the OSHA Act.

11. Should environmental protection and safety be included in a company's safety considerations? Explain your answer.

12. Is it recommended to use an off-the-shelf safety inspection checklist, or should companies create their own custom checklists?

Chapter 10

Subcontracting and Purchasing

Objectives

This chapter is a discussion of subcontractor management, subcontract agreements, and subcontractor coordination. The objectives of this chapter are to introduce the following:

- Reasons why general contractors subcontract work
- Subcontractor's role and the subcontracting business
- Typical subcontractor agreement or the subcontract
- Ethical responsibilities when selecting a subcontractor
- Typical subcontractor quote and its complexities
- Process of "buying out"
- Good procedures and process for subcontractor management
- Best practices for subcontractor coordination
- Typical forms used in procurement of material and equipment

In the past, general contractors used subcontractors only to perform the "specialized" tasks of the construction project and accomplished most of the tasks with their own labor. The current general contractor subcontracts much of the project work, providing primarily supervision for the construction project. Subcontractors are used on the construction project for the following reasons:

1. *Specialized labor for particular construction tasks*

   Skilled craftspeople trained in the specific assembly perform the task correctly, enhancing the quality of the installation. They also complete the task efficiently, with the minimal amount of labor for the appropriate task.

2. *Lower cost for subcontract work*

   As the labor for the subcontractor is specialized and only a narrow range of work is done, subcontractor costs are generally less. When utilizing subcontractors, the contractor has reduced overhead costs as well as reduced labor and payroll costs.

3. *Reduced risk for the contractor*

   Several areas of risk are reduced by subcontracting work rather than accomplishing it with the contractor's own forces. The risk of labor productivity, where actual labor costs need to be less than or equal to the estimated labor cost, is eliminated for the contractor, the subcontractor now being held responsible. Other types of risk general contractors attempt to avoid by using subcontractors include the following:

   - Productivity and/or cost control, from the estimate to the project's completion
   - Lack of expertise in specialized areas
   - Control of potential liquidated damages
   - Cash flow
   - Quality from lack of expertise or the right craftspeople
   - Cleanup, warranties, and other general condition areas

Subcontract management is extremely valuable in today's legal climate. Because much of the risk has been shifted to the subcontractor, contracts between contractors and subcontractors have increased in importance. Informal agreements and understandings generally have been replaced by contractual agreements. The subcontract agreement is a serious legal contract, with binding provisions for both parties. Fulfillment of the obligations of the subcontract agreement is necessary for completion of the construction project. Subcontractors can affect the project's profitability by delay, poor workmanship, and default of contract. Subcontractor management relates directly to the profitability of the project.

Purchasing control also is necessary for a profitable project. **Purchasing** is the activity of procuring material or equipment for the project. The primary difference between purchases and subcontracts is that purchases do not contain jobsite labor, while subcontracts do. Purchasing procedures are part of a controlled and well-managed project. They can include the following:

- Pricing and purchasing material and equipment, both from the central office and from the jobsite

- Tracking and expediting the purchase to coincide with the construction schedule

- Control of the material at the jobsite

- Purchase or rental of construction equipment for the project

Writing subcontracts, material contracts, and purchase agreements are the essence of job purchasing. The process of converting all subcontractor bids to subcontracts and all quotes to purchase orders or purchase contracts is often called **buyout**. This is best accomplished at the beginning of each new job. How thorough and complete one job is during this process may have a large impact on the project's profitability and manageability.

When selecting a subcontractor for the different pieces of work, the contractor must balance scopes and be able to compare quote to quote. This is known as **scope alignment**. The person putting together the scope for each subcontract must understand what is being said in the qualifications, inclusions, and exclusions given on the subcontractor's quote. One is looking for gaps between subcontractors that will later cost the contractor money or overlaps of scope (two subcontractors contracting for the same work) among the subcontractors. Often this scope alignment and scope negotiation will require many phone calls between the general contractor and subcontractor. When the deal is finalized between the general contractor and subcontractor, it is important that the discussions have been well documented. A letter of intent shows good faith and will get things moving for the subcontractor. The final steps of the buyout are to complete a final subcontract agreement that is signed by both parties.

Remember that key elements of the subcontract will tie the subcontractor to the prime contract, list the contract documents, and include inclusion and exclusion items. When discussing exclusion, understand the risks. There is a fine balance between when to be general and when to be specific. The scope is a good area to clarify items such as milestones, bond, liquidated damages, or schedules. Note that if the owner has accepted alternates, they need to be included both in the price and in the scope. The subcontract is made up of mostly "boilerplate" language. These are important provisions, and one should understand the consequences of changes in these clauses. It should be noted that many general contractors are now adding additional "General Conditions" to their subcontracts. These should be reviewed to remove any duplication.

This chapter further discusses the project management function of writing subcontracts, purchase orders, and material contracts; the administration of subcontracts; and the area of purchasing and expediting.

Subcontract Management

The Subcontractor

The contractor's field personnel should have a complete understanding of subcontractors and the subcontracting business to effectively manage subcontractors. Field personnel should understand the following factors about each subcontractor:

- The nature of the subcontractor's business

- The scheduling demands on the subcontractor

- The risks the subcontractor is facing on the project

- The equipment and safety concerns of the subcontractor

The development of a working relationship between the general contractor's staff and the subcontractor's staff can often make accomplishing the goals of both companies easier. The goal for both companies is to make a profit, expand their businesses, move into a more profitable market, and, it is hoped, enjoy the process.

Subcontractors vary from very small firms to large international firms. They specialize in a certain area of the construction project, such as floor covering or mechanical or electrical work. Because of the smaller portion of projects, most subcontractors are concerned with various concurrent projects. The subcontractor's focus is to make a profit from all business activity while servicing customers with a finite amount of resources.

Subcontractors have a wide variety of attributes, which help explain the nature of each subcontractor's business:

- Subcontractors may engage in a number of different types of business in their field: retail, subcontracting, and contracting as a prime contractor on some projects. They might perform residential, commercial building, industrial, or heavy construction.

- Most subcontractors have higher indirect overhead than general contractors. They may have inventory, fabrication facilities, shop facilities, or retail facilities, resulting in higher overhead for physical facilities and personnel.

- Capital requirements for a subcontracting business can be fairly high. Liquid assets, such as inventory and accounts receivable, are higher than that of the general contractor. Some subcontracting businesses, such as excavation and masonry subcontractors, have a fairly large long-term debt for equipment.

- Subcontractors are paid for their work considerably after the completion of that work. "Contingent Payment Clauses" in subcontract agreements state that the subcontractor will not receive payment until the contractor receives payment. Subcontractors may have retainage held for long periods of time, particularly when completing an early portion of a project, such as excavation.

- Many subcontractors have additional subcontractors working for them. For example, a mechanical contractor may complete the plumbing and piping work with its own forces while subcontracting HVAC work, pipe insulation, fire sprinkler, excavation, temperature controls, and other portions of the work.

- Scheduling crews for the subcontractor often relates to keeping crews busy and fulfilling company-wide obligations rather than meeting particular project requirements.

As a separate business entity, the subcontractor has many pressures that are not apparent in the project relationship alone. This "hidden agenda" requires that the contractor be clear, concise, and forthright in contractual and jobsite relationships with all subcontractors.

The Subcontract Agreement

The subcontract agreement is an agreement or contract between the contractor and subcontractor. It is based on the construction documents prepared by the architect and engineer and is an agreement for a specifically described portion of work.

Subcontract Agreement Amount

The amount of the subcontract agreement is normally based on a lump-sum bid by the subcontractor to the contractor. This bid usually is submitted in a competitive environment, with the contractor receiving several subcontract bids for each subcontract area. The contractor requires competitive bids to maintain a low, competitive bid for the owner. Most contractors will choose the low subcontract bid. Negotiation after the receipt of bids is normal to determine any missing or overlapping areas between subcontracts.

Selecting Subcontractor Bids

Fair and ethical bid processing is necessary for the contractor and subcontractors to remain competitive in the marketplace. **Bid shopping**, the practice where contractors supply bid amounts from subcontractors to other subcontractors, is not ethical in most markets. This practice tends to decrease subcontract bids to cost or below cost, resulting in jobsite problems. Other unethical practices, such as contractors demanding cuts in bids, happen occasionally but limit the ability of the contractor to receive competitive bids for future projects. Fair treatment of subcontractors when receiving bids should establish a relationship of trust between the contractor and subcontractor.

One of the consequences of bid shopping is the increasing use of listing laws by states and other governmental agencies. The listing requirement is a part of the bid and is later incorporated into the contract itself. California requires a list of all subcontractors and material and equipment bids in excess of .5 percent of the total bid. This percentage is so small that it requires the general contractor to list most of the subcontracts and purchases on the project. In other states, only the major subcontractors are listed, that is, mechanical, electrical, and so on.

Many subcontractors submit bids late in the bid period, resulting in an incomplete analysis of subcontract bids. These bids are normally made by telephone or fax. But both methods can create confusion that will need to be clarified, usually after the bid period. Comparison of scope and items covered and excluded is necessary prior to writing subcontracts. Negotiations for adding or deleting portions of the work usually are required prior to finalizing subcontract agreements.

A typical telephone subcontractor quote sheet is shown in Figure 10–1. The telephone quote usually does not contain the detail and contract modifications contained in the faxed bid. The trend to fax quotes in the past decade has complicated scope definition at bid time and has caused the general contractor potential problems with subcontract negotiations. Figures 10–2, 10–3A, and 10–3B illustrate a typical subcontract bid quote transmitted by fax. The process of scope clarification after the bid becomes very complicated and often is confused with bid shopping.

Subcontractors describe the scope of their work in relation to construction documents, usually by the section number in the specification. For instance, a masonry subcontractor might describe their scope of work as follows:

> All brick and CMU masonry work, as per Section 04000 of the Specification. Place reinforcing in masonry only. No weather protection.

A short description of the technical specifications is needed for writing scope of work clauses in the subcontract. The general contractor, at bid time, wants to quickly determine the individual subcontractor's proposed scope of work, then make comparisons to other subcontractors who are bidding the same work. If an electrical subcontractor bids on Section 16 complete, without any other inclusions or exclusions, and another electrical subcontractor does the same, the question of which subcontractor to use becomes much easier to answer. If both prices are within 10 percent of each other and both subcontractors are bondable and of good reputation, then the lowest bid of the two would be the logical and correct choice. Scope comparisons and discussions with subcontractors often are necessary to ensure full coverage of the subcontracted area.

Subcontract Agreement Contract Form

Many firms use a standardized contract form for the subcontract agreement. These forms are the products of construction organizations such as the Associated General Contractors of America, Inc., and the American Subcontractors Association. An example of a subcontract agreement is shown in the Appendix.

The advantage of using standard contracts is that they are "tried-and-true," both with parties in the industry and in the courts. These contract forms are familiar to contractors and

FGH construction company

Telephone Subcontractor Quote

Project: _____ Bid Date: _____
Company Name: _____ Estimator: _____
Address: _____ Phone: _____
City: _____ License: _____
State/Zip: _____ Called in By: _____
Division/Scope of Work: _____
_____

Inclusions: _____
_____
_____
_____
_____
_____
_____

Total Base Bid: _____

Exclusions: _____
_____
_____
_____
_____
_____

Alternates or Bid Items: _____
_____
_____
_____
_____
_____

Total Amt. of Alternate

Bid includes products that meet or exceed specifications?   ____yes ____no
Is bid per plans and specifications?   ____yes ____no
Is your firm DBE / WBE / DVBE? (circle one)
Union labor   ____yes ____no   Installed?   ____yes ____no
_____ Addenda?   ____yes ____no   Erected?   ____yes ____no
Tax?   ____yes ____no   Furnish only?   ____yes ____no
Bond?   ____yes ____no   F.O.B.____jobsite____Trucks
                                     _____nearest R. R. crossing
Received by_____   _____Other _____
                                     Delivery _____
Date_____   Time_____   Weight _____

5390 Walnut Avenue, San Francisco,
California, 93422-0027
Phone: (415)555-2346, Fax: (415)555-2300

Figure 10–1   Telephone Subcontractor Quote

subcontractors, containing standard language and requirements. Most contracts have some bias, depending on who writes them. Standard forms cowritten by contractor organizations and subcontractor organizations reduce this bias, however. Both parties have the right to modify sections of the subcontract agreement, subject to specific approval by the other party. Discussion about contract language and modifications is part of the negotiation process. When a discussion cannot be resolved, the contractor must decide on the feasibility of awarding the subcontract to the second bidder. Both parties need to carefully consider their position in these discussions, determining the value of the contract language. The contractor may incur additional

Borland Mechanical Contractors
2839 South 1st Ave.
Atascadero, California 93422
(805) 462-1520
FAX (805) 462-2000
Contractor's License No. #195231

FAX COVER SHEET

This is a Subcontract Bid!

FAX (408) 584-9250

DATE: February 9, 2026   TIME: 1:45 PM

TO (Company): FGH Construction Company, Inc.

ATTENTION: John Anderson

FROM: Bill Franks - Estimator

REFERENCE: Naval Shipyard - Point Magu, Mechanical Repairs to Bldg. 210

The attached is Borland Mechanical Contractors scope letter for the above referenced project. Please review in depth. Any questions should be directed to Bill Franks prior to bid opening. Thank you for this opportunity to bid this project with you.

NUMBER OF PAGES INCLUDING COVER PAGE 3

If you do not receive all the pages, please call: (805) 462-1520

Figure 10–2 Fax Cover Sheet

cost by subcontracting with another team, and the subcontractor may lose the contract. Many contractors will use an in-house subcontract, written by their attorneys. These contracts usually are biased heavily in favor of the contractor. Most contractors will not allow modifications to this custom agreement. Some subcontractors will present their own subcontract agreements, particularly in residential construction. These contracts are usually brief, intended to protect the subcontractors' right to payment. In commercial building construction, some large specialty subcontractors, such as elevator subcontractors, will prefer to use their own subcontract agreement. The bargaining power of subcontractors is enhanced when they are in an exclusive area and/or are a large firm.

Borland Mechanical Contractors
2839 South 1st Ave.
Atascadero, California 93422
(805) 462-1520
FAX (805) 462-2000
Contractor's License No. #195231

FGH Construction Company, Inc.
893 Higuria Street
Monterey, CA 93940

Attention: John Anderson

Reference: Naval Shipyard - Point Magu, Mechanical Repairs to Bldg. 210

Gentlemen:

We are pleased to quote you the Mechanical Proposal for the referenced project based upon the following scope of work listed below:

Division 15 - Mechanical Complete with the exception noted under work included, work not included and standard clarification of our proposal as outlined in attachment "A".

Work Included:

1. All work shown on the drawing as it related to the systems we are furnishing and installing.
2. Louvers as shown on the Mechanical Drawing.

Work excluded:

1. Formed Concrete
2. Painting
3. Temporary plumbing, electrical, and lighting for our construction use.
4. Sewage usage Fees
5. Premium Time
6. Parking Fees

Our lump sum bid is: **$ 345,500.00**
Should you need clarification or have question regarding this fax bid proposal, please call.

Sincerely,

Bill Franks
Estimator

Figure 10–3A   Fax Subcontractor Quote

The subcontract agreement contains provisions from the contract between the contractor and owner and provisions for the relationship between the contractor and subcontractor. The subcontract should contain the following articles or areas:

• Preamble and date/parties to the agreement

• Reference to the construction documents, and applicable sections of the specification

Attachment "A"

Standard Clarification

The following conditions:

1. Cleanup - Borland Mechanical will remove all rubbish and debris generated by our operations to your trash bins onsite and leave our work area in a clean condition (not broom cleaned). Our bid does not include and we are not to be charged any prorated, general clean-up cost or haul off charges.

2. Back charges - FGH Construction will not perform any portion of Borland Mechanical's work or incur any costs for our account, except upon written order and unless Borland Mechanical is in default and have been given written notice under our subcontract.

3. Progress Payments - Progress payments shall be paid to Borland Mechanical in the percentages approved by the Owner for Borland Mechanical' work within five working days following FGH Construction's receipt. Any retention reduction given to FGH Construction will be passed on to Borland Mechanical.

4. Insurance, Liability, and Bond - This bid does not include the cost of Builder's Risk Insurance or the cost of a bond. Borland Mechanical can furnish a bond at your request and costs. Borland Mechanical shall be only liable for acts of our own employees.

5. ....

6. ....

7. ....

Figure 10–3B   Fax Subcontractor Quote

- Scope of work
- Subcontract price
- Payment provisions
- Changes, claims, and delays (including damages caused by)
- Insurance provisions
- Bonding provisions, if required by the contractor
- Materials and workmanship
- Time and schedule
- Obligations of the contractor and subcontractor
- Labor provisions
- Contractual requirements, indemnification, and recourse by the contractor
- Remedy for solution of disputes
- Termination of the agreement

Scope Definition in the Subcontract Agreement

Proper scope definition in the subcontract agreement is one of the keys to successful subcontract management. Each subcontract needs to be fully defined, then compared with the other subcontracts to ensure coverage of all items. All subcontracts should be adequately described, compared, and checked prior to writing and issuing any individual subcontract. Well-defined subcontract scope statements avoid unnecessary arguments about who will handle certain items, reduce change orders, and give the project management team tools to control the cost, time, and quality of the project.

The scope of work must be carefully described for each subcontract. Even when using the standard preprinted subcontract agreement, the exact scope of the subcontract work needs to be added to the agreement. The scope of work description should include the following:

- Description of the work relating to the construction documents, including drawing and specification reference; reference should include dates of the documents, document numbers, and dates of the addenda

- Additional work to be performed by the subcontractor beyond the specification sections

- Exclusions from work described in the construction documents as per the subcontractor's bid

- Any additional specific information relating to the project, such as schedule dates or delivery dates

- Description of included alternates and negotiated additions or deletions to the agreement

Standard clauses almost always precede or follow the scope definition, stating that all work will be "performed in accordance with the owner and contractor contract, contract documents, and the plans and specifications." The terms "per plans and specifications" and "per contract documents" are used to connect the subcontract to all of the same provisions contained in the contractor's contract with the owner. Phrases such as "including but not limited to" should be avoided in the subcontract agreement, as they can lead to multiple interpretations. Figure 10–4 shows a sample scope of work statement in the subcontract agreement.

"SECTION 2. <u>SCOPE</u>

     Subcontractor agrees to furnish all labor, materials, equipment and other facilities required to perform the work to complete:

Project completion date per project master schedule.

Item of work to include but not limited to: Subsurface Investigation, Demolition, Site Preparation, Earthwork, Trenching, Backfilling, and Compacting.

for the project in accordance with the Contract Documents and as more particularly specified in:

Section (s) 02010, 02050, 02100, 02200, 02221, 02700, 02721 of the Contract   Specifications.

See Exhibit "A" which is attached hereto and made a part hereof.

See Attachment No. 2 dated August 25, 1996, for Continuation of Scope of Work."

Figure 10–4 Scope of Work

The subcontract price should reflect the quoted price or newly negotiated price from the subcontractor. Many subcontract agreements require some negotiation on scope, price, or contract provisions. One would expect to see the subcontract price reflect these clarifications and negotiations, but this is not always true. The system that requires the general contractor to set a price using many diverse subcontractor bids, competition leaving small margins, and an all-inclusive scope of work defined by the contract documents does not leave the general contractor with much room to maneuver on price. These negotiations normally take the form of clarification of scope rather than a change in subcontract price.

The **schedule of work** clauses relate to the time frame required for completion of subcontract work. Terms similar to "time is of the essence" are often used, emphasizing the importance of time to the subcontractor. The subcontractor usually is required to follow the contractor's schedule, but most contractors will prepare their schedules with input from subcontractors, including activity duration, sequence with other activities, and material and equipment delivery dates. As the contractor needs to compile a schedule from all subcontractors and suppliers, the project schedule may not conform with the subcontractors' ideal schedules.

Subcontract agreements include **indemnification clauses** that "hold the contractor harmless" from actions of the subcontractor. These clauses give the contractor protection from claims and lawsuits arising from the subcontractor's actions in pursuit of the work covered under the subcontract agreement. The subcontractor is responsible for providing appropriate liability insurance to protect the contractor and owner from lawsuits connected with the subcontractor's workforce or work on the project.

Control of subcontractors on the project is difficult for the contractor. Several standard clauses are included in subcontract agreements to provide some tools for control of the subcontractor by the superintendent. Compliance to the schedule, jobsite cooperation, and quality of the installation are common concerns to the superintendent. The subcontract agreement usually contains the following type of clauses to allow control of the subcontractor:

- Schedule requirements related to termination clauses if the subcontractor does not meet schedule and manpower requirements

- Quality control, inspections, and repair of defective work, also related to termination clauses

- Clauses related to acceptability of subcontractor jobsite personnel and the right of the contractor to have that individual removed from the jobsite

Remedies for solving disputes usually are stipulated in the subcontract agreement. Arbitration is the most common remedy to disputes; however, litigation is occasionally stipulated. Arbitration is normally considered more expedient than is litigation, although the arbitration process can be slow and expensive. The claim procedure for the subcontract is similar to that for the general contract, requiring notification of claim, continuation of work during the claim, continuation of payments, and a step-by-step procedure. The final settlement of the claim will be accomplished by the method stipulated, a form of either arbitration or litigation.

Termination of contract clauses is essential to any agreement. Specific clauses should be included in the subcontract agreement, stipulating the following:

- Occurrences that will cause termination of the agreement, such as noncompliance with contractual terms by the subcontractor or nonpayment by the contractor

- Notice necessary for termination, including form and timing

- Determination of costs of termination

- Remedies for termination or to oppose termination

Termination of the contract by the contractor usually relates to subcontractors' lack of ability to perform their contractual obligations. In these cases, the contractor needs to carefully follow the terms of the agreement, preferably with an attorney's guidance. Replacing a subcontractor usually will result in delays and extra costs. Termination proceedings normally are a last-resort measure, as they often cause more problems than they solve. If the subcontractor is a solvent business entity, it is usually easier to solve performance problems than it is to terminate the contract. In cases where the subcontractor is insolvent financially, termination and replacement of the subcontractor may be the only available remedy.

The major clauses of each subcontract have to be administered and various subcontracts and subcontractors managed. A major concern for the contractor is the subcontractors' meeting schedule, providing an adequate jobsite workforce to meet the schedule. The project superintendent needs to work with subcontractors on a daily basis, monitoring their progress and jobsite workforce. If changes are necessary, immediate action is necessary to avoid project delay. The quality of the subcontractors' installations also needs to be monitored on a daily basis. Poor-quality work must be stopped and corrected before additional work is done incorrectly.

Coordination Meetings

Weekly coordination meetings are normally held, with all applicable subcontractors in attendance. The focus of the subcontractor meeting is the exchange of information on scheduling, interface between the various subcontractors, and the review of updated information, changes, and potential effects on all companies involved. Like any meeting, this should be scheduled at the same time each week, with set agendas; the superintendent should control the flow of the meeting. Generally, all of the major subcontractors should be at the weekly subcontractor meetings for the duration of the job. This is not a difficult task once subcontractors are on-site, but many are hesitant to come to meetings if they feel their time will be wasted. Every contractor has his own method of encouraging subcontractors to attend these meetings, from fining them for missing meetings to providing incentives. When subcontractors are not able to attend meetings, minutes should be sent to them.

Scheduling Subcontractors

Jobsite personnel must understand subcontractors' business motivations in order to manage subcontractors on the jobsite. Subcontractors are involved in many projects simultaneously. Despite trying to achieve a balance of work for personnel and equipment, they inevitably have several jobs that need attention at the same time because of project delays and schedules. Most subcontractors are interested in completing their work in a timely manner. Furnishing subcontractors with schedules of the work and updating the schedule will help meet project demands.

Subcontractor Submittals

Subcontractors are required to submit numerous documents to the contractor during the course of work. Prior to initial payment, the subcontractor must submit certificates of insurance, bonds, material samples/shop drawings/product data, and various certifications and affidavits required by the owner. During the project, the subcontractor may be required to submit certified payrolls, partial lien releases, and other miscellaneous documents.

Changes to the Subcontract Agreement

Control of changes with subcontractors is critical in subcontractor management. Official changes in the contract follow a specific procedure, requesting pricing information, followed by official notice to the contractor in the form of a change order. The contractor, then, needs to provide the subcontractor with written authority to proceed with additional work for the amount negotiated. This change to the subcontract agreement must be in writing. Technically, the work should not be done until formal notification is made; however, the work is often completed prior to completion of the paperwork. Payment is not made, though, until all of the paperwork is complete. Other changes occur during the work on an informal basis. It is often necessary to modify work procedures to accommodate all elements of the work. These changes are normally done at the moment, without regard for cost of the change. Careful communication needs to be accomplished between the contractor and subcontractors to avoid confusion about payment for work. As contracts become more complicated, the subcontract agreement may be explicit about the parties responsible for authorizing additional work.

Quality Control in Subcontract Work

When discussing subcontractor management, another area that must be controlled is quality and workmanship. The contractor's field personnel need to be involved in day-to-day quality control with subcontractors as well as in quality review at the end of the subcontract work or at the completion of the project. The contractor's field personnel must be able to recognize correct work procedures and quality of work for each subcontract. Education of field personnel needs to be done periodically for updates in new and changing techniques. As the contractor is ultimately responsible for the quality of the work in the project, field personnel must be continually involved with quality review of the subcontractors' work as it progresses.

A common dispute between contractors and subcontractors regards the acceptance of the subcontractor's work. As most subcontract work is completed or partially completed prior to the completion of the project, the subcontractors' installations must be accepted by the contractor prior to acceptance of the project by the architect. Often, a subcontractor's work needs to be accepted prior to the start of another subcontractor's installation. For instance, the gypsum drywall subcontract must be completed and accepted prior to the start of painting. Many times a subcontractor's work is completed before other work in the same area, requiring protection and care of the craftspeople working in that area. For example, ceramic tile floor covering is installed before several operations in a toilet room, specifically cabinets, and installation of plumbing fixtures, toilet partitions, and toilet accessories. Any of the other trades could potentially damage the ceramic tile installation.

Most contractors are reluctant to accept responsibility for approving work prior to approval by the owner. It is usually difficult for the subcontractor or the contractor to protect their completed work from other craftspeople on the project. Disputes can easily arise in this area. Many contractors will use clauses in the subcontract agreement requiring the subcontractor to protect their work, deferring acceptance of subcontract work until accepted by the owner. Realistically, the contractor and subcontractors should cooperate to achieve a successful project. The contractor's superintendent and other field personnel must be involved with subcontract installations, avoiding unnecessary disputes.

Some guidelines for accepting subcontractor work include the following:

1. The contractor's superintendent should be aware of the subcontractor's progress and quality of work during the installation.

2. Inspection of the subcontractor's work should be made prior to the subcontractor's departure from the project. If possible, the architect or owner's inspector should be involved in reviewing the subcontract work for quality as well as the contractor's field personnel. If further work or remedial work is required, it is best to complete it before the installation crew leaves the jobsite. It is also best to have the work repaired prior to commencing adjacent or attached work.

3. When a subcontractor's work is the substrate for another subcontractor's work, such as completion of drywall installations prior to painting, the contractor should involve the other subcontractor with acceptance of surfaces and adjoining installations before the start of that subcontractor's installation. Careful inspection and agreement need to be made between the contractor and subcontractors about the acceptability of substrate work.

4. Agreement on the protection of the subcontractor's work must be reached prior to the subcontractor's departure from the project. Some subcontractors and contractors like to photograph or videotape the condition of the work when turned over to the contractor. Finishes often receive minor damage during the final stages of a project. The contractor's field personnel should be active in the final stages of the project, preventing damage and determining the cause of any damage.

Subcontractor Payment

Subcontractors are very concerned about receiving payment for their work at the jobsite. As most subcontract agreements have a "contingent payment clause," which provides that the subcontractor will be paid after the contractor receives payment from the project owner, payments for the work, less the amount held for retainage, are normally received over 90 days after the work is performed. Subcontractors are interested in requesting payment for their work to coincide with the payment period conclusion. Most subcontractors are obligated to pay for materials, as well as labor, considerably before receipt of payment from the contractor. The contractor must provide the necessary payment "cutoff" dates to each subcontractor, allowing the subcontractor to bill the appropriate amounts at the proper time. The payment process is fairly inflexible once established, not allowing for billings between cutoff dates. The contractor is responsible for the amount billed, requiring careful monitoring of subcontractor work completed and the amount paid to the subcontractor. The owner also will monitor the amount of work completed. To avoid reprocessing payment requests and the associated delay, the contractor needs to verify the amount of work completed by subcontractors prior to submitting the payment request. A subcontractor's billing may be listed in several items in the Schedule of Values used by the owner to determine payment, and the subcontractors should list their completion in appropriate sections to facilitate payment processing. As subcontractors often overbill for their work because of cash flow concerns, it is often necessary to verify the amount with material and equipment invoices, certified payrolls, and verification of physical work completed.

Subcontractors' requests for payment usually will include an amount for material stored on the site. Most owners will pay for material delivered and stored on the site. This facilitates having adequate material on the jobsite for the work tasks and does not delay the progress of the project. Most owners are concerned, however, that the amount paid for material coincides with the material actually stored on the jobsite. Verification of the quantity of material stored at the site and the cost of the material, by invoice, often is necessary. The subcontractor usually is concerned about the storage and handling of the material on the jobsite and is responsible for this until it is incorporated into the work. Subcontractors will want to store their material close to the point of installation, if possible, to facilitate efficient installation.

Subcontract Back Charges

Many contractors will **back charge**, a deduction from the amount owed to the subcontractor, costs that have been incurred by the contractor that should have been the subcontractor's responsibility. The back charge normally is deducted from the subcontractor's progress payment. These back charges can include a wide variety of items, such as the following:

- Charges for equipment use

- Charges for material used by the subcontractor, furnished by the contractor

- Charges for labor furnished to the subcontractor for their contractual responsibilities

- Charges for cleanup of waste on the jobsite

- Charges for delays caused by the subcontractor

- Charges for repair of the subcontractor's work by the contractor or other subcontractors

The contractor should notify the subcontractor concerning the reason and amount of the back charge before applying it to the payment. The subcontract agreement will normally allow for back charges within specified limits. An agreement on the back charge should be reached between the contractor and the subcontractor, although this is not always possible. Unnecessary disputes arise in this area that could be resolved with communication between the contractor and subcontractor. Some guidelines for back charges include the following:

1. Notify the subcontractor of cost of equipment use prior to the time of the equipment. Agreement should be made in each instance and recorded, with each party keeping a copy of the record of hourly cost and hours used.

2. Record the use of materials, with both parties receiving copies of the record. *Example:* The plumbing subcontractor needs a cubic yard of concrete for thrust blocks on a water line. The contractor is pouring concrete at the time, and arrangement is made for the cubic yard to come off of one of the contractor's concrete trucks. A record is made by the field engineer that a cubic yard of concrete was furnished, at market value, indicating the time and date and containing signatures of the contractor's field person and the plumbing foreman. The amount is then deducted as a back charge from the next payment made to the plumbing subcontractor.

3. A similar procedure to the one just described will be used when a subcontractor uses contractor personnel for work in the subcontractor's scope.

Example

A temporary ramp is needed by the mechanical subcontractor for installation of a piece of equipment. The contractor furnishes two carpenters for 8 hours for construction of this ramp. Record is made of the hours and the applicable rate, with the date noted and signed by the superintendent and mechanical foreman. Deduction of the amount is then made at the next payment.

4. Back charge for cleanup might be agreed upon at the start of the project or might be made as a result of the subcontractor not cleaning up waste. Agreement for the scope of work and cost should be made prior to commencing the cleanup activity.

5. Back charging for delay is difficult, as it is normally disputed by the subcontractor. Discussion of the impact of a delay should occur, resulting in an agreement between both parties.

6. Repair of a subcontractor's work by another party usually is done when the subcontractor refuses to repair the work. This repair cost is normally part of a dispute between the contractor and subcontractor. Careful documentation must be made indicating notices sent to the subcontractor, date of the repairs, exact nature of the repairs, and detailed listing of labor hours and material used. Photographs and videotapes can assist in this documentation.

Withheld Payments

Instances may arise when the contractor will withhold payments from the subcontractor as a reserve to cover payment of obligations incurred by the subcontractor. The contractor and subcontractor normally agree in the subcontract agreement to an amount of retainage to be held, but occasionally additional amounts must be withheld from the subcontractor's payment. Some reasons a contractor would withhold payment include the following.

- As a reserve to cover repair or replacement of work in place

- As a reserve to pay second-tier subcontractors when they have furnished notice that they have not received payment

- As a reserve to pay labor, fringe benefits, and labor taxes when the subcontractor is not making appropriate payment

- As a reserve to pay equipment or material suppliers when they have not received payment from the subcontractor

These payments withheld are dispersed as necessary, under provisions contained in the subcontract agreement. Because these instances contain many legal issues, the contractor should consult an attorney prior to withholding payments from the subcontractor.

Subcontractor Coordination

If subcontractors are able to pursue work in a productive and profitable manner, they normally cooperate with the contractor and other subcontractors. This facilitates an overall positive jobsite attitude, optimizes the work schedule, and increases quality in the project. The contractor, then, should try to facilitate subcontractors' work by being ready for the installation and by providing working conditions favorable to the installation and completion of the subcontract. On the surface, a little extra coordination and cooperation for the subcontractors may appear to increase jobsite costs for the contractor. In reality, the extra cooperation reduces costs related to project efficiency, project duration, and completion of punch lists and quality reviews.

Scheduling subcontractors and the use of the subcontractors in the schedule can be crucial to the profitability of subcontractors on the project. When preparing the schedule, the contractor should be aware of the sequential relationship of the subcontractors' work, the duration of the work, and the delivery of materials. Fair and honest representation of the subcontract work in the schedule provides the subcontractor with realistic expectations to complete the work profitably. There are a number of scheduling philosophies, using the subcontractor as a tool to push the schedule along, usually at the expense of the subcontractor. These tactics have short-term benefits, at best, resulting in disputes, poor-quality work, and subcontractor default on the project. The project schedule should be used as a tool to realistically indicate the work plan and help all process participants achieve or exceed the plan. There are certain subcontracts in every project that can provide the pace of the project. The contractor needs to identify these pacesetters and facilitate their work, using the following techniques:

- Discuss the fastest course possible with the subcontractor, realizing that optimization of the time frame is beneficial to all parties. Determine a reasonable duration for the installation.

- Determine what needs to be done prior to the start of the subcontract.

- Establish achievable start and finish dates for the activity well in advance of the start of the work.

- Determine material delivery constraints, such as shop drawing reviews, and minimize any possible delays in ordering and delivering the material.

- Determine use of the contractor's lifting equipment to facilitate the installation.

- Determine appropriate jobsite storage of material and equipment.

- Be prepared for the subcontract work rather than just expecting it to happen.

- Be flexible to changes and seek quick and efficient solutions to any changes.

Today's general contractor is offering more preconstruction services, which include scheduling, value engineering, conceptual estimating, constructability studies, and life cycle costing. To accomplish these tasks accurately and professionally, a general contractor will rely on long-term subcontractor relationships. Full project information in the early stages of a project, including cost and schedule of subcontract work, can provide subcontractors with a competitive edge in negotiating contracts. In many private projects, owners and architects rely on bidder designs in mechanical and electrical specialty areas. In this type of bid work, the general contractor assumes a great deal of risk if a highly sophisticated subcontractor who understands the design and engineering of the job is not used. In this type of arrangement, the contractor assumes responsibility for the design of the applicable portions of the work as well as for the normal construction responsibilities. Mistakes in the design of a bidder-designed contract can cause major problems in the successful completion of the project. Both mechanical and electrical specialty contractors, capable of design and construction of the systems, are available in most construction markets. These specialty contractors can provide budget information during the early stages of a project and final construction estimates when designs are complete. These can be very efficient arrangements, saving cost and time, if specialty contractors are competent in their work and can work closely with the general contractor. General contractors should establish close working relationships with subcontractors in most specialty areas for work in negotiated and "cost-plus" contracts.

Subcontractor Safety and Waste Management

Additional project management and subcontract management relates to safety, waste management, and cleanup activities of the subcontractor. General contractors have found that these key elements are often ignored by the subcontractor, particularly by those that emphasize high productivity from their crews. Subcontractors do not always understand the relationship of safety to project profit. Many subcontractors expect the contractor to clean up and dispose of waste created by the subcontractor's crews, saving the subcontractor the cost of cleanup. The contractor needs to discuss the responsibility of safety programs and project cleanup with subcontractors prior to the start of each subcontractor's work. Continual reminders of these responsibilities need to be made by the subcontractor's field personnel throughout the project. Back charging the subcontractors for cleanup costs is commonly done when subcontractors do not implement their responsibilities in cleaning up after their work. Occasionally, contractors will negotiate with the subcontractors to clean up the entire jobsite on a periodic basis.

Waste management is a relatively recent development, a result of higher landfill costs and increased environmental regulations. Many owners are requiring construction waste to be managed by efficient reduction, reuse, and recycling. The appropriate clauses must be added to the subcontract agreements, requiring subcontractors to plan, separate, and recycle their construction waste. Coordination of this waste management effort by the contractor is necessary. The contractor may wish to assume all of the waste management responsibilities on the project at a negotiated cost to the subcontractors. This central waste management effort may be more effective and evident than relying on individual subcontractors.

The Subcontractor's Subcontracts

Many subcontractors subcontract out portions of the work. These "second-tier subcontracts" are responsible for providing specific work to the subcontractor. As there is no contractual relationship between the contractor and the second-tier subcontract, the contractor has less direct control of that portion of the work, relaying all directions through the subcontractor. The subcontractor, though, is responsible for this second tier subcontracted work to the contractor. Responsible full-service subcontractors, such as the mechanical subcontractor responsible for all of the work specified in Divisions 21, 22, and 23 of the Contract Documents, are often more desirable to the contractor, as the superintendent deals with one foreman rather than four or five different foremen for different subcontractors. These situations rely on the ability of the subcontractor to manage subcontractors, similar to the responsibilities of a general contractor. It is recommended that the contractor include a clause in the subcontractor agreements that indicates that any work that the subcontractors have accomplished by subtier subcontractors be tied to the primary set of Contract Documents by the contractual agreement between the subcontractors and subtier subcontractors.

Purchase of Materials

Subcontracting is only part of the purchasing process. When only material is being procured, short forms and different methods are used to timely obtain and properly deliver the needed material or equipment to the jobsite. Material and specific building equipment to be incorporated into the project, without jobsite labor included, are purchased under a purchase order or a "material contract."

Material Contracts

The material contract is not used by all general contractors, but when it is, it usually is used for major purchases of bulk materials, materials and equipment to be furnished to others, or equipment to be installed by the general contractor's own forces. It should be understood that the majority of general contractors in commercial construction do not furnish a great deal of labor on the jobsite, as 75 to 100 percent of the work is accomplished by subcontractors. In the area of heavy and industrial construction, some contractors accomplish the majority of the work with their own forces, including mechanical and electrical work. As an example, the installation of waste and water treatment equipment can be a competitive advantage if the general contractor has the expertise to complete this installation with its own crews. The discussion of material contracts has been placed after subcontract writing because some of the same elements can be found on the material contract. The description of the materials or equipment to be furnished is analyzed much like a subcontract scope of work, relating it to both the original quote from the vendor and the specific specification furnished by the owner.

Key elements of material contracts are the delivery articles and use of liquidated damages for late deliveries. These articles often will specify particular dates for delivery of material or equipment to the jobsite. Tied to these dates are liquidated damages for late delivery. These liquidated damages are not a penalty but rather are anticipated costs for problems caused by the late delivery of goods ordered. The contract will generally carry a clause that allows changes to be made during the submittal and shop drawing process without voiding the contract. A key element when shop drawings are involved is that the coordination between this equipment and other elements of the structure is needed. This type of contract also could be used for supply only of specialty fabricated items. This contract should include an article of compliance to all applicable laws and should define how payment will be made. Material contracts should be carefully compiled, with the advice of an attorney, and contain the correct applicable wording. While subcontracts are covered by contractual law, material contracts are covered by the Uniform Commercial Code. The subtle differences between these two areas of the law require special attention to the material contract when custom contracts are used.

Figure 10–5 is an example of a material contract used for purchase of material at a predetermined cost.

Purchase Orders

The purchase order is a control document used to define items to be ordered, the payment terms, and the quoted price; how it may be shipped or delivered; the delivery time; and the cost account for the purchase. The purchase order system generally has the following components:

- Actual purchase order number
- Link to the cost control system to allow committed costs to be entered
- Indication of who made the purchase and for which project
- Coordination of delivery slips, purchase orders, and invoices

AGC CALIFORNIA

SHORT FORM PURCHASE ORDER

Order No. ____________________

Name of Project ____________________

SELLER: ____________________

BUYER: ____________________

DELIVER TO: ____________________

DATE: ____________________

1. MATERIAL TO BE PROVIDED:

Description/ Item No.	Estimated Quantity	Unit Price	Extension*	Delivery Date

*Approximate Amount of Material Contract (Based on Estimated Quantity)

Ship to ____________________

Via ____________________ Mark ____________________

Deliver F.O.B. ____________________ With Freight Allowed to ____________________

Mail Invoices in Triplicate to ____________________

____________________ Terms ____________________

2. **PAYMENT.** The price specified shall include all taxes and duties of any kind levied by federal, state, municipal, or other governmental authority, which either party is required to pay with respect to the materials covered by this Agreement. The obligation of Buyer to make any payment hereunder is subject to the condition precedent of payment by Owner to Buyer therefor, except payments withheld by the culpable acts or omissions of Buyer.

3. **LIABILITY AND INDEMNIFICATION.** Seller assumes all risks in furnishing the material and work ordered hereunder. Seller shall be liable to Buyer and shall indemnify Buyer for any added costs, loss, damages, claims, expenses or royalties Buyer incurs as a result of, arising out of, or incurred in connection with the performance or nonperformance of this Agreement, including actual attorneys' and experts' or consultants' fees incurred in good faith, except when arising from Buyer's sole negligence.

4. **DELIVERY.** Time is of the essence of this Agreement. Should delivery for any reason fail to be timely, Seller shall be liable for all damages suffered by Buyer as a result of such failure, including, without limitation, any liquidated damages under Buyer's Prime Contract. Failure to furnish materials within the scheduled time shall give Buyer the right to cancel any undelivered balance of this order without additional charge.

© Associated General Contractors of California, Inc. 1988

Form AGCC-7
3/95

-over-

Figure 10–5 Materials Contract

Courtesy of Associated General Contractors of California, Inc.

Most contractors will use a book of purchase orders that are serialized or numbered as well as duplicates so that loose purchase orders are not floating around. The purchase order number also is a way to ensure payment to the vendor. The purchase order establishes accounting information for both the buyer and the seller. For the vendor (seller), it may indicate a credit purchase. It establishes delivery and tax information for the seller.

5.   **COMPLIANCE.** Seller's performance shall in all ways strictly conform with all applicable laws, regulations, safety orders, labor agreements and working conditions to which it is subject, including, but not limited to, all state, federal and local non-discrimination in employment provisions, and all applicable provisions required by the Prime Contract and by Buyer's own internal safety program, and all local regulations and building codes. Seller shall execute and deliver all documents as may be required to effect or evidence compliance.

6.   **COMPLIANCE WITH LICENSE LAW.** CONTRACTORS ARE REQUIRED BY LAW TO BE LICENSED AND REGULATED BY THE CONTRACTORS STATE LICENSE BOARD. ANY QUESTIONS CONCERNING A CONTRACTOR MAY BE REFERRED TO THE REGISTRAR OF THE BOARD WHOSE ADDRESS IS:

CONTRACTORS STATE LICENSE BOARD
P.O. BOX 26000
SACRAMENTO, CALIFORNIA 95826

7.   **BONDS OR INSURANCE.** Seller shall furnish one of the following to Buyer as required:

Supply Bond in an amount specified by Buyer (choose one)
__ The premium for the bond will be paid by Buyer
__ The premium for the bond is included in the price of this Agreement

Insurance in amount and type specified by Buyer; the specifications and policies are hereby incorporated by reference (choose one)
__ The premium for the insurance will be paid by Buyer
__ The cost of insurance is included in the price of this Agreement

8.   **TERMINATION.** Buyer may terminate or suspend at its convenience all or any portion of this Agreement not shipped as of the date of termination or suspension of this Agreement. Seller shall receive payment for work actually performed. Seller shall not be entitled to any recovery on account of profit or unabsorbed overhead with respect to work not actually performed or on account of future work, as of the date of termination or suspension. No termination or suspension shall relieve Buyer or Seller of any of their obligations as to any material shipped prior to Seller's receipt of the termination or suspension order.

If Seller fails to perform any obligation under this Agreement, Buyer may terminate this order for default. In the event of a termination for default, Buyer may, in addition to all other rights and remedies, purchase substitute items or services elsewhere and hold Seller liable for any and all excess costs incurred, including attorneys' fees and experts' and consultants' fees actually incurred.

9.   **ATTORNEYS' FEES.** In the event either party becomes involved in litigation or arbitration in which the services of an attorney or other expert are reasonably required arising out of this Agreement or its performance, or nonperformance, the prevailing party shall be fully compensated for the cost of its participation in such proceedings, including the cost incurred for attorneys' fees and experts' fees. Unless judgment goes by default, the attorneys' fee award shall not be computed in accordance with any court schedule but shall be such as to fully reimburse all attorneys' fees actually incurred in good faith. California law shall apply to all disputes arising out of this Agreement or its performance or nonperformance.

We acknowledge receipt of, and accept Purchaser's order: This order is hereby approved:

_____   _____
SELLER   BUYER

By _____   By _____

Title _____   Title _____

Date _____   Date _____

Contractor's License Number: _____   Contractor's License Number: _____
       (If Required)   (If Required)

NOTE: Before execution, users should insure that this form meets their specific needs. Some construction material procurement agreements may require the use of specialized provisions not included in this form. This document has important legal consequences; users are encouraged to consult with an attorney with respect to its use or modification.

AGC
CALIFORNIA   -2-

Figure 10–5   Materials Contract (*Continued*)

Purchase orders also can be used to establish a fixed unit price when the order quantity is not yet determined or when multiple deliveries are needed. Lumber for concrete formwork often is ordered this way. As businesses become more computerized, linking specific purchases to potential claims, changes can be accomplished without much effort, which allows the estimator to review costs in more detail. Figure 10–6 is an example of a purchase order for a construction project.

Purchase Order

VENDOR: _____

_____

_____

_____

Purchase Order No. _____

All Invoices, Correspondence,

Packages, Etc. must carry P.O. No.

SHIP TO: _____

_____

_____

_____

To Be Delivered _____   Picked Up _____

(Shipping Terms) _____

FOB Above Address _____

Freight Collect

Delivery Required By:	P.O. Date	Terms	This P.O. is:		
			Original		
			Confirmation Only		

Quantity Ordered	Unit	Description (note: Subject to terms & conditions on Reverse Side)	Cost Code	Unit Price	Total Amount

Total Cost _____

Remarks:

Note: Send all invoices to:

Shipping Address _____

Home Office Address _____

Address Shown Below:

_____

_____

FGH CONSTRUCTION COMPANY, INC.

By: _____

_____

5390 Walnut Avenue, San Francisco, California, 93422-0027
Phone: (415)555-2346, Fax: (415)555-2300

Figure 10–6   Example of a Purchase Order

Expediting and Tracking Material and Equipment

The use of material contracts and purchase orders helps the general contractor expedite critical equipment and materials. Expediting can be defined as the tracking, the confirming, and/or the accelerating of delivery of an item that has been purchased. When purchasing is done from a central or home office, expediting is part of the purchasing agent's job description. When purchasing is site based, the project engineer may track and expedite the items. If a company uses a central purchasing method, it never completely moves away from incidentals being purchased by the jobsite. Some firms believe that central purchasing provides the company with greater control and a broader number of vendors' quotes from which to choose, thus giving the contractor opportunity for a better price. Figure 10–7 shows an equipment tracking or expediting form used for guaranteeing delivery of equipment on time.

Creston, California
WATER TREATMENT PLANT
EQUIPMENT AND MATERIAL EXPEDITING FORM

Qty.	Equip./ Material desig.	Description	Mfg.	Spec. Section	Supplier	Contact	Phone Number	Lead Time (Wks.)	CPM Scheduled Date	Revised Date	Submittal Date	Received Date

Figure 10–7   Equipment and Material Expediting Form

Summary

Subcontracts, material contracts, and purchase orders are all used to control the cost of the project and work flow as defined by the schedule. All parts of project management are tied to one another. The way the subcontract is written, its scope for the subcontractor, and its general conditions all relate to the way the project manager and superintendent will accomplish the work on time, within the budget, and at the required quality. The use of a subcontract gives all parties a better understanding of what is expected and helps the general contractor manage the project more effectively.

Subcontractors are used extensively in construction projects primarily to do the following:

- Enhance project quality

- Reduce cost through specialization

- Reduce risk for the contractor

The subcontract agreement, the agreement between the contractor and the subcontractor, contains the following attributes:

- Based on the bid and subsequent negotiations with the subcontractor

- Standard forms are often used for the contract form

- Careful scope definition is necessary

- Remedies for problems are contained in the agreement

Subcontractor management by the contractor is necessary in the management of a successful project. Some areas of concern for subcontractor management include the following:

- Coordination meetings

- Scheduling work activities

- Submittal control

- Administering changes in the work

- Quality control

- Payment control, including back charges and withheld payments

- Coordination of work activities among subcontractors

- Safety and waste management

Control also is necessary in the purchase of material and equipment. Purchase orders and material contracts are used to do the following:

- Control costs

- Report costs to the appropriate project activities

- Control delivery of material

Additionally, the tracking of material and equipment is necessary in controlling purchases and rentals for the construction project.

Review Questions

1. Name the four factors that the field personnel should understand about each subcontractor.

2. In the past, general contractors used subcontractors only to perform specialized tasks. What are current-day general contractors doing differently in this area?

3. Why are subcontractors used on construction projects?

4. Define the term *purchasing* and explain how it differs from subcontracting.

5. What is the major risk the general contractor tries to avoid by subcontracting work?

6. Define "bid shopping" and state the consequences to the subcontractor.

7. List the major articles or areas that a subcontract should contain.

8. What are the major keys to successful subcontract management, and why is it considered so important?

9. Why would a contractor "back charge" a subcontractor?

10. What is the major difference between a subcontract, a material contract, and a purchase order?

Chapter 11

Project Quality Management

This chapter discusses quality—its definition, its relationship to the overall success of the project, and the methods to implement continuous improvement plans. The objectives of this chapter are:

- Explain quality as a key component to a successful project
- Illustrate quality as it relates to construction
- List the typical elements needed for quality management programs
- Explain the concept of total quality management
- Identify the essential points a company must integrate into quality program as defined by Dr. W. Edwards Deming
- Write a quality management plan
- Prepare a flowchart of the building permit process

The construction industry often defines *quality* as conformance to standards and specifications. In current quality management terminology, though, quality is defined as *meeting or exceeding the customer's expectations*. We assume that the construction documents express the customer's expectations, but we probably need to go further to satisfy the customer. For instance, the construction documents may call for certain models of door closers on doors in the building. There is a wide range of adjustment on those closers that will slowly to quickly close the door. The customer will need to have the door adjusted to their level of use. The contractor needs to determine the tension that will satisfy the customer's needs. Satisfying the customer is one of the goals of the project; however, we sometimes lose that perspective while trying only to satisfy specifications and standards. Satisfied customers are often repeat customers.

Quality is not related to price. A relatively low-priced item can be installed in a high-quality manner when that item is installed properly in accordance with the manufacturer's recommended procedures and it functions as intended. High-quality work does not have to be reworked or repaired. The intent of a quality program is to provide work that is done correctly the first time. This work not only satisfies the customer but also is optimally produced, resulting in the minimal cost.

Many contractual relationships emphasize quality assurance/quality controls (QA/QC). Quality assurance normally refers to a plan to achieve quality, and quality control refers to inspection, testing, and necessary remediation. QA/QC is currently being included in the broader term of **quality management**. Quality management is the continuing plan of the contractor to provide quality work in every phase of the project. A quality culture develops within the company from the top to the bottom, providing high-quality work throughout the company.

For several years, other industries have been actively involved in quality management programs, such as total quality management, ISO-9000, and Six Sigma. Although some construction firms have adopted extensive quality management programs, the construction industry generally has been slow to embrace quality-oriented cultures. Pressure from customers has forced the construction industry to improve its level of quality management. Contractors are realizing that they need to do more than simply comply with building codes to satisfy their customers.

Defining Quality in the Construction Process

The three primary elements of a construction project are cost, time, and quality. All three of these elements are interdependent on each other. If there is pressure to keep cost down, quality may be impacted. If there is considerable time pressure, both cost and quality will be impacted. Figure 11–1 indicates the interdependency of these three elements.

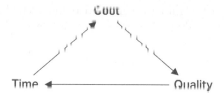

Figure 11–1   Relationship of
Cost, Quality, and Time in the
Construction Project

Some contractors will say that they can optimize two of the three parameters, but the third will suffer. For instance, if the project is built in a compressed time frame and high-quality work is maintained, then the cost of the project will increase. Current thought asserts that all three goals can be met, because quality can be obtained through efficiency. If the work is done correctly the first time, then cost and time will be optimized as well. Unusual time, cost, or quality restraints will have a definite impact on the other two goals.

We must realize that "meeting the customer's expectations" may not always be within the constructors' control. The constructor assumes that the plans and specifications reflect the customer's expectations. In practice, though, the design and resulting construction documents may not exactly express the customer's expectations but rather may express the designer's expectations. In contractual situations where the contractor is involved in the design phase, such as construction management or design-build, the contractor may have more of a role in ensuring that the product meets the customer's needs and expectations.

Total Quality Management

Total quality management is a process of bringing quality to the construction project. The quality of a construction project is the product of innovation, quality improvement, and productivity improvement, implemented by an involved and responsible workforce. The construction industry has always been involved in this; however, the industry has depended on decisions from strong leadership rather than involving employees at all levels to participate in improving the quality of the product and process. The contractor can achieve a strong total quality management program that involves employees in improving the product. The measure of success of a quality management program is customer satisfaction. The continued success of the contractor is directly related to this.

Total quality management should create opportunities for improvement in construction methods, processes, and the delivery of the product to the customer. It should also provide a process for continuing development of these opportunities in the construction project. The workforce, field management, and company management need to be committed to providing a high-quality product to the customer.

The concept of total quality management comes from the work and leadership of the late Dr. W. Edwards Deming, whose formula for a company's business success is based on the relationship between improved quality and improved productivity. A successful project, then, would have the following elements:

• Installations executed properly, one time only

• Teamwork among project participants, including field management, skilled craftspeople, and subcontractors

• Commitment of all who are involved to accomplish the task as efficiently as possible

• Recognition of the quality of the project by the customer and potential customers, ultimately resulting in increased sales

The advantages of total quality management and continuous improvement of construction may be difficult to see in the short term—it may seem like adding costs without benefit. Construction owners, however, recognize the quality of the construction product and firms that are committed to satisfying their customers. These owners select construction firms that make their needs and the quality of the project top priorities.

The training and skill of the workforce is an important element of total quality management. The construction employer should train its employees in the quality installation of materials and systems, if the employee is not already so trained. Trade unions offer employees apprenticeship programs where they can acquire the necessary skills. Continuing training is necessary for employees to keep them aware of changes in products and techniques. It also aids in achieving increased quality in the construction project.

The process of continuous improvement or the total quality management process generally is defined by six broad steps:

1. Make suggestions for areas of improvement
2. Break down into parts and provide measurement tools
3. Create solutions to the suggestions
4. Implement and observe the solutions at work
5. Acknowledge the individuals and award their ingenuity
6. Incorporate the solutions on a broad scale

To implement the continuous improvement process, management, staff, and individual employees must understand the building blocks that constitute quality. These blocks include the following:

- Construction work activities made up of smaller components
- Quality defined by client satisfaction
- Elimination of rework and mistakes achieved by prevention
- Quality measured by attaching costs
- Quality improvement pertaining to productivity
- Quality improvement through individual commitment and teamwork

Deming lists the essential points a company must integrate into its system to become successful in total quality management:

- Create consistency of purpose to improve product and service (plan to stay in business)
- Adopt the new philosophy (stop tolerating poor quality)
- Cease dependence on inspection to achieve quality (improve the process)
- End the practice of awarding business on the basis of price tag alone (seek longer-term supplier relationships and reduce the number of suppliers)
- Constantly devise and implement improvements for every process in the systems of planning, production, and service
- Institute modern training (for everybody)
- Institute modern methods of supervision (the responsibility of foremen must be changed from sheer numbers to *quality*)
- Drive out fear (encourage employees to speak up)
- Break down barriers between departments

- Eliminate slogans, exhortations, and targets for the workforce

- Remove barriers to pride in workmanship (poor supervisors, poor materials, inadequate equipment, lack of training, and so on)

- Institute a vigorous program of education and self improvement for everyone

- Require commitment by all employees to accomplish the transformation and create a structure of top management that will stress the use of the aforementioned points

Some of Deming's essential points do not pertain to methods used by the construction industry in its business, but the majority of them can be applied when put into the context of an overall quality strategy, which begins with the management of the organization committing to a process of high-quality work attitudes and business practices. Training, the creation of vision and mission statements, and adherence to a high-quality principle are all elements to the implementation of a quality strategy. Surveys should be employed among customers and employees concerning their reactions and thoughts pertaining to quality. Teamwork and commitment are first provided by the establishment of continuous improvement groups. Quality improvement suggestions must be implemented, and outside subcontractors and suppliers must be brought into the process. If the company creates a continuous improvement plan toward quality, the process will continue to expand and work.

The Quality Plan

To achieve a successful quality management program, upper management needs to commit the entire organization to concentrating on the quality of the construction product. Once upper management decides that a quality emphasis is necessary to sustain the company's operations currently and into the future, the company can obtain quality management program goals and develop a plan for implementing those goals. Without full and continued upper-management support and commitment, the program will be short lived, without producing measurable quality gains.

The goal of the program should concentrate on continually and consistently improving the quality of the constructed product. Some objectives of the quality management program could be the following:

- Increasing and maintaining customer satisfaction with the construction work

- Decreasing defects in the construction work

- Decreasing the amount of warranty repair

- Maintaining quality work consistently from project to project and crew to crew

- Obtaining efficiency in the construction work and consistently "doing it right the first time"

These objectives need to be clearly defined initially. The objectives need to relate to what the plan is intended to accomplish. The objectives need to be realistically examined to see if success can be realistically achieved with those objectives. Objectives also need to be defined that can be measured in some way to determine if success has been achieved. Each of the objectives needs to be matched with a measurement method. For instance, if "decreasing the amount of warranty repair" is established as an objective, then establishing the current amount of warranty repair and tracking the number of valid warranty repair calls in the future will be needed. If the number of calls and, accordingly, the amount of cost of warranty calls decreases, then it can be inferred that some success in meeting that objective was achieved.

The quality management program uses a continuous "Plan–Do–Check–Act" methodology for implementation of the quality management program, as shown in Figure 11–2. The use of this program is a continual cycle, applying lessons learned as it progresses.

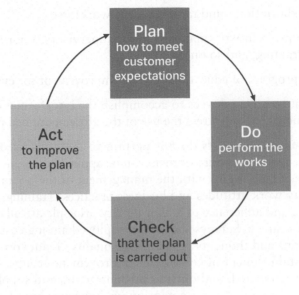

Figure 11–2   Plan-Do-Check-Act
Methodology

The **Plan** phase includes the full plan for the company program as well as the plan for the particular project's quality management. The company quality management plan should be a detailed written plan that covers the following areas:

- Company commitment to the quality management plan

- Establishment of a quality director and/or quality committee. The quality director is often from operations but can be any individual within the company that can lead an effective quality management program. Typically, the quality director or manager adds the quality management position to one's current position in the company.

- Definition of quality responsibilities throughout the company structure. All management positions and field labor positions should have responsibilities within the quality management program that need to be defined within the written plan/manual.

- Management of the quality management program. The plan should address the process of the quality management program within the company and its interaction with company participants.

- Identification of relevant requirements, codes, and standards for the work. Construction has many sources of directions for the correct materials and methods of installation. This information can be found in federal, state, and local regulations; building codes; project construction documents; industry standards; manufacturer's recommendations; and company standards. It is important to identify these criteria and train the crews to meet the applicable standards.

- Identification of materials needed for the construction work, their source of supply, and control of the material to provide a quality installation. This includes procedures for inspection and control of purchased material.

- Procedures for subcontractors to comply with the quality management program. Subcontractors are responsible for a large portion of the work and need to be involved with the quality management program. Consistent procedures for subcontractor quality management should be specified.

- Procedures for assuring that subcontractors have the proper conditions for the optimal execution of their work, such as job-ready conditions, environmental conditions, and jobsite access.

- Identification of labor classifications necessary for the work, including jobsite leadership of the work.

- Identification of labor attributes necessary for the work, such as training, experience, and certifications.

- Formulation of a method to correlate employees with the necessary training, experience, and certifications and to ensure that all employees are current with the necessary requirements. Ensure that documentation of this compliance is kept and updated.

- Determination of inspections for material delivery, job-ready conditions, work in progress, completion, and punch list.

- Plan for remediation of defects prior to completion of the project.

- Formulation of a continuous improvement plan, including identification of areas to improve, training of applicable personnel, and confirmation of effective application.

- Determination of the relative success of the program by using measurable indicators, such as the number of zero-item code inspections and the number of valid warranty calls.

- Procedures for regular audit of the success and use of the quality management program at jobsites by the quality program manager.

- Procedures for an annual audit of the quality management program with upper management, including analysis of the success of the program and the plan to improve the plan for the next year.

The plan phase will also include implementation of several of the elements of the company's quality management plan. This area includes implementation of identifying applicable standards, training of the crew, and ensuring that the material and subcontracts meet the standards.

The **Do** phase involves doing the work efficiently and "right the first time," applying the principles in the quality management plan.

The **Check** phase involves inspection of the work and the necessary repair of defective work prior to turning over the project to the customer. Inspection of the work needs to be done by a knowledgeable individual with authority within the firm. Use of a simple checklist form containing major elements of the installation facilitates these inspections. Inspection needs to be made at the completion of every installation.

The **Act** phase includes continuous improvement and the evaluation of the entire program. Continuous improvement can be done in many ways. One continuous program involves identification of currently occurring defects from the inspection forms coupled with training to all applicable employees on the correct method of installation. By addressing one defect per month, the contractor can effectively address many defects in a short period of time.

During the Act phase, the contractor needs to analyze the effectiveness of their program and address the weaknesses of the program. By analyzing measurable indicators of the success of the program, the contractor can show justification for the program while identifying areas for increased concentration.

Example of Specialty Contractor Quality Management

Assume that a specialty contractor has realized that they have received a large number of repair calls from new work recently completed. These maintenance calls cost an average of about $500 per each and are assumed by the company under warranty. Company management had always assumed that as their employees were trained craftsmen, they completed high-quality and acceptable work. The company had never had a specific quality management program. Because quality seemed to be the problem with excessive warranty items, they found a quality management program sponsored by a local contractor's association.

As profits were negatively affected, the company president became involved in the process of implementing a quality management program. Despite that an additional effort would be necessary to implement an effective quality program, it would save money and help the company's reputation. The company president heartily endorsed the new quality management program, and empowered a group of project managers to form and implement an effective quality management program.

The first step was to identify all codes, instructions, regulations, manufacturer's recommendations, specifications, and company standards relative to their frequent tasks and contracts. Appropriate material, fasteners, and equipment need to be identified. Skills, training, and certificates also needed to be identified for the installations. Management needed to identify how the crew related to these requirements, and form the appropriate crews for quality installation. Crews needed to be trained according to standards, materials, equipment, and methods for their installation on the jobsite.

Typically, specialty contractors accomplish most of the actual work on a construction project. The general contractor can also use the above planning for their own work on the jobsite. The optimum quality management program becomes a culture on the jobsite, and all contractors and subcontractors need to participate.

The next phase of the quality management process is to check if the work was done properly. This inspection is based on the standards and requirements established for the installation. Typically, the most complete inspection is accomplished by a third party rather than the individual involved in the installation. Sometimes, the foreman will do the inspection, but it is usually more thorough if done by a third-party inspector. Repair of the defect is done immediately. After each inspection, the defects are recorded to determine the most prevalent ones. The entire crew should receive training on the problem areas, thus eliminating the problem company-wide.

The company then needs to act on its findings. Foremen should emphasize items that have been used for the in-progress training. At the end of the year, management needs to determine the cost or savings of the quality management program. Upper management is interested in results: fewer warranty calls, less cost in installations, and greater customer satisfaction. One of the challenges of this program, similar to all new programs, is to keep it going after the initial trial.

The Jobsite Quality Control Team

Prior to the start of the project, quality control responsibilities need to be assigned. Some projects, such as federal projects, may require that a full-time quality control engineer be assigned to the project. This position needs to recognize, along with a list of responsibilities for that position, what is relevant to specification and jobsite requirements.

Quality control responsibilities often are allocated to superintendents, assistant superintendents, engineers, and field engineers in addition to their other responsibilities. Their role in quality control should be explicitly expressed and related to their assigned activities. A checklist of specific project quality concerns can be used as part of this assignment. Figure 11–3 shows an example of a quality control assignment and checklist for concrete work.

The primary objectives of quality control assignments are to do the following:

- Avoid duplication of effort

- Ensure that every quality aspect is covered

- Provide a clear delineation of responsibilities

- Provide effective guidance on the project to achieve quality work

- Provide documentation of materials, installation, and tests

Organization of the quality control effort before the project starts is essential for comprehensive quality control throughout the project.

Quality Control Checklist
Concrete

Project: City Hall Renovations, Springfield, CA

QC Assignment: Fred Smith, Field Engineer

Submittals:
- Request, Submit, Approve Mix Designs:
  - 3,000 psi
  - 4,000 psi
    - Standard
    - Exposed Aggregate
    - Colored (Red)
  - 5,000 psi
  - 6,000 psi

- Request, Submit, Approve Rebar Packages:
  - Footings, Foundations
  - Tilt-up Panels
  - Elevated Slabs

- Miscellaneous Product Submittals:
  - Sealer
  - Expansion Joint material
  - Water stop

General:
- Receive Concrete tickets from drivers, file
- Receive, organize, chart test results for cylinder breaks
- Organize rebar—keep cut sheets and drawings for each area
- Integrate material handling with safety talks
- MSDS on jobsite for:
  - Concrete
  - Form oil
  - Sealers
- Provide training in proper concrete procedures as necessary.

Footings:
- Assure compaction in trenches
- Dewater footing trenches—Do not pour in standing water
- Assure no frost in footing subgrade
- Forms to level and square
- Assure proper placement of reinforcing
- Assure ease of concrete placement
- Pour within temperature parameters: 40 deg. F to 80 deg. F
- Order trucks with sufficient time between trucks
- Assure imbeds and dowels are placed in correct locations

Figure 11–3   Partial Concrete Quality Control Checklist

Testing and Inspection

Both testing and inspection are required by most contracts to protect the owner, public, architect, and contractors. The inspection process should be done by independent agencies outside of the contract process to avoid any vested interest. Inspection and testing, if they are done correctly, will bring an unbiased review of the installation and product requirements. Inspections and tests must occur at many steps during the contractual process. Materials that are mass manufactured may not have specified testing or quality control by field personnel, but in all cases, some form of in-house or outside testing and quality control has been performed at the manufacturing plant. Many products require labels from institutes or other agencies, such as Underwriters Laboratories labels on electrical devices to show conformance to product standards and federal regulations.

Most projects are subject to inspection by the local code authority or building inspector. Most municipalities or local jurisdictions have plan review personnel, as well as field inspectors, in their offices. The building inspector's main task is the enforcement of local building codes. Each municipality or local code authority has its own building code, which is normally based on a standard code. These building codes have been established, written, and continuously updated by national or regional code organizations. The primary building codes currently used in the United States are the International Building Code and the International Residential Code. Other codes apply in mechanical, electrical, energy, and life safety areas. Some of the codes used for these areas are state energy codes, state indoor ventilation and air quality codes, the Uniform Plumbing Code, the International Mechanical Code, the National Electric Code, the International Fire Code, the International Fuel Gas Code, and Liquefied Petroleum Code. All of these codes are periodically updated and revised.

Additional codes are incorporated into local building codes, such as access requirements (American Disability Act/ADA standards), zoning ordinances, health codes, and other regulations that protect the environment, safety, and health of the general public.

Building codes are written to protect the environment, health, life, and safety of the public. Other types of codes to protect the public include hospital, fire and fire suppression, restaurant health, and other specialized inspection areas. The building inspector is concerned with the general design, structural stability, and construction of a building. The first step in ensuring compliance to building codes is submitting plans for a plan check. If the building is a mixed-use facility with many complicated or specialized functions, the designer will work with the city's or county's planning and zoning department, as well as the building department, throughout the initial design. The plan check fee and permit fee can be paid by the owner prior to beginning the work, or they can be included in the cost responsibilities of the contractor. Figure 11–4 is an example of typical building permit fees. Fees for the plan check normally are in addition to the basic permit fee. Many cities have cited higher costs in inspection and plan review and have enacted higher building permit fees. But these are not the only costs incurred in obtaining the permit; many jurisdictions today impose other fees to pay for the costs of increasing city infrastructure, such as school fees, floodplain fees, and road and bridge fees.

Often code compliance changes are required by the plan check. If this is completed prior to signing a contract with the general contractor, it will allow the owner time to have these items priced and incorporated into the contract before the main contract is signed, which eliminates the need for a change order the first day of the project. As one of the first requirements of the project, an official stamped set of plans must be kept on the jobsite for use by the inspector while the inspection is made. Figure 11–5 is a typical flowchart for the building permit process.

Figure 11–6 illustrates an example of a building permit that has been issued after the application and review have been completed. Figure 11–7 shows a sample jobsite inspection card.

The building inspector can use two additional inspection forms. One is the Correction Notice, shown in Figure 11–8, and the other is the Stop Work Notice, shown in Figure 11–9. In some instances, the on-site inspection record will provide space for correction comments, but the larger Correction Notice provides a more detailed comment area for noting necessary corrections. In most cases, a correction notice is issued, unless the correction is life threatening or the correction requires immediate action. The Stop Work Notice is used when public safety is threatened. If the work being performed is outside the permit, the Stop Work Notice also is used.

Total Valuation	Fee
$1.00 to $500.00	$23.50
$501.00 to $2,000.00	$23.50 for the first $500.00 plus $3.50 for each additional $100.00, or fraction thereof, to and including $2,000.00
$2,001.00 to $25,000.00	$69.25 for the first $2,000.00 plus $14.00 for each additional $1,000.00, or fraction thereof, to and including $25,000.00
$25,001.00 to $50,000.00	$391.75 for the first $25,000.00 plus $10.10 for each additional $1,000.00, or fraction thereof, to and including $50,000.00
$50,001.00 to $100,000.00	$643.75 for the first $50,000.00 plus $7.00 for each additional $1,000.00, or fraction thereof, to and including $100,000.00
$100,001.00 to $500,000.00	$993.75 for the first $100,000.00 plus $5.60 for each additional $1,000.00, or fraction thereof, to and including $500,000.00
$500,001.00 to $1,000,000.00	$3,233.75 for the first $500,000.00 plus $4.75 for each additional $1,000.00, or fraction thereof, to and including $1,000,000.00
$1,000,001.00 and up	$5,608.75 for the first $1,000,000.00 plus $3.65 for each additional $1,000.00, or fraction thereof

Other Inspections and Fees:

1. Inspections outside of normal business hours .... $47.00 per hour[1]
   (minimum charge—two hours)
2. Reinspection fees assessed under provisions of Section 305.8. .... $47.00 per hour[1]
3. Inspections for which no fee is specifically indicated .... $47.00 per hour[1]
   (minimum charge—one-half hour)
4. Additional plan review required by changes, additions or revisions to plans .... $47.00 per hour[1]
   (minimum charge—one-half hour)
5. For use of outside consultants for plan checking and inspections, or both .... Actual costs[2]

[1] Or the total hourly cost to the jurisdiction, whichever is the greatest. This cost shall include supervision, overhead, equipment, hourly wages, and fringe benefits of the employees involved.

[2] Actual costs include administrative and overhead costs.

Figure 11–4   Typical Building Permit Fees

Reproduced from the 1997 edition of the Uniform Building CodeTM copyright © 1997, with permission of the publisher, The International Conference of Building Officials

The following list summarizes the most important aspects of the building inspector's responsibilities:

- Inspectors are trained personnel in the specific area of inspection.

- Inspectors are independent and do not enjoy any type of gain from their decisions.

- Inspectors do not direct the contractor.

- Inspectors must make decisions regarding conformance to specifications or codes.

- Inspectors can accept or reject work.

Other areas of compliance used by the outside inspecting agency, owner's representative, or project architect are codes and applicable laws, standards, and manufacturers' literature and recommendations. The building code is only one of many codes that may be part of the specifications. Some areas have adopted seismic standards that are not included in the building codes. Federal programs and laws such as the Americans with Disabilities Act, the

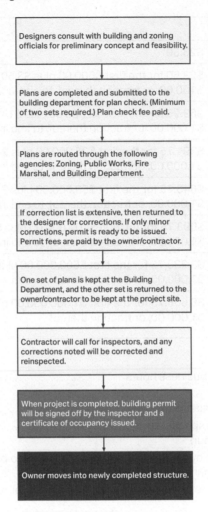

Designers consult with building and zoning officials for preliminary concept and feasibility.

Plans are completed and submitted to the building department for plan check. (Minimum of two sets required.) Plan check fee paid.

Plans are routed through the following agencies: Zoning, Public Works, Fire Marshal, and Building Department.

If correction list is extensive, then returned to the designer for corrections. If only minor corrections, permit is ready to be issued. Permit fees are paid by the owner/contractor.

One set of plans is kept at the Building Department, and the other set is returned to the owner/contractor to be kept at the project site.

Contractor will call for inspectors, and any corrections noted will be corrected and reinspected.

When project is completed, building permit will be signed off by the inspector and a certificate of occupancy issued.

Owner moves into newly completed structure.

Figure 11–5   **Flowchart of the Building Permit Process**

Occupational Safety and Health Act, and regulations set by the Environmental Protection Agency are among a few additional requirements that must be followed. Most specifications reference explicit standards to be used as guidelines for inspections, comparisons to the norm, testing methods, and other foundations needed for inspecting. The list of reference standards and testing agencies is long, the most common being the American Society for Testing and Materials (ASTM), American Concrete Institute (ACI), and the Underwriters Laboratories (UL) label. Additionally, some specifications reference other specification standards, such as the Federal Specifications, Military Specifications (MIL specs.), and American Association of State Highway and Transportation Officials (AASHTO). Figure 11–10 is an example of specification language used to reference associations and their standard methods of installation and other quality standards.

Other field testing that may be required by the building department or specifications falls within the category of special inspections, which requires employment of an independent testing company by either the owner or the contractor. Typical specification language could read as shown in Figure 11–11.

City of Pullman, CA
Construction Permit

Permit Number: _____

Project Address _____   Date Received: _____
Legal Description _____   Date Issued: _____
Assessor's Parcel No. _____   Zone: _____ Lot Area: _____

Contractor/Builder/Owner	_____	Arch./Engr./Designer	_____
Address (Mailing)	_____	Address (Mailing)	_____
(City/State/Zip)	_____	(City/State/Zip)	_____
License No.	_____	License No.	_____
Phone	_____	Phone	_____

Project Description: _____
_____
_____

Valuation: _____

Fees: **Requirements/Conditions:**

Building Permit   _____   _____
Plumbing Permit   _____   _____
HVAC Permit   _____   _____
Electrical Permit   _____   _____
Grading Permit   _____   _____
Demolition Permit   _____   _____
Sign Permit   _____   _____
       Subtotal: _____   _____
Building Plan Check   _____   _____
Fire Safety Plan Check _____   _____
       Subtotal: _____   _____
Water Impact   _____   _____
Water Meter Installation _____   _____
Wastewater Impact   _____   _____
School Assessment   _____   _____
Flood Assessment   _____   _____
       Subtotal: _____   _____
Total Fee: _____   _____
Paid to Date: _____   _____
Balance Due: _____   _____

I have read and signed the "Owner Builder," "Workers Compensation Declaration," and the "Certificate Of Exemption From Workers Compensation Insurance."

Notice to Applicant:

If, after making any of the foregoing declarations, you become subject to any Labor Code or License Law provision, you must comply with such provisions or this permit shall be deemed revoked. I certify that I have read this application and state that the above information is correct. I agree to comply with all city ordinances and state laws relating to building construction and hereby authorize representatives of this city to enter upon the above-mentioned property for inspection purposes. Unless noted under "Requirements/Conditions," this permit will become null and void if work or construction authorized is not started within 180 days, or if construction or work is suspended or abandoned for a period of 180 days any time after work is commenced. A new permit will be then required to proceed with the work.

Signature   _____   Date   _____
Printed Name   _____   Receipt No. _____

Figure 11–6   Example Building Permit

City of Pullman, CA

| Building Division: | 533-8956 | Permit No. | _____ |
| Inspection Requests: | 533-8900 | Date Issued | _____ |

Notice: Inspectors Available: 8 - 8:30 a.m. 533 - 8958

Address of Project: _____

Type of Project:

Building	New ( )	Add. ( )	Alteration ( )	Repair ( )
Electrical	( )			
HVAC	( )			
Plumbing	( )			
Change of Occupancy ( )				
Other ( )	_____			

| Contractor/Building | Phone Number | License Number |
| Arch./Engr./Designer | Phone Number | License Number |

Project Description: _____
_____
_____

| Legal Description | Assessor No. | Zone | Lot Area |

Front Side of Card

SITE		ROUGH INSPECTIONS		SPECIAL REQUIREMENTS		
Grading		Roof Nailing		Description	Yes	Received
U'Grd. Utilities		Framing		Soils/compaction Report		
Septic/Sewer		Wiring		Rough Grading Verified		
Setbacks		Drain/Waste/Vent		Height & Setback Verified		
FOUNDATIONS		Water		Engineered Septic		
Footings		Gas		Special Inspection		
Piers		HVAC		Truss Plan		
Stem/Pad		Shear Nailing		Encroachment		
Hold Downs		Framing Hdwr.		Final Grading Verified		
Garage/Slab		Fireplace		Temporary Power		
RETAINING WALLS		**INSULATION**		Utility Agreement		
Footings		Underfloor				
Steel		Walls				
Drains		Ceiling				
Final		Other				
UNDER SLAB		**SURFACE COVERING**		**OCCUPANCY APPROVAL**		
Drain/Waste/Vent		Lath		Building (Temporary)		
Water		Drywall		Planning		
Gas				Public Works		
HVAC				Fire		
MISC.		**POOLS & SPAS**		Health		
Hood		Pre-Gunite		Police		
Suspended Ceilings		Pre-Deck		Electrical (REL)		
Shower Pan		Pre-Plaster		Gas (REL)		
Gas Test		Fence				
Sewer Lateral						
Sprinklers						
Misc.						

Back Side of Card

Figure 11–7   Jobsite Inspection Card

City of San Pullman, California
Building Department

CORRECTION NOTICE

Project Address: *5962 J street*

I have this day inspected this structure and these premises and have found the following violations of city and/or state laws governing same:

Platform for Hot water tank needs to be raised to the required height of 18" and seismic strap installed around tank.

When corrections have been made, please call for re-inspection

Date *6/13/2026*   Inspector *Bill Jones*

DO NOT REMOVE THIS TAG

Figure 11–8   Example Correction Notice

City of San Pullman, California
Building Department

STOP WORK
Notice

Address: *5962 J street*

This building has been inspected and

Your building appears to encroach into the setback shown on your site plan

is found to be in non-conformance and is not acceptable. All work is to stop and corrections immediately made. Before proceeding call *634-9222* This a serious issue and must be addressed directly with our office.

Date *6/13/2026*   Inspector *Bill Jones*

DO NOT REMOVE THIS NOTICE

Figure 11–9   Example Stop Work Notice

SECTION 00800
STANDARDS AND ABBREVIATIONS

Part 1 - General

1.01 Description

The list below represents standards and abbreviations used in the Drawing and Project Manual. These standards to be incorporated into these documents by name are given for the contractor's use in providing installation and quality standards for the contractor's work. When in conflict with the project manual, the project manual will govern.

Part 2 - Manufacturer, Associations, Institutes, and Standard Abbreviations

Aluminum Association, Inc.	AA
American Arbitration Association	AAA
Brick Institute of America	BIA
Metal Building Manufacturers Association	MBMA

....

End of Section 0800

Figure 11–10 Standards and Abbreviations, Example Specification Section

---

SECTION 01410
TESTING LABORATORY SERVICES

Part 1 - General
1.01 Work Included
    A. Work includes but is not limited to the following:
        1. Inspection and testing required by laws, ordinances, rules, regulations, orders, or approvals of public authorities: See conditions of the Contract.
    B. On-site monitoring and Laboratory and Field tests required and standards for testing:
        1. See requirements specified in this section and other Specification Sections throughout the Project Manual.
1.02 Related Work
    A. Coordinated related work ....
    B. Owner will employ and pay for an Independent Testing Laboratory or Laboratories to perform inspection and testing services specified herein unless otherwise noted.
        1. Contractor's cooperation with the Laboratory is required to facilitate their required services.
        2. Employment of a Laboratory does not relieve Contractor's obligations to perform any contract work and any other testing as required/deemed necessary to meet proper performance standards.
        3. In general, test requirement for individual section is found in Part 3 - Execution of specification section.
1.3 Quality Assurance
1.4 References
1.5 Duties of Laboratory:
1.6 Contractor's Responsibilities
    A. Cooperate with engineering and laboratory personnel; provide access to work, and to manufacturer's operations.
    B. Secure and deliver to laboratory adequate quantities of representational samples of proposed materials.
    C. Provide to Laboratory:
        etc.
1.7 Tests, Inspections, and Methods required
1.8 Identification of Asbestos Materials

End of Section 01410

Figure 11–11 Testing Laboratory Service, Example Specification Section

Areas that normally require outside laboratory and inspection services include the following.

- Soil testing: compliance to compaction density requirements (an example of a typical specification section showing soil testing requirements is illustrated in Figure 11–12)

- Concrete testing: slump, cylinder compressive strength

- Reinforcing steel placement: confirmation of placement locations

- Welding testing/inspection: visual, X-ray testing

- Bolt torque: tested torque on example bolts

- Aggregate testing: hardness, material composition

- Asphalt testing: mix design, strength

- Layout and vertical alignment (an example of a specification section for layout requirements is shown in Figure 11–13)

".......... 5. Soils Consultant and Soil Testing

A. The Contractor.

B. It is essential that subgrade preparation and compaction of fill be performed carefully and in accordance with the plans and specifications; failure by the Contractor to perform site preparation work properly could result in structural damage to the building and other construction feature; damage shall be rectified by the Contractor

C. A qualified soils consultant who is a registered professional engineer in California shall inspect stripping of topsoil and site preparation in the building and paving areas. A minimum notice ...

D. A qualified and bonded soil test firm shall:

1. Certify in writing that the imported fill material used by the contractor meets gradation and sand equivalent requirements of the specification hereinafter.
2. Do the necessary sampling and laboratory work to develop moisture/density curves for the fill material.
3. Make field density tests as specified in Sections 02210, 02221, and 02241, and submit all test results to the Architect promptly. Test ...
4. Furnish the Architect a letter upon completion of grading, signed and sealed by a registered Professional Engineer ...
5. Submit a final written report to the Architect covering ...
6. The cost of testing shall be paid for by the Owner, except as provided in Section 01410.

Figure 11–12   Soil Testing Requirements, Example Specification Section

---

"..........3. Construction layout and Staking

All construction grading and utility staking shall be done under the supervision of a Civil Engineer or Land Surveyor registered in the State of California. The use of lasers is encouraged for providing straightness and level work. The use of straight edges and carpenter level to set flow lines is not acceptable."

Figure 11–13   Layout Requirements, Example Specification Section

An independent testing lab could provide the following tests on cast-in-place concrete, using its own field inspector:

- Placement and condition of all reinforcement
- Verifying the mix used, the time from batching to placement, and the amount of water added on all concrete trip tickets
- Verify admixtures used
- Check concrete slump
- Cast cylinders for strength tests
- Properly store and break cylinders

All contractor field team members have responsibilities for ensuring quality, with the construction superintendent assuming the primary responsibility for its implementation in the construction product. The superintendent should perform quality checks on the contractor's own work and the work of the subcontractors. Inspections should be similar for technical conformance to specifications and aesthetics. The material or equipment furnished, the installation of the material or equipment, and the final finishes are equally important. The quality of an installation relates to its durability as well as to its initial appearance. Instances of poor workmanship should be noted by the contractor, the architect, and/or the owner's representative. Immediate repair or rework must be done to correct work not meeting the proper standards. As mentioned in the previous discussion about total quality management, rework is expensive; thus, doing it right the first time is the best way to achieve a high-quality product. Generally, patching and other forms of corrective measures do not provide a satisfactory final architectural finish that pleases everyone, including the contractor.

Checklists can be developed and used to ensure that the superintendent or other quality control personnel include all aspects of an installation when preparing and implementing punch lists.

A preliminary punch list for an acoustical ceiling subcontractor involves the following:

1. Remove tools, equipment, and excess materials
2. Restore any damaged finishes from the installation
3. Properly store replacement tiles as required by specifications
4. Color should be from same manufactured lot and of matching colors
5. Texture and finish should match specified and approved material
6. Is the ceiling flat, square, and true?
7. Do the cut tiles fill the spaces completely?
8. Are the joints at the ends of walls mitered or butt joints?

Figure 11–14 shows the specification on acoustical ceilings.

All technical specifications have quality issues detailed throughout each section. The specification notes allowable tolerances and defines shop drawing requirements and samples needed for review along with manufacturer's test data. The specifier also comments on job conditions needed for proper installation and later walks through the installation required by the subcontractor while referencing the Acoustical and Insulating Materials Association performance data.

Short checklists can be taken from the specifications, manufacturer's literature, and other standards. With today's digital cameras and word processing programs, examples of acceptable workmanship and what specific standards should look like are much easier to produce. When completing a project, the review of what worked and problems that occurred should be documented and discussed as part of the process to eliminate any future quality issues.

Quality is specified in different places and in different ways. Most specifications have a clause that states that "all work will be performed in a workmanlike manner." This same

Section 095 10 - Acoustical Ceilings

Part 1 - General

1.01 Related work specified elsewhere

1.02 Description

Provide acoustic ceiling treatment where scheduled or indicated on drawings.

1.03 Allowable Tolerances

Unless otherwise noted, level within 1/8 inch in 12 feet.

1.04 Submittals

Before acoustical ceiling materials are delivered to the jobsite, the following shall be submitted to the Architect.

A. Shop Drawings: ....

B. Samples: ....

C. Show proposed methods of seismic bracing to conform with requirements of UBC Table 23-J. Submit complete calculations defining compliance with seismic bracing requirements of UBC.

1.05 Job Conditions

Maintain temperature and humidity conditions approximating those in completed building before, during, and after installation of acoustic ceiling materials. Delay installation until building is enclosed and all "wet" finish work has dried.

Part 2 - Products

2.01 Suspended Tile Acoustical

Part 3 - Execution

3.01 Installation

In accordance with acoustical and insulating materials association performance data and as follows:

Etc.

End of Section 09510

Figure 11–14   Acoustical Ceilings, Example Specification Section

clause further specifies that all work performed will "be of good quality and free from defects and defaults." If the quality has not been specified precisely, generally the implied warranty is not held.

Summary

This chapter has attempted to create a broad picture and understanding of quality and quality issues. Quality is not a simple goal to achieve. The work environment for construction is not the controlled setting of manufacturing plants. The product is always new in some form, and the details are somewhat different from the last project. Documents differ in detail and accuracy from job to job, the workmen have varying skills, and the multitudes of constructors use different information about specific construction techniques.

The chapter has also discussed the process of inspection and of implementing quality improvement. The relationship of total quality management and the phrase "continuous improvement" were related to the construction industry, emphasizing the importance of these areas to the modern-day contractor. Quality, customer satisfaction, improved productivity, and future work are all interrelated in current and future construction practices.

Review Questions

1. Define the word *quality.*

2. List the standards of quality used in construction.

3. List the elements that a construction quality management program might include.

4. What is total quality management, and who is credited for its growth?

5. What are the six broad steps that define the process of continuous improvement?

6. Name the type of codes used by municipalities.

7. Draw a flowchart for the building permit process.

8. Discuss the responsibilities of a building inspector.

9. Name five areas that could require outside laboratory and inspection services.

Chapter 12

Time and Cost Control

This chapter contains a discussion about the use of time and cost controls during the project. The objectives of this chapter are to introduce the following:

- The reasons for using time and cost controls during the project
- Project duration controls and the use of the project schedule as a tool for monitoring and controlling the duration of activities and the project
- The appropriate scope of schedule activities
- The use of sequencing in the project schedule
- A realistic duration for work activities
- The use of the schedule during the project for the project participants
- The use of the schedule to solve problems during construction
- The reasons for the use of cost control during the project, including the specific uses and impact of those uses
- Cost control methods
- The relationship between productivity problems and the responsible party/solution

The contractor must control both the duration of the project and the cost of the project, the major parameters of the project. The contractor commits to completing the project in a specific time frame and at a finite cost. Many contractors feel that both time and cost are naturally controlled by the construction process and field personnel. Although that premise is basically true, the contractor needs to use management techniques to plan and accurately monitor the actual progress and cost to that which is planned and estimated. The contractor is then able to modify operations to meet the time frame and estimated cost.

Traditionally, the contractor's field personnel did their best to complete the project as quickly as possible, with minimal cost. The results of this effort during the project were unclear. It would appear as though the project would be completed on time, and the project cost seemed to be within the budget. The effectiveness of control of time and cost on the jobsite was evident at the end of the project: if the job was completed on time and if the project made a profit or loss. In recent years, however, the use of construction scheduling and computerized cost control accounting provides a means of monitoring the effectiveness of the controls during a project, allowing field personnel to adjust productivity factors, crew size, and subcontractor activity to bring the project to acceptable progress.

Small as well as large construction projects can benefit from time and cost control. Large projects use specific individuals dedicated to scheduling and cost control. This should not be thought of, however, as a luxury available only to larger projects. A construction schedule and cost control information can help any contractor achieve optimum results during the construction process.

The purpose of this chapter is to introduce control techniques and relate them to activities during the construction period. This chapter does not detail the use of these systems since there are numerous texts available on scheduling, project management, and cost control techniques that deal with these subjects.

Project Duration Control

The construction project owner will always need a project completed within a specific time period, whether explicitly stated in the contract documents or not. The owner's date for project completion establishes a parameter and a maximum duration for the project. The contractor must estimate the necessary means of achieving the owner's completion date. If there is not enough time to complete the project using normal construction shifts and techniques, the contractor is expected to use multiple shifts or other methods to complete the project by that time limit. There usually are liquidated damages, a daily monetary amount charged to the contractor for compensation of costs incurred by the owner, when the facility cannot be used.

The owner's completion date, however, rarely has a direct relationship to the actual amount of time needed to construct the project. This date is often based on the owner's need for the facility rather than the expected construction duration. A school project will be required to be completed in July or August, allowing time for equipment move-in so that the facility can be in operation in early September at the start of the school year. A retailer will want its facility completed in late summer to be able to stock goods and train personnel prior to the holiday retail season. These completion dates establish a maximum construction duration, but the contractor may be able to complete the facility prior to the completion date.

Completion of construction in the minimum time will reduce the contractor's jobsite overhead and enable the contractor to pursue other work. To optimize profits in both the specific project and the aggregate, the contractor needs to complete the projects in the shortest amount of time while not increasing cost with lost productivity or overtime costs. The contractor needs to plan the project carefully, for without planning and diligence in maintaining the plan, the construction project can extend for a long duration, costing the contractor considerable resources. A project planned according to construction sequence and realistic projected duration of activities rather than one based on the prescribed completion date can help the contractor complete the project earlier than scheduled.

The plan for the construction of the project includes careful consideration of the elements and relationships in the project. No two projects are ever alike. Each has its own set of materials, systems, subcontractors, weather conditions, soil conditions, delivery dates, sequences, and durations. Previous projects help one become aware of the duration of certain specific activities. However, two projects of similar scope might have completely different time frames for completion because of the time of year started, weather delays encountered, sequencing, and delivery of materials. If two exact projects were started on the same day, the two superintendents would sequence the projects differently, encounter different problems during construction, and complete the projects at different times.

The project plan is the plan of construction conceived by the project superintendent, along with the purchasing restraints already in place (subcontracts and purchase orders) to most efficiently achieve the objectives of the project. It is important to remember that the project plan is generated by the personnel who will manage it. The project superintendent must be intimately involved in planning the project in addition to other personnel. Too often the plan and subsequent schedule are developed by personnel who are not involved with the day-to-day management of the project, resulting in a wide difference between the schedule and the actual project sequence and duration.

The project plan involves more than just a schedule of activities. It must consider all project needs and how the solutions to those needs affect the duration of activities and the project itself. Some planning considerations include the following:

- Activities on the project

- Duration of the activities

- Sequencing of the activities

- The interrelationship of subcontract activities

- Equipment requirements for the project

- Utilization of subcontractors

- Field management personnel

- Crew size and project staffing of craftspeople

- Anticipated material delivery dates

- Weather planning: anticipated lost days, weather protection

- Anticipation of delays: other contracts, labor strikes, owner-based changes

- Alternative solutions to sequencing

Careful analysis of the entire project is needed to tie activities together to form a plan and subsequent schedule. When a scheduling consultant is used, the superintendent and other field personnel must formulate the plan for the project and convey that information to the scheduling consultant.

Prior to scheduling, the activities must be identified, the sequences must be established, and the durations of the activities must be estimated. This information could be identified jointly by the scheduler and the superintendent, but the definition of the information should be done by the superintendent. Some considerations when compiling these data are discussed next.

Scope of Activities

Each activity in the construction schedule must be identifiable, with the following attributes:

- Able to be described as a separate function, such as "formwork for footings"

- Must have a labor crew, with attributable crew hours for the activity

- Must have a specific duration attached definable for the work, such as "10 working days"

- Must be able to be monitored by comparing planned duration with actual duration during the construction process

A construction activity has an identifiable block of time that must be included in the construction sequence. It can contain several different steps, trades, and estimate line items, or there could be a time restraint before further work can be done. Two typical construction activities and their components could be the following.

Example

Prep and Pour Concrete Slab

Subgrade preparation

Spread and prepare gravel base

Install embedded items

Install underslab electrical, plumbing, and ductwork

Set forms

Install reinforcing steel

Set screeds, expansion joints

Pour concrete

Finish concrete

Duration: 3 days

Cure Concrete Slab

Wet cure concrete slab

(Time restraint—no relating work to be done until curing complete)

Duration: 10 days

The appropriate scope of the activity is important when formulating the plan and schedule. The size of the project helps determine the scope of the activities. When preparing a short-term schedule, small units are appropriate. When preparing a large project, larger units are appropriate. Short-duration items, however, can create some problems with the schedule. Any fluctuation can affect these items, easily throwing the actual construction off schedule. Short durations also can inflate the schedule by requiring too much time for individual parts.

Using the previous "Prep and Pour Concrete Slab" activity, the following example illustrates the short time needed and inflated time created by adding all of the subactivities together.

Example

Prep and Pour Concrete Slab

Subgrade preparation	2 hours
Spread and prepare gravel base	4 hours
Install embedded items	2 hours
Install underslab electrical, plumbing, and ductwork	8 hours
Set forms	4 hours
Install reinforcing steel	2 hours
Set screeds, expansion joints	4 hours
Pour concrete	2 hours
Finish concrete	6 hours
Total hours	34 hours

The estimated 34 hours are more than 3 days (24 hours) previously established for this activity. Of course, some of the activities could be done concurrently, saving the overall duration; some of the activities are ample estimates for the work, resulting in an inflated duration. It is easy to see that if one activity takes a little longer, caused by a long coffee break, an unexpected material delivery, an illness, or a number of other factors, the construction would be easily thrown off schedule.

An overly long duration also is not appropriate for monitoring actual against projected time. Assume that the first example, "Prep and Pour Concrete Slab," is for a 5,000 sq. ft. concrete slab. If the concrete slab was much larger, for instance, 50,000 sq. ft., the item of "Prep and Pour Concrete Slab" may be too large to monitor and may be separated into five sections, of 10,000 sq. ft. each, and a duration of 3 working days per section, using a larger crew. "Prep and Pour Concrete Slab, Section 1," and so on would be more accurate for monitoring the construction, as the actual slab pouring and finishing will be accomplished in five sections here.

In most construction schedules, activity duration should be no shorter than 1 day. Situations exist, such as a plant shutdown for a short-term repair or for additions that must be scheduled in small increments, such as hours. A guideline can be established for activity duration, such as between 2 and 20 working days, but this should not totally eliminate necessary activities that are shorter or longer.

A descriptive list of the items included in each activity is a good organizing tool for checklists to determine that all activities are included in the plan. Descriptions of the activities are also good references during the project to determine if the activity is complete. Some activities may resemble others in a brief description, so the full description is necessary to identify the activity and its scope.

Sequence of Activities

The plan of the project will determine the sequence of the activity. In any project, several different sequences could be used to accomplish the project, depending upon the strategy of the superintendent, considering the project conditions. The example shown in Figure 12–1 illustrates two different sequences of a portion of the project, either of which might be applicable regarding crane mobilization costs, weather conditions at the projected time of the activities, subcontractor availability, crew availability, and duration available for the activities within the scheduled completion.

Distinct reasons may exist for the superintendent choosing one sequence over another. For quality reasons, the superintendent may want to pour the slab without a pour back between the existing and new slabs. Sequence 1 would facilitate that condition. When selecting a particular sequence, it may be necessary to compare durations and costs associated with the sequence, similar to the comparison in Figure 12–2. In this example, sequence 2 has a shorter duration of 1.5 days and a cost that is lower by $1,900. In most circumstances, the shorter duration and lower cost would be the reasons to choose sequence 2. Mitigating reasons may exist, however, making sequence 1 more desirable, such as quality concerns, construction details and connections, availability of the crane, availability of the concrete finishers, and a variety of other reasons.

Project Description: This portion of the project involves an addition to an existing gymnasium. The existing building consists of concrete tilt-up wall panels and metal roof joists, with a concrete slab-on-grade. The existing building has a hardwood gymnasium floor applied above the concrete slab. The concrete panels at the end of the existing building are to be removed, and used as the panels at the end of the addition. The addition attaches to the existing building, and is constructed of tilt-up concrete wall panels and metal joists, with a concrete slab on grade, similar to the original building.

Sequence 1:
1. Mobilize crane
2. Remove tilt-up walls to be relocated, store on site
3. Build temporary weather partition at end of existing building
4. Excavate for footings
5. Prep and pour footings
6. Prepare subgrade
7. Pour slab on grade
8. Slab cure
9. Prep and pour panels on slab
10. Mobilize crane
11. Lift panels into place
12. Set joists and deck
13. Backfill at "pour-backs"
14. Pour concrete slab at "pour-backs"

Sequence 2:
1. Excavate for footings
2. Prep and pour footings
3. Prepare subgrade
4. Pour slab on grade
5. Slab cure
6. Prep and pour panels on slab
7. Mobilize crane
8. Remove and relocate existing panels
9. Lift new panels into place
10. Set joists and deck
11. Backfill at "pour-backs"
12. Pour concrete slab at "pour-backs"

Figure 12–1   Example Sequence Comparison

Comparison of Sequence 1 and Sequence 2
Addition to Gymnasium

Sequence 1:

Activity	Duration (Days)	Cost
1. Mobilize crane	0.5	$ 1,000
2. Remove tilt-up walls	0.5	$ 1,100
3. Temporary partition	2	$ 1,300
4. Excavate footings	2	$ 840
5. Prep & pour footings	5	$ 2,500
6. Prepare subgrade	5	$ 1,200
7. Pour slab on grade	2	$ 7,500
8. Slab cure	5	$ 200
9. Prep and pour panels	15	$ 8,500
10. Mobilize crane	0.5	$ 1,000
11. Lift panels into place	0.5	$ 1,400
12. Set joists and deck	1	$ 2,600
13. Backfill at "pour-backs"	2	$ 1,000
14. Pour concrete "pour-backs"	1	$ 700
Total	42	$30,840

Sequence 2:

Activity	Duration (Days)	Cost
1. Excavate footings	2	$ 840
2. Prep and pour footings	5	$ 2,500
3. Prepare subgrade	5	$ 1,200
4. Pour slab on grade	2	$ 7,500
5. Slab cure	5	$ 200
6. Prep and pour panels	15	$ 8,500
7. Mobilize crane	0.5	$ 1,000
8. Remove and relocate ex. panels	0.5	$ 1,200
9. Lift new panels into place	0.5	$ 1,400
10. Set joists and deck	1	$ 2,600
11. Backfill at "pour-backs"	3	$ 1,300
12. Pour concrete "pour-backs"	1	$ 700
Total	40.5	$28,940

Figure 12–2   Example Sequence Cost Comparison

In the examples shown in Figures 12–1 and 12–2, the sequence was assumed as "finish to start"; that is, the activities were completed before the next activity started. This is not always the case, though, as one activity may start after a portion of the preceding activity is completed. Numerous concurrent activities occur on the jobsite. If all construction sequences were the finish-to-start type, the project would be estimated at a much longer duration. What follows are common relationships available with most commercial scheduling software.

Finish to Start: The second activity does not start until the first one is completed.

Example

Foundation wall needs to be completed with forms stripped prior to setting the stud wall on the foundation wall.

A period of time can exist between the finish and start, or a lag between the two activities.

> ### Example
>
> The concrete slab must be completed prior to installation of the interior studs. As the slab needs to cure and harden before framing labor and equipment is on the slab, the contractor could insert a 5-day lag, allowing the slab to cure for a week prior to installation of the framing.

Start to Start: Two activities may need to begin at the same time, such as installation of carpet and resilient floor covering, with the same subcontractor installing both but using separate crews. A lag might occur between the two starts as well.

> ### Example
>
> Drywall installation may have a fairly long duration, such as 20 working days. Drywall, however, will begin in a certain area and progress away from that area. Some areas will be ready for painting 5 days after the start of the drywall operation. Time would be wasted if the painter waited until all of the drywall was completed. The relationship, then, would be a start-to-start with a 5-day lag, with painting beginning 5 working days after the drywall. Obviously, coordination is necessary to ensure that the painter knows where to begin and that the area is clean and ready for the painter when scheduled.

Finish to Finish: This relationship is used when two activities should be completed at the same time despite the fact that they might have different durations.

Logical sequencing, however, is most important in planning and scheduling. Care should be taken to ensure correct sequencing, with the necessary activities preceding each activity. Considerable disruption can be caused by careless sequencing. If subcontractors are scheduled to arrive and work on the project, they will require that the necessary adjoining and substrate work be completed, and they will often leave the jobsite if this preliminary work is not done. The schedule is a guide and should be changed if the logic is not correct. The logic, or proper sequencing, is the key to a successful project. All parties involved should review the logic of the project prior to completion of the schedule.

Duration of Activities

The duration of an activity must be accurately predicted. When determining the duration of a construction activity, consider these factors:

- The duration of an activity needs to be relative to the amount of labor hours included in the estimate. Input from the estimator is often necessary to determine the intended crew size and amount of labor. Construction activities do not always coincide with the estimated items, so some interpretation of the estimated hours is necessary. This information should be combined with the superintendent's view on how the work will be accomplished.

- The duration of the activity should relate to the quantity of work accomplished. It is important to factor crew size against the quantity of work to be performed. The duration of concrete formwork activities will certainly vary from a situation where there are two carpenters and a laborer to eight carpenters and four laborers. When the crew is properly sized for the project, the productivity rate should not be affected by using a larger crew, but the duration of the activity should be shorter.

- Weather concerns also should be considered in the duration of the activity. The time of year in which the activity will be accomplished has a large influence on the duration of the activity. For example, a built-up roofing activity might have a 10-working-day duration during warm weather. If this activity was intended to be completed in December in the northern half of the United States, the duration should be longer to allow for weather conditions appropriate for installation, without freezing or precipitation. A contractor might allow 20 days during that period, hoping the work would be done within the 20-day window. Another contractor might change the sequence, either completing the roofing prior to November or after March.

- Consideration of delivery of all items may affect the duration of the activities. Delivery is a factor in the sequencing of the activity, but it also can affect the duration.

- Subcontractor involvement in the activity may affect the duration. Duration control can be facilitated by the contractor by ensuring that the crews and the number of crews are available at the proper time. The contractor cannot as easily affect the performance of subcontractors. Some cushion should be allowed in the duration for subcontractors arriving on the project.

Duration, in most schedules, is expressed in working days, not calendar days. Five working days would indicate a week in most cases. For cases on accelerated project phases, the construction week consists of 7 days. Use of "working days" for the duration works best, with the project calendar being adjusted for longer workweeks or holidays.

The Project Schedule

The project schedule is a manifestation of the project plan—a written or graphical depiction. The schedule is a communication tool to share the project plan among project participants. It has many forms: a simple, noncalculated bar chart; the Gantt chart, a calculated bar chart; a network chart showing interdependencies, some time scaled; and tabular schedules, listing dates. It should always be remembered that the contractor is trying to communicate one's plan to other participants: architects, owners, construction managers, subcontractors, and suppliers. The exact method used may vary, depending on the target for the information. A construction manager, for instance, would normally be quite knowledgeable about schedules and therefore probably would request network reports, tabular reports, and the Gantt chart. The owner, however, may not be interested in reading anything other than the Gantt chart. The contractor should ensure that the appropriate report is given to each party, possibly with additional clarification. Some contractors will send everyone a 3- or 4-inch-thick stack of reports, expecting the recipient to discern applicable information. These reports usually are either filed or thrown away, without any exchange of information.

As most scheduling software produces many reports and graphs, there is a tendency to become overwhelmed with the information, losing track of what is important during construction. The following list contains some schedule information relevant to the parties involved in the construction process:

Owner:

Completion dates: project and milestones for partial completion

Current status of the project: problem areas and projected changes to dates

Dates and relationship of owner-furnished items and separate contracts

Current activities in progress

Schedule for owner-provided services, such as testing

Architect:

Completion dates: project and milestones for partial completion

Current status of the project: problem areas and projected changes to dates

Relationship of submittal review to construction schedule

Current activities in progress

Schedule for inspection/observation, particularly for sub-consultants

Contractor:

Detailed relationship of activities

Current status of activities

Relationship of projected delivery dates of material and equipment to activities

Schedule of subcontract activities for coordination

Duration of activities to schedule crews

Interrelationship of activities

Opportunities to condense construction duration without increasing cost

Opportunities to level crew size

Current activities that are behind or that are expected to exceed their projected duration

Subcontractor:

Expected schedule for particular activities: date required on jobsite and duration allowed for work

Relationship of other activities that directly affect the subcontract activities

Current status of project, relating to particular subcontract activities

Relationship of subcontract material and equipment to activity

Suppliers:

Date material or equipment due at jobsite

Anticipated order date, after review of shop drawings and submittals

The majority of scheduling is currently done with scheduling or project management software, which organizes, calculates, levels, and provides numerous views of the schedule, including network, Gantt charts, and tabular listings. (Chapter 14 describes some popular scheduling and project management software.) As mentioned previously, a plan should be established prior to inputting data into scheduling software, with a list of activities, durations, and predecessors prepared. A partial list of activities for input into scheduling software is illustrated in Figure 12–3.

Full scheduling software normally calculates the **critical path** for the project. The critical path is the calculated path for the project that considers the dependencies of predecessors. In considering the predecessors for each activity, the longest predecessor duration establishes the start date of the activity. The completion date established by the critical path is the earliest possible date, considering the dependencies of the activities. Any change to an activity on the critical path will directly affect the completion date of the project. Activities not on the critical path have a **float,** or a period of time in addition to the activity's duration, prior to the start of the successor activity. The float allows some flexibility with noncritical items and flexibility in duration and the actual start of the item. For example, if an item has 5 days float and its scheduled early start date is Monday, August 7, the item can start any day from August 7 through August 11, assuming that its duration remains constant. If the activity actually starts on

Activity Number	Activity	Duration	Predecessors
1	Mobilize	5 days	
2	Clear site	5 days	1
3	Mass excavation	10 days	2
4	Structural excavation	10 days	3
5	Plumbing excavation	4 days	2
6	Prep & pour footings	7 days	4 + 5 days
7	Underslab plumbing Rough-In	10 days	5
8	Foundation wall	20 days	6 + 3 days
9	Prep slab subgrade	4 days	7, 8

Figure 12–3 Schedule Data

August 7, 5 additional days could be added to the duration, possibly using a smaller crew than originally anticipated. If the activity is started 10 working days later than initially anticipated, either the duration of the activity would have to be shortened by the additional 5 days, possibly by enlarging the crew, or the activity will affect the critical path and thus the completion date by the 5 days. Careful monitoring of activities and their effect on the critical path of the project is necessary throughout the project.

Updating of the project is necessary on a periodic basis, either weekly, biweekly, or monthly. The primary purpose of this update is to determine which activities are behind schedule and what their effect will be on the completion date of the project. After determining the activities that are behind schedule, the project management team must analyze the effect and what steps, if any, must be taken to bring the project back to a schedule that will achieve the projected completion date. As mentioned earlier, the project plan should be flexible to allow for changes in activity sequences, crew sizes, and shifts worked. The initial schedule should always be maintained as a reference for the project, comparing updated progress to the original plan.

A variety of methods are used to update the schedule and communicate the updates to those involved in the project. Most scheduling software programs have updating features. When using these features, always be sure the original schedule is used as a comparison. The revised completion dates from the computerized schedule updates should be viewed as data to compare to the initial completion date, allowing the contractor to manipulate activities to meet the initial schedule date. The target date can change, however, with project scope changes and project events that cannot be avoided. Change orders can change the duration of the project by granting a time extension in a specific number of days. If a new completion date is established, justification for the new date should be made. Completion date changes should be infrequent, however, as the owner depends on the project being completed by the established date.

Because the schedule is a communication tool, the schedule updates should be done in a manner that effectively communicates the variance in schedule, if any, and the steps that are necessary to remediate any problems. Some schedulers will use the network diagram or bar chart to indicate the current status of activities by color coding the charts. For instance, red would indicate behind schedule, green would indicate on schedule, blue would indicate ahead of schedule, and yellow would indicate that the activity was late but had not yet affected the schedule. This color coding allows the project management team to quickly identify problem areas. Tabular reports usually are available to indicate the activities showing variance. As many of the construction activities are subcontract items, the contractor needs to work with the subcontractors closely, indicating the problem and identifying the solution. The example that follows indicates a comparison of the original schedule with the updated schedule and shows the remedial schedule that is necessary, including dialogue with subcontractors.

Example

Figure 12–4 illustrates a partial construction schedule, showing the finish stages of a project. The completion date for the project is August 26. The owner has used this date for moving into the facility and hiring additional personnel. There is a liquidated damages clause in this project, stipulating $1,000 per day liquidated damages for late completion of the project.

Figure 12–5 shows the schedule as impacted by actual progress. Activity 15401, Plumbing Rough-In for the interior walls, was completed a week later than scheduled, resulting in delaying the start of the drywall activity. As these activities were on the critical path, the project completion would be delayed until September 3. The superintendent for the contractor needed to analyze the alternatives caused by this delay:

- Could the completion date be extended to September 3? In this case, the completion date could not be changed because of the owner's arrangements and insistence to impose liquidated damages if the facility could not be used at the scheduled completion date.

- Can durations of activities be compressed to save the 5 working days from the schedule? The superintendent examined each item, starting with critical path items, and discussed activity durations with the applicable subcontractors. The superintendent came to the conclusion that scheduled durations could not be compressed sufficiently to return the project to the original completion date.

- Can different sequencing be used to return the project to the scheduled completion date? The superintendent realized that by coordinating the area of work of the drywall contractor, the painting contractor could start work a week earlier. This earlier start was acceptable to the painting subcontractor. Ceramic tile would also start a week earlier than originally scheduled, which was also acceptable, as the ceramic contractor had received delivery of the ceramic tile. Figure 12–6 illustrates the different sequence by starting the painting a week early. This remedial schedule results in the project's maintaining its original completion date of August 26.

A variety of methods can be applied to get the project back on schedule, including the following:

- Altering the sequencing of the activities, bringing some activities up in time, and changing the critical path.

- Altering the duration of the activity or activities showing a problem, which can be done by increasing crew size, adding multiple shifts, or increasing productivity for the activity; an activity also can be split into other activities, separating the essential predecessor elements from those that could be done later.

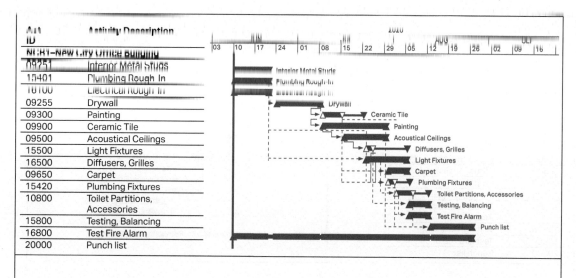

Act ID	Activity Description	Orig Dur	Rem Dur	Early Start	Early Finish	Total Float	%
NCB1–New City Office Building							
09251	Interior Metal Studs	10d	10d	10JUN03	21JUN03	0	0
15401	Plumbing Rough-In	10d	10d	10JUN03	21JUN03	0	0
16100	Electrical Rough-In	10d	10d	10JUN03	21JUN03	0	0
09255	Drywall	10d	10d	24JUN03	08JUL03	0	0
09900	Painting	15d	15d	09JUL03	29JUL03	0	0
09300	Ceramic Tile	5d	5d	09JUL03	15JUL03	5d	0
09500	Acoustical Ceilings	10d	10d	16JUL03	29JUL03	0	0
16500	Light Fixtures	10d	10d	23JUL03	05AUG03	0	0
15500	Diffusers, Grilles	3d	3d	23JUL03	25JUL03	7d	0
09650	Carpet	5d	5d	30JUL03	05AUG03	0	0
15420	Plumbing Fixtures	3d	3d	30JUL03	01AUG03	3d	0
10800	Toilet Partitions, Accessories	4d	4d	02AUG03	07AUG03	3d	0
15800	Testing, Balancing	5d	5d	06AUG03	12AUG03	0	0
16800	Test Fire Alarm	5d	5d	06AUG03	12AUG03	0	0
20000	Punch list	10d	10d	13AUG03	26AUG03	0	0
		55d	55d	10JUN03	26AUG03	0	0

Figure 12–4 Original Construction Schedule

- Reevaluating the duration of the successor activities to see if time can be gained later in the project. (Note: This can be dangerous territory—rationalizing that things will get better. Careful analysis is necessary before making this decision.)

The schedule and progress updating of the schedule during the project provides the contractor with a tool to help control the project's duration. The schedule itself merely gives an indication of the project's status. The creativity, experience, and management skill of the project team allow for the effective management of project activities and control of the completion date.

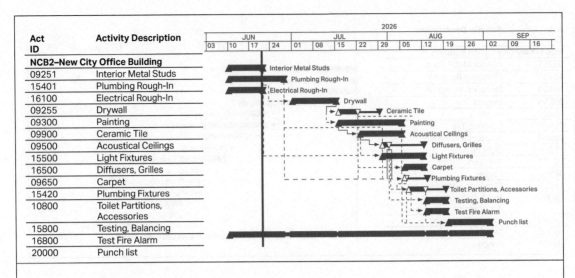

Act ID	Activity Description							
NCB2–New City Office Building								
09251	Interior Metal Studs							
15401	Plumbing Rough-In							
16100	Electrical Rough-In							
09255	Drywall							
09300	Painting							
09900	Ceramic Tile							
09500	Acoustical Ceilings							
15500	Light Fixtures							
16500	Diffusers, Grilles							
09650	Carpet							
15420	Plumbing Fixtures							
10800	Toilet Partitions, Accessories							
15800	Testing, Balancing							
16800	Test Fire Alarm							
20000	Punch list							

Act ID	Activity Description	Orig Dur	Rem Dur	Early Start	Early Finish	Total Float	%
NCB2–New City Office Building							
15401	Plumbing Rough-In	10d	6d	10JUN03A	28JUN03	0	41
09251	Interior Metal Studs	10d	0	10JUN03A	21JUN03A		100
16100	Electrical Rough-In	10d	0	10JUN03A	21JUN03A		100
09255	Drywall	10d	10d	01JUL03	15JUL03	0	0
09900	Painting	15d	15d	16JUL03	05AUG03	0	0
09300	Ceramic Tile	5d	5d	16JUL03	22JUL03	5d	0
09500	Acoustical Ceilings	10d	10d	23JUL03	05AUG03	0	0
16500	Light Fixtures	10d	10d	30JUL03	12AUG03	0	0
15500	Diffusers, Grilles	3d	3d	30JUL03	01AUG03	7d	0
09650	Carpet	5d	5d	06AUG03	12AUG03	0	0
15420	Plumbing Fixtures	1d	1d	06AUG03	06AUG03	5d	0
10800	Toilet Partitions, Accessories	4d	4d	07AUG03	12AUG03	5d	0
15800	Testing, Balancing	5d	5d	13AUG03	19AUG03	0	0
16800	Test Fire Alarm	5d	5d	13AUG03	19AUG03	0	0
20000	Punch list	10d	10d	20AUG03	03SEP03	0	0
		60d	51d	10JUN03	03SEP03	0	21

Figure 12–5 Updated Schedule

Several occasions arise during the construction project when it is necessary to prepare short-term or special-use schedules. These usually are separate from the primary schedule and can be in a different scale, such as hours. Some occasions for using short-term schedules include the following:

• Detailed clarification of a larger item in the construction schedule, which may be used to schedule crews, or coordinate several different crews

• Schedule of a power shutdown or other utility interruption, which might be done in hours

• Installation of a piece of equipment, coordinating the crafts involved

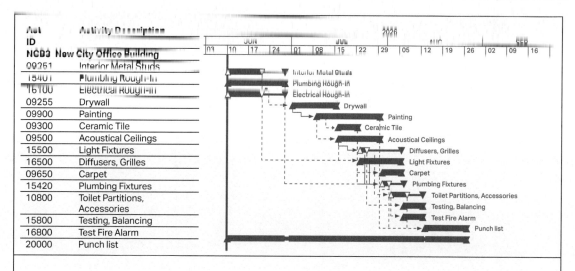

Act ID	Activity Description	Orig Dur	Rem Dur	Early Start	Early Finish	Total Float	%
NCB3–New City Office Building							
15401	Plumbing Rough-In	15d	15d	10JUN03A	28JUN03	0	0
09251	Interior Metal Studs	10d	10d	10JUN03A	21JUN03A	5d	0
16100	Electrical Rough-In	10d	10d	10JUN03A	21JUN03A	5d	0
09255	Drywall	10d	10d	01JUL03	15JUL03	0	0
09900	Painting	15d	15d	09JUL03	05AUG03	0	0
09300	Ceramic Tile	5d	5d	16JUL03	22JUL03	0	0
09500	Acoustical Ceilings	10d	10d	16JUL03	29JUL03	0	0
16500	Light Fixtures	10d	10d	23JUL03	05AUG03	0	0
15500	Diffusers, Grilles	3d	3d	23JUL03	25JUL03	7d	0
09650	Carpet	5d	5d	30JUL03	05AUG03	0	0
15420	Plumbing Fixtures	3d	3d	30JUL03	01AUG03	3d	0
10800	Toilet Partitions, Accessories	4d	4d	02AUG03	07AUG03	3d	0
15800	Testing, Balancing	5d	5d	06AUG03	12AUG03	0	0
16800	Test Fire Alarm	5d	5d	06AUG03	12AUG03	0	0
20000	Punch list	10d	10d	13AUG03	26AUG03	0	0
		55d	55d	10JUN03	26AUG03	0	0

Figure 12–6 Remedial Schedule

- Schedule of the completion of a specific area of the project for early owner occupancy
- Schedule of the move-in activities of the owner
- Schedule for remediation of work behind schedule
- Specific schedule for a trade or section of the work

These short-term schedules often are prepared in the field by project personnel. Because their purposes are specific, their formats will be customized to the particular situations (see Figure 12–7).

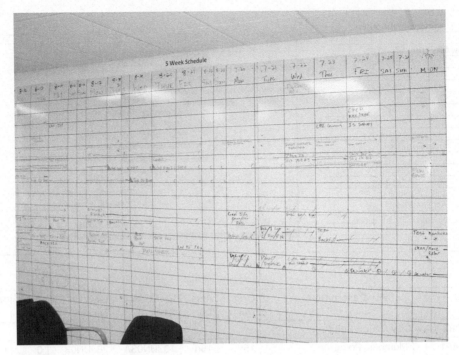

Figure 12–7   Jobsite Short-Term Schedule

© Mincks, William

Project Cost Control

Comparison of the actual cost with the estimated cost during the project provides an accurate measure of the current success of the project. Cost comparison data during the construction activity provide the contractor with opportunities to adjust the factors involved with the activity. Active cost control enables the contractor to achieve a profit on construction activities.

A number of computer software programs are available for cost accounting and cost control. These programs compare the actual cost with the estimate, providing accurate cost information to the project team immediately after input. The software, however, only computes and collates the data. The entire project management team must understand the parameters of effective cost control and follow these parameters as they set up the estimate; the cost accounts; labor, material, and equipment reporting; productivity management; and project management. Conscious effort by the project manager, superintendent, field engineers, and foremen can make a cost control system work.

There are several different reasons contractors use cost control methods on construction projects. Cost control can range from a simple collection of costs for labor, material, equipment, and subcontractors, organized in projects or subprojects, to detailed compilation and analysis for every work activity. The overhead cost of cost control increases as the detailed collection and expected reporting detail increases. Therefore, contractors need to determine how much information they want from their cost systems, according to their managers and the needs of their risk partners, such as banks and bonding companies, and compare this to the staff costs to compile this information. Cost control involves construction expertise from construction engineers or project controls specialists as well as accounting staff.

In a simple cost control system, the labor, material, equipment, and subcontract costs are compared to the estimated cost for the project or subprojects to determine if the project achieved the target cost. By adding the appropriate amount of indirect overhead, usually by using a percentage of the costs, the contractor can determine if the project was profitable; that

In revenue exceeded the cost of direct and indirect costs. The contractor wants to compare the actual profit with the anticipated profit to determine if the accounting and operations systems are synchronized. The following example looks at a small contractor's cost control system.

Case Study

Jim is a small contractor. He usually has about 12 projects per year. When he started business, he accumulated all of his costs to pay his bills, such as payroll, material invoices, equipment rental, and subcontractors. As Jim estimated and managed each project personally, he felt that he was making the optimum profit on each project. Jim kept a journal that indicated what was spent and to whom and often included a note indicating the project or item, such as "Miller kitchen, floor covering." Since his jobs were quite small, Jim often would buy lumber or hardware for several projects in one invoice and usually wouldn't bother to divide those invoices into individual projects. Jim made reports to the IRS for payroll withholding tax, and reported his revenue and other taxes to the state quarterly. He kept his invoices and his journal and every year in March took them to his brother-in-law, who was an accountant. They would determine how much he earned for the previous year and would file this amount with the IRS by April 15. Jim was able to determine if he made a profit for the year, about 3 months after the year end, and was in compliance with rules and regulations.

Jim's business was steady and he was able to make a living with it. He worked long hours, though, usually 12 hours per day on the job and purchasing material and usually 2 or 3 hours in the evenings paying bills, doing payroll, and writing in the journal. Jim felt that he could make more profit, undertake larger projects, and work fewer hours if he expanded his business and his staff. Jim looked to larger projects but found that he needed relationships with a bonding company and a bank. Both of these entities required him to keep better books on his construction costs. They suggested that he needed to know how much profit he was earning on each project and really should compare his estimated costs with his actual costs. After talking to a new accountant, Jim wondered if the expansion was worth the extra expenses of a bookkeeper and accounting services.

Jim then talked to a friend who had been a fairly large contractor for several years. His friend explained that Jim needed to know where he profited and where he did not so that he could concentrate on profitable projects. Regardless of the type of work, geographical location, owners, or architects, it was necessary for Jim to draw some conclusions about why these projects were profitable. Jim's friend also explained that it was important to compare actual costs with the estimated costs to see where the additional profit or loss was being generated. Jim could use the results as historical data for the actual cost of an item or to see which crews or individuals were producing more work. In fact, if Jim got the comparison immediately, as is possible with computers, he could identify a productivity problem and take immediate action to solve the problem.

Jim was convinced that he should implement a cost control program. It took a while for Jim and his foremen to get used to coding time cards to the activities accomplished that day, but they adapted to the new system. As Jim's business grew, the sophistication of the reporting grew, and Jim was able to use the information he generated to manage his work more efficiently. He was able to manage crew productivity, produce accurate historical data for his estimating system, select projects that have a good profitability potential, and manage his costs. Because he used accepted accounting practices, he could prove to his bonding company and banker that he was a good risk partner. This allowed him to expand his business by constructing larger projects.

Cost control can be used to do the following:

- Determine project or partial project profitability

- Determine the source of overruns to allow immediate steps or measures on future projects

- Compare work activity actual cost to the estimated cost for that activity. Analysis of this information can do the following:

- Determine crew productivity levels

- Identify productivity problems (several productivity problems/solutions are listed later in this chapter)

- Specify ways to solve problems during the process and therefore limit or eliminate potential losses

- Use the comparison data for historical data

- Use the analysis of problems for "lessons learned" that can be applied to future work

- Compare costs incurred to the baseline estimate to determine which costs are within the initial project scope and which costs are additional costs (This comparison is used to isolate costs for change orders or the necessary compilation of additional costs.)

The section that follows is a discussion of some of the important factors in a cost control system.

Realistic Cost Control Activities

The primary objective in setting up a project cost control system involves the correlation of the cost control activities from the estimate with reportable construction activities. The cost control activity should be related to a crew assignment so that reporting labor hours can easily be tracked. The activity should not be so small that reporting hours becomes difficult for the foreman. The items should be narrow enough to identify a problem, facilitating a solution. Cost control activities will be used as historical data in estimating future projects and can be applied to several projects, not just one. Obviously, the formation of these activities is very subjective. The example shown in Figure 12–8 examines concrete foundation walls for a project. The controllable cost here will be the formwork labor, as it continues for a period of time longer than the weekly labor (payroll) reporting.

The data in Figure 12–8, comparing actual with estimated hours, provide an idea about the productivity of the crews for the concrete foundation wall. Comparing the actual with the estimated figures results in a variance that can be projected to a total variance if the same rate of productivity continues. Item 03113, Strip Formwork, is currently over its estimated cost by $471.36. Because only 16 percent of that item has been completed, management has a chance to review conditions and discover why that item is a bit behind. It is possible that the learning curve is impacting that item, but other conditions, such as crew size, equipment, weather, or other factors, may have affected that item's productivity. Management can take steps to modify the condition, such as reducing the crew size from three to two laborers, which may be more efficient.

Each firm will have its own format for a cost control system. The major concerns in maintaining an effective cost control system include the following:

- Ensuring that the cost control accounts are of the proper scope. The cost control account should be understandable. Labor should be able to be easily assigned to the cost control account. Estimate line items should be able to act as cost control accounts.

- Relating the crew assignment directly to the cost control activity. The crew assignment should be clear and understandable.

- Cost account results should be able to be used as historical cost data.

- Field personnel should realize the purpose of cost control and report the costs accurately.

The estimate was based on a unit price cost per cubic yard of concrete.
Unit Prices, Material: $ 60.00/CY; Labor, $ 80.00/CY; Equipment, $ 60.00/CY
Estimate line item:

Section	Item	Quantity	Material	Labor	Equipment	Total
03310	Concrete Foundation Walls	1,000 CY	$ 60,000.00	$ 80,000.00	$ 60,000.00	$200,000.00

Is this item adequate for cost control? Can we definitively track the costs, identify a problem, and be able to take action to solve the problem? Possibly, but definitive information is not really available. We need to look at the situation with definable crew tasks, which are not too small. The following is a breakdown of the concrete walls in definable categories associated with crew makeup and cost.

Section	Activity	Crew	Labor Cost	Crew Cost	Hrs	Total Cost
03112	Set Formwork	6 carpenters 2 laborers	$28.45 $25.30	$221.30	240	$53,112.00
03113	Strip Formwork	3 laborers	$25.30	$ 75.90	60	$ 4,554.00
03202	Install Rebar	3 ironworkers	$32.15	$ 96.45	68	$ 6,558.60
03302	Pour Walls	6 laborers	$25.30	$151.80	64	$ 9,715.20
03303	Sack Walls	2 laborers	$25.30	$ 50.60	120	$ 6,072.00
	Total foundation wall labor					$80,011.80

With this breakdown, it will be easier to track the cost progress of labor for the concrete walls. Each crew is definable, with definable crew hours for each activity. The crews will be doing tasks that can be described in a simple set of instructions and drawings. The progress can be measured by the quantity of work completed.

Section	Activity	Quantity	Quant. to Date	% Complete	Crew Hours	Craw Hrs to Date	Cost to Date	%comp x Budget	Variance	Projected Variance
03112	Set Formwork	2500 LF	900 LF	36%	240	80	$17,704.00	$19,120.32	$1,416.32	$3,934.22
03113	Strip Formwork	2500 IF	400 LF	16%	60	20	$ 1,200.00	$ 728.64	($471.36)	($2,946.00)
03202	Install Rebar	2500 LF	800 LF	32%	68	16	$ 1,543.20	$ 2,098.75	$ 555.55	$1,736.10
03302	Pour Walls	1000 CY	320 CY	32%	64	16	$ 2,428.80	$ 3,106.88	$ 680.06	$2,125.20
03303	Sack Walls	40000 SF	3200 SF	8%	120	8	$ 404.80	$ 485.76	$ 80.98	$1,012.00

Figure 12–8   Cost Account Analysis

• Comparison of actual and estimated cost should be done immediately, providing data to field management personnel.

• A feedback system should be in place to receive information from the crew relating to the cause of variances between estimated and actual costs.

• The crews need to be thanked when they accomplish the task under the estimated cost.

• Crews need to be encouraged when costs are over the estimate. There usually are factors that cause labor to overrun the estimate—active project management finds the problem and solves it.

Inefficient productivity usually has a reason or reasons for not achieving the target. Several different reasons exist for low productivity, and several solutions exist to solving the problems. The most common response to low productivity is encouraging the crew to work faster. There may be other solutions, however. Management should examine possibilities such as improving its role in activities, obtaining additional funding for activities (such as change orders), and managing subcontractors, with possible back-charges for impacted delay costs.

The chart in Figure 12–9 includes the most common reasons for low productivity and offers some possible solutions to those problems.

Field management is not always aware of the problems or source of problems because sufficient dialogue does not occur between the crew and management. Conversations with crew foremen and crew members often indicate the problem. Easy reporting, such as a questionnaire of yes-and-no questions, can provide enough input to field management to start an immediate investigation of the problems.

Productivity Problem	Possible Solution
Poor instructions/layout	Field management; improve instructions
Incorrect installation techniques	Field management; provide training to crew
Inexperienced/Untrained crew	Field management; train crew; hire new crew
Poor or incorrect details for the installation	Architect: clarification; possible change order
Incorrect sequencing	Field management; rearrange schedule
Poor, insufficient, or incorrect shop drawings	Supplier: revise drawings, possible back-charge
Insufficient time allowed	Field management: reassess crew time; rearrange schedule; revise historical cost data
Wrong or not enough tools and equipment	Field management: supply crew with proper tools
Insufficient, incorrect, or late delivery of materials	Field management: assess problem—supplier or field management? Arrange for material ASAP
Defective materials	Supplier: replace materials ASAP; possible back-charge
Poor material location requiring rehandling	Field management: relocate material; revise jobsite proper material handling
Wrong crew size	Field management: adjust crew size—could be larger or smaller
Attitude of crew	Field management: find source of problem; solve problem: may have to change some personnel
Unknown (latent) conditions	Field management: notify architect; possible change order
Poor environmental conditions: heat, light, ventilation	Field management: provide necessary equipment to adjust environmental conditions
Interference or additional instructions by other parties, outside of contract channels	Field management: discuss with appropriate party; possible change order
Late, unwarranted rejection, or beyond scope inspection	Field management: discuss with appropriate party; possible change order
Weather conditions	Field management: determine if weather is beyond normal; possible change order

Figure 12–9   Productivity Problems and Solutions

Summary

Control of time and cost are two of the most important tasks of the field management team. Controlling the project to minimal time and cost is the contractor's prime objectives. Time relates to cost, as shorter durations should reduce the cost of jobsite overhead on the project. Time and cost control, however, are normally separate tasks on the jobsite. This can be accomplished by individuals being assigned solely to the controls area or by project field engineers.

The project plan is the superintendent's method for constructing the project. It will have its own activities, durations, sequences, interrelationship of activities, equipment usage, personnel, material delivery constraints, weather constraints, and predictable delays. It is flexible and responsive to changes; its activities must be monitored, updated, and revised to reach each goal. The project's sequence, controlled by the superintendent, can be analyzed for time impact and associated costs.

The schedule is the communications tool of the project plan. Various forms of schedule representation are available and should match the comprehension level of the parties involved. Scheduling software can be used that will calculate the critical path and float of noncritical items.

Cost control compares the estimated and actual cost. Cost control accounts should match activities done in the field. Prompt comparison of costs can provide field management with opportunities to adjust methods, with the actual cost meeting or being less than the estimated cost.

Review Questions

1. What are some considerations in preparing the project plan?

2. What are some considerations that are necessary to determine duration of activities?

3. What are some information items the contractor uses from the project schedule?

4. What schedule information should be sent to subcontractors?

5. What are the three primary methods to use to get the project back on schedule?

6. What is the comparison made in cost control?

7. What are some of the reasons a cost control system is used for a construction firm?

8. What are the major considerations for a cost control system?

9. What would be some solutions to the following productivity problems?

   Incorrect installation techniques

   Insufficient shop drawings

   Poor crew attitude

   Unknown conditions

Chapter 13

Waste and Environmental Management and Sustainable Construction Practices

Objectives

This chapter discusses waste management on the jobsite and the subject of sustainable construction practices and techniques. The objectives of this chapter are to introduce the following:

- Setting processes and the methods for waste management on the jobsite
- The superintendent's role in managing a sustainable construction process
- Sustainable design and construction
- LEED certification and the role that construction and the jobsite play in the process

Waste management is not new to the construction process. It is considered during the entire project, from the estimate to the implementation and completion of the physical construction. Today's jobsite management is well aware of the problems of hazardous waste recognition, safety in handling, the regulation requirements, and the reduction and control during the production process. The project team has long understood the problems associated with waste, that is, what causes it, the hazards it can cause, and the potential impact to our environment. Contractors instinctively try to eliminate waste and rework, plan for the reuse of material where feasible, and participate in the discussion to create sustainable buildings. Waste material by its nature is wasted dollars, and when the project can reuse material, such as formwork, all attempts are generally made to reuse material. No contractor or project team member knowingly orders extra material or throws away good material when it could be returned, reused, or recycled. But saying all this, the industry is quickly incorporating new materials and designing new systems that the project team may not have ever incorporated into a project before. The economics and the political winds have greatly changed in the past few years with owners wanting to participate in "green building" or "sustainable construction."

Creating the Jobsite Environment Management Plans

The idea of creating a waste management plan is a relatively new idea, and a quick survey of today's construction sites would find very few documented waste management plans in place. In the near future, waste management plans will be as common as the other types of formal plans generated for the management of the project. A typical outline for a waste management plan might include the following:

A. Waste Management Goals and Planning
  1. Waste will be controlled by use of a detailed waste management plan.
  2. The plan will set specific goals that are measurable.
     a. Goals for recycling and salvage (by weight of total waste anticipated on the project) are set at ___ percent.
     b. Goals for reducing waste will be documented and passed on to the company as a whole.
     c. Goals for other sustainable processes will be set for each different phase, system, or parts of the project.
B. Communication and Education Plan
  1. Communication Plan
     a. Internal
     b. Specialty Contractors

2. Education Plan

   a. Internal

   b. Specialty Contractors

It is important that the project team communicates the project goals. This is not a top-down process but a collaborative process that includes the crafts to the chairman. This project will implement a continuous improvement plan for waste, environmental considerations, and sustainable education.

C. Evaluation Plan

  1. Recycling operations tracking

  2. Communication checklist

  3. Short form waste audits

  4. Full waste management audits

  5. Cost and materials tracking

  6. Final report

D. Specific Topics:

Design Phase

  1. Waste prevention in the design documents

  2. Create and suggest green alternates

Construction Phase

  1. Waste prevention during operations

    a. Waste due to theft

    b. Waste due to operations

  2. Waste prevention during purchasing

  3. Recycling and reuse of waste on site

  4. Understanding local and state material recycling and salvage requirements

  5. Storm water pollution prevention requirements

  6. Create and suggest "green" alternates to the specified materials

  7. Understand the required documentation for LEED and Green Globes

Operations Phase

  1. Operations and Maintenance

    a. Produce documents for owner so that equipment can be operated as designed and is being maintained as specified by the manufacturer. (Some new equipment has narrow operation limits to keep it at peak environmental performance.)

Waste Management in the Design Phase

Contractors are often active in the design phase when involved in design-build, construction management at risk, and agency construction management contractual relationships. This early involvement in the process provides the opportunity to help build realistic specifications for reducing waste in the construction process.

Designers are typically aware of the physical attributes of materials; however, they don't usually consider the waste generated by the use of the material in the construction process. The contractor is aware of the efficient use of material and its waste in each application. This insight can help the designer choose the optimal material for each particular use.

The specification needs to reflect what the owner is intending to accomplish concerning waste management. The specification should include requirements to achieve reduction of waste, such as requiring detailed waste management plans from the contractor and trade contractors on the jobsite.

Waste is generated in a systematic process that can be scheduled. Begin making schedule requirements that will illustrate when and how waste will be generated. The schedule should be used to better understand waste generation and how best to recycle, reuse, or dispose of the different kinds of materials being used on the project.

High-performance buildings are relatively new, and the use of "green" alternatives is not common today, though in the near future most buildings will have some sustainable features. Contractors are in a unique position. They have installed and constructed with many of these new green materials, know their costs, and understand the different estimating and costing methods associated with them. Contractors are in the position to positively help in the life cycle costs of buildings and can create solid green alternatives. Life cycle costing is a key to creating the economics for the use of many new materials that may cost more on installation but in the long term create savings in other areas. Not only can green products be less expensive in the operations of buildings, but they can also produce better working environments for the people using the facilities.

Waste Management in the Construction Phase

Waste Due to Theft

Many of the green materials used in construction are expensive and not readily available, making them susceptible to jobsite theft. When implementing jobsite security systems, emphasis should be planned for the "green" materials. Theft and vandalism will create unanticipated waste that will cause extra costs and delays. Today's site surveillance is relatively inexpensive and effective using Internet cameras and wireless technology.

Waste Due to Operations

This is an area in which contractors typically excel. They continually analyze their construction processes to decrease waste. A typical analysis of a project waste stream is shown in Figure 13–1. Note that Residential Construction waste stream is different than Commercial

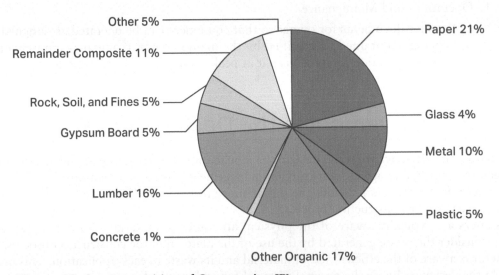

Figure 13–1   **Composition of Construction Waste**

© Queen's Printer for Ontario, 2004. Reproduced with permission.

Figure 13–2 Waste Management. Clear signage on waste bins.
iStock.com/ChrisSteer

Construction and Heavy Civil Construction waste stream. Each project will have its own waste stream characteristics. Once the project's waste stream (materials and amounts) is identified, methods for recycling, disposal, and handling can easily be developed.

The contractor should have documented procedures for waste reduction and provide records of the waste management on the project. Storage practices should be reviewed for every project and preplanned. Storage for specialty contractor material also needs to be considered in this plan.

Waste Prevention During Purchasing

Much waste prevention can happen during the purchasing process. Questions need to be asked:

- How is the material packaged?
- Is the packaging material green?
- Can the packaging material be used in other ways?
- How is the material shipped?
- Is there a plan or a buyback program for returning pallets and containers and/or excess material?

Most contractors and specialty contractors have never asked questions of their suppliers or of each other that would help both reduce the waste stream and create a greener completed building. Today, materials are typically over packaged; by knowing which products don't create a dumpster full of nonrecyclable packaging, the project can save labor and costs involved in that activity. This is also a prime time to plan for future recycling if products are packaged in recyclable packaging. The process of purchasing materials is an area that can directly involve the specialty contractors. When subcontractors are in charge of their own material purchases and have the incentive to create less waste, they do so. Projects that have much of the material supplied by the general contractor for the subcontractors will see an increase in the waste from those subcontractors. Because installation of materials is production based, subcontracts must contain incentives and directions in the area of waste.

Recycling and Reuse of Waste On-Site

Recycling and reuse of waste does not just happen; it is a planned activity. There is more to recycling than supplying separate bins for a jobsite's waste. It is important to understand the project and its waste stream to have a cohesive, well-thought-out plan for the recycling,

Figure 13–3   Crushing Waste Material for Reuse at the Jobsite

reuse, and/or discarding of all waste material that is generated on the jobsite. This plan should include documentation of how the waste is generated and a plan of implementation for dealing with such items as scrap lumber, the disposal and reuse of concrete rubble, the reuse of plant material, and the disposal or reuse of drywall. This list goes on and on, relating to the nature of the project and the project's requirements. It should be noted that recycling and its accountability can happen only through education of all participants involved in the project. Sometimes personnel or company policies will defeat the purpose of a good waste and recycling plan on a project, such as the policy that craftspeople are not allowed to remove excess material from the project.

Understanding Local and State Material Recycling and Salvage Requirements

When considering any program of material recycling and salvage, it is imperative to know which materials can or cannot be put in landfills, which materials can be mulched, and which materials need to go to special disposal sites. As part of setting up a project, research needs to be done on local disposal and recycling options. Again, this is an area where questions have to be asked and answered:

- Where are the disposal sites?

- Are they close to the project?

- What type of waste is accepted for disposal or recycling?

- Are waste transit services offered, or does the contractor need to deliver the materials to the disposal site?

- What is the disposal fee?

- Does it center on poundage of waste or per item (appliances)?

- Are the fees the same for green and nongreen waste?

Today, all local governments have legislation on sustainable practices. The contractor needs to adhere to its local and federal laws concerning material recycling and salvage. It can be very expensive to dispose of material in an improper manner just to save tipping fees.

Figure 13–4   Trash Chute Used for Safety and to
Prevent Dust

Storm Water Pollution Prevention Requirements

Preventing storm water runoff is not only a green requirement; it is federal law. The jobsite creates many different kinds of pollutants that can enter our streams, lakes, and other sources of freshwater. Every vehicle on site is fueled by gas or diesel, which is considered a hazardous material with specific cleanup and reporting requirements but is not the only hazardous material found on the jobsite. Properly disposing of excess concrete and concrete washout is another site consideration. A site needs to be ready for the potential storms that will occur, thus the need for storm water pollution prevention plans that begin with recognizing the hazardous materials on the jobsite. The plan also should illustrate how those materials will be handled during the process of completing the project and in case of inclement weather. The plan should also include identification of responsible parties and detail possible penalties if the plan is not implemented.

Formal storm water pollution prevention plans (SWPPPs) need to be formulated for each project, considering the specific jobsite needs. Creating stable soil conditions; using grasses during construction, filter fences, wattles, exit grates to knock off dirt from equipment tires; and providing adequate dust control contribute to a more sustainable project. Doing business today and running the jobsite has different responsibilities than in the past. Monitoring trucks and other equipment for leaks and having the proper spill kits on hand and crews trained in the cleanup process are examples of new, regulation-driven management areas of the project.

Create and Suggest Green Alternatives to the Specified Materials

Generally the contractors understand their materials, but today there is a wave of new green materials. Green materials include materials with recycled and recyclable content, low amounts of volatile organic compounds, and low environmental impact. It is imperative for the contractor to investigate and learn about these new materials as they come on the market. A new plan should be created and introduced into the firm solely for the purpose of green material research. This could be accomplished by creating a new position or as easy as the contractor setting a couple hours aside each week for green research. Reporting of new, applicable green materials should be an agenda item in monthly meetings and documented in the meeting minutes. The contractor plays a very important role in understanding, making suggestions, and being a key player from design to commissioning of the project. Individuals and members of a construction firm must continue to have a process to evaluate these new materials, both from the idea of suggesting or even creating green alternatives and to provide value on service life and other important costing ideas.

Understand the Required Documentation for LEED and Green Globes

Each member of the construction team must understand one's role in the documentation process and installation process. Most certifications require a specific level of documentation. Waste management, waste diversion, reuse, source reduction, and recycling are all difficult if not done from the beginning of the project. Important job documents that could affect profitability and performance can be lost forever if not done at the time the activity happens. Contractors generally will have requirements to keep record drawings as the project progresses but will also have documentation requirements associated with LEED and Green Globes requirements. These can be accomplished by specific reference in project subcontracts but also need to be part of the ongoing review of subcontractor requirements, similar to the procedure used with record drawings.

Specialty and Subcontractors' Role in Waste Management

Specialty contractors knowledgeable in green practices and the use of green materials pertinent to their field of work play a large, positive role in waste management. They can also add to making the project team a potential leader in the technical areas of sustainable practices. They can be an important source of information about sustainable construction practices and the design of high-performance buildings. As design-build continues to move into the mainstream of delivery processes, the subcontractors' role in the design will also continue to increase, as they are best equipped to understand how design decisions will impact the project specifics. They are at the cutting edge of new product development and are being constantly bombarded with the literature and the discussion of these new products and methods of installation. The wise subcontractors understand green practices and learn about new green developments in their field. A wise contractor contracts and builds positive working relationships with subcontractors who are knowledgeable in green practices and savvy of new green materials and their uses.

Storm Water Management

Storm water management generally starts with the requirement and development of a SWPPP. This became a federal requirement in 2000 by order of the Environmental Protection Agency (EPA). The development of the SWPPP should be done by the individuals who have operational control over the construction site. A major part of this plan requires the control of the construction process in both the planning of the site and the planning of jobsite activities. SWPPP plans are required by the EPA and are regulated under the National Pollutant Discharge Elimination System (NPDES) storm water program. A plan is required for all construction projects/activities (including other land-disturbing activities) that disturb one acre or more. Construction storm water runoff has been determined to cause environmental damage to our rivers, lakes, and coastal waters in the form of animal, plant, and fish destruction, sedimentation and erosion; and pollution. While these issues are addressed in the storm water management plan, they must also comply with the Clean Water Act.

Storm water regulations are still in a dynamic state. Additional and new regulations came into effect on March 10, 2003. The new regulations stated that coverage was now to be one to five acres from the construction site that could be disturbed during the construction process. This also includes smaller sites that are part of a larger common plan for development or sale. The previous regulation covered sites that disturbed more than five acres.

Owners and the contractors on these construction sites are required to create and implement SWPPPs. Permit coverage is applied for and received from an authorized state department. If the state where the project is being performed is not authorized by the EPA to issue NPDES permits, the EPA will issue the permits. Most states are authorized to implement the NPDES permit program, including the storm water program.

When the EPA is the permitting authority, contractors must follow the Construction General Permit (CGP), which states provisions that need to be followed to meet and comply with NPDES storm water regulations. Sites that are one acre or more, which also include smaller areas that are part of a common plan designated for development or sale, are protected under the CGP. The CGP replaces previous EPA permits.

Contractors wishing to obtain a permit may contact the Notice of Intent (NOI) Processing Center via their online form or call (866) 352-7755 for questions about filing by mail.

Final 2008 Construction General Permit

In 2008, the EPA released a final CGP that deals with discharges of storm water from certain construction sites. This 2008 CGP uses primarily the same terms and conditions as the 2003 CGP, though it is issued for a two-year time period and applies only to new discharges. Concerning comments on the proposal, the EPA reorganized the content of the permit to better clarify existing requirements. Contractors that are covered and using the 2003 CGP may continue to operate under the terms of conditions of that permit and need not file a new NOI.

The Environmental Protection Agency (EPA) has issued a national regulation to limit and permit storm water discharges from construction activities and sites. This latest Construction General Permit (CGP) is dated 2012 and replaces CGP 2008. The EPA references this as the National Pollutant Discharge Elimination System (NPDES) for general permit for storm water discharges.

Indoor Air Quality and Other LEED Documentation and Requirements During Construction

Sustainability in design and construction is one of the latest major trends in the construction industry and the country as a whole. The goal is to positively change our interaction with the environment while continuing to grow and not have the negative impact on our surroundings that often happened in the past. Today, going green is more than an option. The good news about green construction techniques and sustainable movement is that new markets and clients are being created as society taps into the mainstream of the green building movement. Profits will still be generated for contractors who follow and include green in their building practices. As government requirements continue to grow, contractors who become knowledgeable about sustainable construction practices and can create in-house requirement documentation will continue to create market position.

The left diagram in Figure 13–5 illustrates the traditional conventional method relationship between schedule, cost, and quality. Today, two additional elements have been added: people and environment. This is called the sustainable method, which is rebuilding relationships between these new two elements and the past three elements. Both address the construction

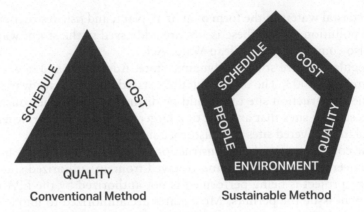

Figure 13–5   **Construction Goals**

process, but the right diagram in Figure 13–5 illustrates the new paradigm in the construction industry today. This right diagram was adapted from the Pentagon's reconstruction and its sustainable direction.

When one thinks of indoor air quality, the work environment and the properties of the physical building are the two areas that come to mind. Today, indoor air quality starts with the creation of a Construction Air Quality Plan (CAQP). Note that this plan has a number of key elements:

1. Exclude pollution sources.
2. Choose nonpolluting materials.
3. Manage moisture and humidity.
4. Ventilate effectively.
5. Protect the material and equipment to be installed from fabrication, delivery, and installation.
6. Document both by photos and by written descriptions.
7. Create a method to measure the effectiveness of the plan.

The plan should be divided into three areas:

1. What happens during construction?
2. What happens during commissioning?
3. What documentation and records are needed for owner occupancy as it relates to the other two items?

Note that the CAQP prevents poor air quality during construction along with providing quality air after construction. When using the building equipment to provide air during construction, specific techniques should be used to ensure that the construction process has not become a source of poor air quality for the occupying owner. Special consideration in the area of mold mitigation is also a prime air quality issue often overlooked. A mold prevention plan could and should be part of an overall air quality plan. Today, mold has become a major area of litigation in the design and construction industry. "Sick-building syndrome" is often associated with the issue of mold. Having the right CAQP in place and having it communicated to all levels can eliminate these problems after construction is completed.

During Construction

Indoor air quality is not just a building goal but also a great concern during the construction phase. Many traditional construction practices contribute to poor air quality after occupancy; for instance, ducts would arrive at the jobsite with exposed ends, open to all jobsite contaminants.

It was believed that when the air handling equipment was started, the accumulation of dust and other potential contaminants would be expelled out of the duct into the building, eliminating any air pollution problems. This has not been proven to be true, and most projects are now moving to the installation of clean ducts and the planned use of high-efficient filters during the first start-up of air-handling equipment. Air can contain other gases that come from the use of glues, paints, fillers, and other chemicals during construction. Some construction materials, such as manufactured wood products, contain formaldehyde and other potentially harmful chemicals. The term "off-gassing" is used to describe the emission of noxious gasses from manufactured products. The construction team needs to avoid such materials or have them off-gas prior to installation in the facility. This ensures that gases will not be trapped into a new structure. The carpet layers will often expose their carpets to the outside air for a period to remove any possible problems.

The other major air quality issue is the accumulation of mold due to moisture trapped in the building. Mold has been the number one existing building problem and insurance industry concern of the past 10 years. Lawsuits concerning mold have substantially affected the residential construction market in some areas.

During Commissioning

Commissioning is defined by Thomas Glavinich in his book *Contractor's Guide to Green Building Construction*: "Building commissioning is the systematic process used to verify that the completed building and the systems that comprise it operate in accordance with the owner's project requirements that were documented during the planning stage of the project and served as the basis of design." Commissioning attempts to create documentation that validates the original assumptions and green design aspects of the original design. It provides the owner third-party certification. A major part of commissioning is the validation of indoor air quality, the systems that provide the air quality, and the filter processes used in the building. Verification of equipment performance and creating a baseline for continued performance checks are all done during most commissioning periods. The practice of commissioning is more comprehensive than traditional testing and balancing done during project closeout. Commissioning is intended to confirm that the entire facility performs as intended.

Jay Enck, a member of the technical committee on building commissioning of the American Society of Heating, Refrigerating and Air Conditioning Engineers (ASHRAE), notes, "Commissioning typically helps to ensure good indoor environmental quality, reduce energy and water consumption, and improves how well the building is operated, all of which are the intent of LEED." The ASHRAE has been a leader in the development of guidelines for commissioning and the commissioning process. The commissioning process needs to have a written process that guarantees that the project has met and continues to meet the goals set forth to be considered a sustainable project. Many organizations today have developed guidelines for just this purpose. These guidelines generally fall into two major categories:

1. **HVAC commissioning:** The ACG Commissioning Guideline focuses on HVAC commissioning (www.commissioning.org)

2. **Full building process from design through construction:** California Commissioning Guide (www.cacx.org)

It should be noted that there are also other commissioning guidelines available for renovated buildings and other types of capital projects, both public and private. For the purposes of this discussion, we will focus on these two major areas. When considering the commissioning process for any project, there are a number of different approaches to choose from. One such process starts with a "Request for Proposal for Commissioning Services." A short time ago commissioning was not even being performed. Now there are companies that can fulfill these services, provide the required testing, do the system verifications, and provide start-up help. When discussing HVAC commissioning, the role of the contractor that does the original installation and who is really the responsible party for final performance must have a clear guideline of their contractual obligation through clear and full specifications. An example of specifications for HVAC commissioning is provided by the ACG guidelines referenced earlier in this paragraph. Here is a short excerpt from these sample specifications describing the "Commissioning Agency" and the "Contractor Responsibility."

A. SPECIFICATION 01660 – COMMISSIONING OF HVAC SYSTEMS

Part 1 – GENERAL 1.1 COMMISSIONING AGENCY

The commissioning agency (CA) has been contracted directly with the owner for this project. The CA has overall responsibility for planning and coordinating the commissioning process. However, commissioning involves all parties to the design and construction process, including the contractor.

1.2 CONTRACTOR RESPONSIBILITY

This Section of the specifications defines the contractor's responsibilities with respect to the commissioning process. Each contractor and sub-contractor shall review this Section, and shall include in their bids for carrying out the work described, as it applies to each Division and Section of these specifications, individually and collectively.

1.3 DESCRIPTION OF WORK

The purpose of the commissioning process is to provide the owner/operator of the facility with assurance that the mechanical systems have been installed according to the contract documents, and operate within the performance guidelines set out in the design intent documents. ....

Additional system verification and start-up checklists should be developed along with functional performance test checklists. Again from the ACG guidelines, the following list has been determined that commissioning should be done if the equipment has been designed and installed into the building, and a checklist has also been provided.

Equipment list:

Air Handling Unit

Controls Air Compressor

Hot Water Boiler

Chiller

Heating and Cooling Coils

Cooling Tower

Exhaust Fan

Fan Powered Variable Air Volume Boxes

Unitary Heat Pump—Water Source

Pumps

Return Fan

Roof Top Unit—Gas Heat/Dx Cooling

Supply Fan

Variable Air Volume Boxes

Point To Point Checks

When considering commissioning on the complete building, commissioning will start in the pre-design phase and will have activities in each of the different stages of design and construction. In the following schedule, a list of activities is outlined under each design and construction stage. This list comes from the California Commissioning Guide but is a very good outline for any project.

Commissioning Process Overview

Pre-Design Phase

- Select a commissioning lead.
- Pre-design phase commissioning meeting.
- Begin developing owner's project requirements.
- Develop initial commissioning plan outline.

Design Phase

- Design Phase commissioning meeting (If pre-design meeting didn't occur).
- Perform commissioning-focused design review.
- Update commissioning plan.
- Develop commissioning requirements for the specification.
- Begin planning for verification checklists, functional tests, systems manual, and training requirements.

Construction Phase

- Construction phase kick-off meeting.
- Review submittals, monitor development of shop and coordination drawings.
- Review O&M manuals.
- Perform ongoing construction observation.
- Perform verification checks.
- Perform diagnostic monitoring.
- Perform functional testing.
- Develop commissioning report and systems manual.
- Develop re-commissioning plan.
- Verify and review training of owner's staff.

Occupancy and Operations Phase

- Resolve outstanding commissioning issues.
- Perform seasonal/deferred testing.
- Perform near warranty-end review.

The Commissioning Process Overview is from the California Commissioning Guide, 2006, www.cacx.org/resources/documents/CA_Commissioning_Guide_New.pdf, written by the California Commissioning Collaborative 2006.

It is interesting to review the list of activities or tasks that are to be performed during the construction stage. All of these activities are normal activities with the exception of "Develop Commissioning Report and Systems Manual" and "Develop Re-commissioning Plan." And even these two activities are not completely out of normal tasks required by the specification. Having a "System Manual" could be required and often is required as part of the owner operations manual.

During Occupancy

As owner occupancy occurs, the contractor should provide the documents that will ensure that the owner will be able to maintain and operate the equipment. The owner should be provided with all documentation and/or training for schedule concerns on maintenance items, such as air filters, that will need to be addressed and executed by their maintenance people. As an alternate, the contractor can arrange for an outside vendor who will provide continuous service and filter changing into the future for the owner. As we move into a new climate in the building industry, contractors will also need to think about a longer maintenance and warranty period to ensure that these high-performance buildings continue to operate as specified.

LEED Evaluation and Reporting

LEED is an acronym for Leadership in Energy and Environmental Design. As there are many new books on LEED, sustainability, and the green building movement, this text will not try to duplicate these complete works, but an overview would be helpful in the overall discussion of jobsite management and the role that LEED evaluation and reporting plays. The roles, level of understanding, and knowledge of the parties involved in leading and managing construction continue to increase, as does the responsibility for implementing, documenting, and completing these sustainable projects. LEED is in the forefront of creating measured workable direction in the sustainability of buildings and the sites they occupy. Even as of this writing, the testing for individuals to become LEED-accredited professionals is changing. The authors refer the reader to the U.S. Green Building Council website at www.usgbc.org for additional information.

Summary

This chapter is a combination of reviewing in-place environmental requirements and new trends in sustainable construction and green building techniques. The number of books on green building fundamentals and LEED requirements seems to grow exponentially daily. Contractors have always understood that the projects they build include an environmental piece, but until only recently, as the number of regulations continues to grow, have they aggressively embraced the issue of waste management and been held accountable. Waste management today is as important as safety management, budget management, schedule management, and other jobsite management systems. Jobsite management is more complex and includes many more areas to manage than in the past. Owners are expecting and demanding new levels of knowledge, expertise, and sophistication when it relates to the environmental side of construction.

Review Questions

1. Name four waste management activities that can be determined during the design phase.
2. What is a typical outline for a waste management plan?
3. What are the waste management inquiries that need to be asked during purchasing for the project?
4. What are typical local and state requirements for material recycling and salvage?
5. Why is the contractor qualified to suggest "green material" alternatives?

6. What does SWPPP stand for?

7. What are the key elements of a construction air quality plan?

8. What is building commissioning?

9. When considering commissioning on the complete building, list the different phases.

10. According to the example of the specification for HVAC commissioning provided by the AGC guidelines in this text, what is the purpose of the commissioning process?

Chapter 14

Building Information Modeling (BIM)

Objectives

This chapter is a discussion about the use of Building Information Modeling (BIM) in the construction process. As the use of BIM is evolving quickly with technological advances, this discussion concerns the basics of the modeling system. The objectives of this chapter are:

- The Building Information Modeling system and its components
- Compare the difference between two-dimensional (2D) construction documents and three-dimensional (3D) models
- Outline the advantages of using BIM
- Explain the use of BIM during the construction phase
- Review the use of BIM for the project owner

Building Information Modeling (BIM) is a computerized system representing the construction process. It uses three-dimensional (3D) drawings (Figure 14–1), with additional information provided within the system. Additional information, such as description of qualities, specifications, cost components, and schedule, can be contained within the model to provide a comprehensive set of construction documents. BIM is ideal for many uses in the design and construction process, providing better communications, understanding, efficiencies, and problem solving. BIM can be applied throughout the design and construction process.

Design and construction has depended on two-dimensional (2D) drawings and a separate manual of contractual requirements and specifications for communicating the intent of the project into the actual construction of the physical project. These documents use standard representation of the project elements through a variety of symbols and drawing conventions. The users of the drawings, particularly the constructors, need to be able to convert these 2D drawings to a 3D full-scale actual facility. The constructors use their expertise to provide the means and methods of construction, along with material data, installation standards,

Figure 14–1 Dimensional View of a Building

code requirements, fabrication drawings, cost estimates, schedules, and other information. The constructor needs to compile all of this information and assemble the project to satisfy the owner's needs. This is normally a complicated process necessitating considerable communication and understanding by all involved in the project.

Although the 2D construction document system has been used successfully for a very long time, there are some aspects of the system that can be improved. Computer-assisted design and drafting (CAD) systems initially provided uniform 2D construction documents. These documents were clear, uniform, and more efficient for design teams to produce. Hardcopy sets have been produced by CAD systems, which have evolved into electronic files available for jobsite computers and mobile devices. As the use of CAD systems increased, technological advances also provided opportunity for more comprehensive documents.

Communication of the Design

Although architects and engineers were comfortable using 2D drawing systems, communication of the intent of the drawings was not always understood by the parties using the drawings. Construction owners don't always have expertise in reading construction documents. As the customer and users have varied backgrounds, the architects and engineers aren't always able to adequately communicate the design of the project to those who will use the project. This disconnection in communication results in delays in design and construction, and often results in changes to the project during construction. As architects realize that the construction owner needs to understand the appearance of the project, they often have renderings prepared, showing a more realistic look of the building exterior. With the use of the 3D BIM model during the design period, the architect/engineer is able to more accurately communicate their interpretation of the owner's needs in the facility. The owner, then, is facilitated to provide insightful review, resulting in more accurate construction documents. Fewer changes, then, will need to be added during the construction period, allowing the contractor to proceed with construction. With fewer changes, the project costs will be lower and time will be saved during the construction process.

The 3D models provide a more accurate view of the proposed project than the traditional 2D drawings. With 3D drawings, the owner/user can visualize the volume of the project and project elements in some detail. Fly-through views can show interior views as well as exterior views. As detail of the model develops through the design process, increasing detail can be available for all of the stakeholders in the project (Figure 14–2).

Figure 14–2   3D Building Interior Image

AvDe/Shutterstock.com

Inclusion of Additional Information

One of the problems with the traditional construction document system is the number of accompanying documents necessary to understand the full description of the project, including materials and systems. Contracts, specifications, and other information are traditionally contained in bulky hardcopy volumes that are difficult to use at the point of use. By being able to embed material and system information within the BIM model, the viewer can easily access information that is not conventionally included in the same location as the visual image of the construction drawings. As the process moves to construction from design, more information can be included within the model for cost, schedule, and current progress.

Laser scanning can be used to reflect exact existing conditions in renovation projects that can be used in the BIM model. This process increases the accuracy of the BIM model, and provides reliable information for estimators and constructors. When the construction documents actually depict existing conditions, estimators can identify the costs necessary for the construction work, eliminating or reducing contingencies. Architects and engineers can also use these tools in preparing documents for remodels, renovations, and connections to existing facilities. Laser scanning is used primarily for existing facilities, particularly the interior of the facility.

Drones are used to photograph exterior features. Aerial views of land and real estate can be achieved easily and safely using drones. Photography from drone access can be used for construction updates, as well as land management and marketing. Laser scanning with drones is developing along with increased artificial intelligence in the scanning software.

Use of the BIM Model During Construction

Building Information Modeling (BIM) can provide additional information to enable constructors to be able to accurately estimate, layout, problem solve during construction, and manage the construction process. The model can be manipulated to examine areas that may be obscure in traditional drawings. The view of subsurface conditions for excavation, piping, waterproofing, and other operations can be enhanced by 3D images with the ability to turn, invert, and manipulate the image. This examination can provide the estimator an accurate view of the conditions to be able to determine the amount of material and make a realistic estimate of the installation time and labor necessary for the particular situation (Figure 14–3).

This ability to see all views of the location and conditions enables field personnel to develop strategies to efficiently execute the installation. Field personnel can determine access, safety considerations, activity sequence, tools, equipment, additional materials, labor skills, and methods to install the material consistent within quality standards at minimum costs from the detailed 3D drawings and information provided in the model. When accurate, detailed information is available, more accurate pricing and cost control are possible. Field personnel are able to view the 3D model for installation strategies, rather than guess regarding what will work in those conditions.

BIM models can be used to animate the sequence of construction, which can be used to clarify the scheduling sequence. Schedulers can examine and manipulate the sequence of steps to increase the accuracy in detail and in time with the project requirements. Examination of the BIM model animating the sequence of activities can reveal unforeseen steps and roadblocks, which can be analyzed and solved prior to having a field installation impact. Sequence animation can clarify responsibilities of suppliers, trades, and subcontractors.

In some construction projects, materials and installed equipment are bar-coded and have radio frequency identification tags (RFID) attached (see Figure 14–4). By connecting these tools to the BIM model, accurate depiction of the progress of construction can be made. This in-progress construction model can be used for analysis of the schedule to save time or speed up production. The accurate depiction of progress can be used to communicate with owners and other concerned entities. It can also be used to verify installations and the extent of installations for payment applications.

Figure 14–3   Schedule Information in BIM Model

Autodesk screen shots reprinted courtesy of Autodesk, Inc.

Figure 14–4   RFID Tags

Embedded Cost and Schedule Information

The BIM model can facilitate understanding of each installation by embedding information about the material, its cost, and scheduled delivery dates. This information can be easily accessed in the model and can provide immediate answers to questions and problems. If delivery information is updated, the schedule can continue to reflect the current conditions. The detailed information available in BIM models can provide enough information for systems to be prefabricated by subcontractors. Some prefabrication of systems has been done in the past, but the depth of the information available allows more prefabrication. High-quality prefabricated systems can speed up the construction process and increase the quality of the installations.

Clash Detection

BIM and the associated software can perform clash detection. Clash detection is identification of locations that building elements could incompatibly intersect (Figure 14–5). These clashes can happen frequently when using traditional 2D drawings, as the vertical position is not usually shown on the traditional drawings. When the different elements conflict in location in the field, delays result in repositioning the pieces of the systems. These delays can affect several trades simultaneously, consuming a great deal of time. The conflict between elements often results in conflict between trades during construction. If these conflicts are eliminated, considerable time will be saved and unnecessary disputes between trades will also be eliminated.

Figure 14–5 Example of Clash Detection in BIM Model. The clash area is typically highlighted in red.

Autodesk screen shots reprinted courtesy of Autodesk, Inc.

Using 3D drawings with clash detection software, architectural, structural, plumbing, HVAC, fire sprinkler, and electrical drawings can be compared for intersection. The clashes can be identified, and elements can be repositioned to avoid these clashes. This can be done during the design phase to eliminate cost and time contingencies for moving building elements.

The design documents do not detail all elements of structural and MEP installations. The design drawings are further detailed by the fabricator/installer of the system, such as the HVAC contractor, the structural steel fabricator, or the fire sprinkler contractor. These shop drawings show the exact configuration and location of structural elements, ductwork, piping, and building equipment. If these shop drawings are inserted into the BIM model, accurate field clash detection can take place prior to fabrication of the elements, avoiding costly field delays. By eliminating these delays, change orders will be decreased. The work will tend to flow better, reducing construction duration.

Accurate Construction Dimensions

When the BIM model is complete, including accurate shop drawings and product information, accurate dimensions can be provided for the field. In traditional construction drawings, horizontal dimensions are shown explicitly and scaled for installation; however, the field personnel usually need to do some field calculations. The BIM model can produce exact dimensions for daily use in construction activities. The model can produce additional dimensions, such as vertical dimension and diagonals. This can reduce the time of installation and increase the accuracy of the installation. By doing the tasks correctly initially, the work is completed optimally.

As all information in the BIM model is current, including all approved changes, it provides the crews, the subcontractors, the inspectors, and management full information that is definite, not interpreted. This information can be used by all on the project. The BIM model eliminates the use of out-of-date or incorrect drawings and information. By using local networks and the cloud, all of this information can be made available to appropriate personnel on a variety of computers and mobile devices.

Use of the BIM Model after Construction

The BIM model can be used by the facility manager during the operation of the facility for many maintenance and operations activities. The BIM model can provide accurate as-built information. As material information is embedded in the model, necessary information is easily available by accessing the model. Operations and maintenance information can also be embedded within the model, providing full information for facility operators.

The use of the model varies on projects, depending on the project size, the capabilities of the designers, contractors, and the owner's interest in BIM for the improvement of the project. Continuing use of BIM from the start of design through the construction process takes advantage of BIM benefits. Use of BIM during the construction requires the addition of technical management to input information and maintain the operation of the BIM system.

Access to the BIM model

With the increasing use of BIM in the field, contractors are adapting to full dissemination of the model to the personnel using it. BIM capabilities have been added to jobsite offices. Additional viewing stations have been installed in construction activity locations in the field. Sophisticated gang boxes are being used, which contain large electronic screens, computer, and Wi-Fi connection to allow superintendents and foremen to access the models in the field.

Information is also available on mobile devices, such as tablets, for foremen and the installation crews. These electronic tools provide access to more information and different perspectives at the work location. The use of printers for detail drawings also facilitates the use of the BIM model, its dimensions and information, for the crew. The crew can easily access this information, rather than carrying a large roll of drawings and bulky specification manuals.

Summary

Building Information Modeling provides value and progress to the design and construction process. It provides a realistic look at the facility and its components. BIM provides accurate transfer of information throughout the process. During the design process, BIM facilitates communication of the facility in detail to all of the stakeholders. Through the use of BIM, construction owners can understand the project and make changes early in the process, with less cost impact. During construction, BIM facilitates detailed coordination of systems resulting in less wasted time and higher productivity. The BIM system can also be used in efficient facility management and operation.

Review Questions

1. What is meant by the term "Building Information Modeling"?

2. What are weak points of the conventional 2D construction document system?

3. How can 3D drawings enhance communications between the construction owner and the project designers?

4. What advantages are available with 3D drawings with the construction crew?

5. What additional information is provided in the Building Information Model?

6. What possible cost savings can be realized during construction with BIM?

7. What are RFID tags and how can they be used with BIM?

8. How can the BIM model facilitate accurate dimensioning of the construction work?

9. How can the BIM model of the project be used after the completion of construction?

10. Describe some of the ways that BIM can be accessed at the jobsite.

Chapter 15

Changes and Claims

Objectives

This chapter discusses the type of changes that occur on construction projects, what causes changes to occur, and how changes can be handled, documented, and resolved. The objectives of this chapter are:

- Breakdown the types of changes
- Define the terms used in the discussion of changes
- Illustrate the change order process
- Summarize the process of moving from an unresolved change request to a claim
- Give example of a typical form that might be used in the change order process
- Explain the idea and importance of time extension as well as costs of change orders

Changes in the Construction Project

Changes will occur in every construction project. These changes can be small, such as clarifications to drawings or specifications, or quite large, dramatically affecting the scope of a project. Changes are a normal part of the construction process, as many factors must be considered during its duration. The owner, architect, and contractor must be aware of each change process and be equipped to deal with these changes professionally, objectively, and quickly. The contractor's field personnel must understand the process, be able to assess each situation accurately, and be able to work with the owner and architect regarding each change.

Changes can be made at no cost and with no change in duration, perhaps clarifying a construction detail or an installation method. Changes also can result in greater or lesser costs and require an addition or a reduction in contract time. A change order is a settlement for including a change in the contract; thus, a change order normally costs the owner more than the work that was included in the original contract amount. The optimum price on construction work for the owner is contained in the original bid if construction documents are completed within industry standards. Owner decisions on items that affect the scope of the contract should be made prior to the completion of construction documents and receipt of bids. Building a project from change orders is much like building an automobile from the auto parts store—the cost would be prohibitive. Change orders are not a means for the contractor to make enormous profits, but they reflect the cost of changing the installation during the project, with a specified markup on each item. The costs are fairly high, because most change order work must be done quickly and amended to the original work package. The specified markup for overhead and profit, particularly in public projects, may be more than the contractor used to bid the project under competitive market conditions. The change order should be viewed as a means for the owner to pay for project elements that were not included in the original documents rather than as an opportunity for the contractor to make unreasonable profits.

Changes can occur for many reasons. A discussion follows.

Owner-Directed Change of Scope

Extra work is added to or deducted from the project, and it is clearly a change of scope to the contract. Owners will occasionally add or deduct portions of work that qualify as a change in scope. A change in the scope of the work is when the amount of work is changed from that contained in the contract, as indicated by the contract documents. A change order is almost always authorized for this kind of change, although the cost of the change will influence the owner's decision to accept it.

Constructive Change

The architect or owner representative causes the contractor to perform work outside the contract. This change could occur from a simple defective specification to a directed change in the contractor's method of accomplishing the work at hand. Construction document errors and omissions can fall into this category.

Consequential Change

This occurs as a consequence of the preceding two changes. It is the impact cost that occurs on the other work that is being accomplished. Sometimes delays, resequencing and rework of other work, or the cost of extended overhead will occur. This type of change is generally the hardest to price, understand, and explain and sell to the owner and architect on the project.

Differing Site Conditions

This also can be an area for a contract change. This change usually applies to differing subsurface conditions than are indicated by contract documents or are available from geotechnical reports. Occasionally, actual conditions will not appear as assumed by the designer and as indicated in the construction documents. For instance, many times in renovation projects the designer does not have all of the construction details and plans from the original project that existed prior to the redesign. Unknown, or latent, conditions can appear after the start of construction, which can cause a change to the contract.

Jobsite Discovery of Hazardous Materials

This often causes work to stop. Compliance with federal and state codes must be reviewed and adhered to when handling hazardous material for removal, storing, or dumping. Figure 15–1 is an example of a typical clause in the General Conditions to the Contract regarding the discovery of hazardous materials.

In this case, the contractor would notify the owner of any discovery of hazardous materials, as described in the specification. The owner then needs to decide on the best way of handling the material. A change order might be written to the contractor to remedy the problem. If the owner chooses the option to hire an outside contractor, as allowed in the specification, the original contractor may request a change order for the costs and time associated with the necessary delay for remediation work.

Code Revisions

Changes can occur as a result of outside agencies, such as the local building code authority, reviewing the project after the construction contract has been awarded. If the contract has been signed before the final plan check by the inspection agencies, change orders must be written to modify the change of scope caused by the review. The construction documents are often reviewed prior to pricing the project by contractors, but occasionally some reviews are made subsequent to issuance of the construction contract.

4.5 Hazardous Materials

A. **Owner** shall be responsible for any Asbestos, PCBs, Petroleum, Hazardous Waste, or Radioactive Material uncovered or revealed at the site which was not shown or indicated in the Contract Documents to within the scope of the Work and which may present a substantial danger to persons or property exposed thereto in connection with the work at the site. The **Owner** will not be responsible for any such material brought to the site by the **Contractor**, Subcontractor, suppliers, or anyone else for whom the **Contractor** is responsible.

Figure 15–1   Hazardous Material Clause, General Conditions of the Contract

Vendor Coordination

Additional problems can occur near the end of a project when the contractor is requested to coordinate with vendors that supply and install outside equipment. Often, initial drawing and submittal coordination are not adequate to finalize the installation and operation of the equipment. Most of this equipment being discussed is noted as N.I.C. (not in contract) or O.F.C.I. (owner furnished, contractor installed). Additional installations, such as mechanical piping, might be necessary to facilitate equipment installation.

Product Substitution

Occasionally products specified are not available as market conditions shift. New products are developed, product lines change, and vendors and manufacturers drop one product for another. Sometimes the new product completely fills the requirements specified by the original item, but often it will take longer to obtain, cost more, and require a longer installation time, which can require changes in time and/or money because they can be a possible change of scope.

Change Orders

The change of scope or the addition of extra work is generally a tangible type of change. Owners can basically see the extra materials being added to the project and understand that they are paying for and receiving something additional. The extra work will require a change in the documents or a design change. As a project progresses, owners' needs may change, and they may want to change or add to the scope of the project. Construction contracts contain provisions allowing owners to make changes to the work. A contract clause providing owners with this right might be worded as shown in Figure 15–2.

It should be noted that the change is authorized by a written notice and not verbal communication, so both parties are provided with a clear definition of the work being required and who authorized the work. It is extremely important that the contractor know who can authorize a change order. This is an important issue that should be clarified at the preconstruction meeting.

Some contracts include unit prices for work that may be encountered during the project. For instance, the construction documents may request a unit price for solid rock removal beyond a specific quantity. Assume that the specification calls for 100 cubic yards of solid rock removal to be included within the contract price and requests a unit price for material beyond the 100 cubic yards. The specification would describe how the solid rock is to be measured, by bank cubic yards or loose cubic yards. The amount of rock removal over 100 cubic yards would be priced by the stipulated amount per cubic yard and incorporated in a change order.

In a unit-price contract, where quantities are specified, compensation for variance with the specified quantities may be available. The contract clause in Figure 15–3 can allow adjustment for quantity variance in a unit-price contract.

An allowable quantity variations clause in the contract gives the contractor additional protection for this type of change. This clause permits the renegotiation of a price when the quantity changes substantially, which in this case is defined as an increase or decrease in excess of 25 percent. It should be noted that not all unit-price contracts allow for adjustment of quantities. Careful examination of the contract documents is always necessary to determine the methods allowed within the contract.

Article 10 - Changes in the Work

10.1 General

   A. Without invalidating the Agreement and without notice to any surety, the owner may at any time or from time to time, order additions, deletions, or revisions in the work; these will be authorized by a written Field Order and /or a Change Order issued by the Architect.

Figure 15–2   **Changes in the Work Clause, General Conditions of the Contract**

Article 10 - Changes in the work

10.2 Allowable Quantity Variations

A. In the event of an increase or decrease in bid item quantity of a unit price contract, the total amount of work actually done or materials or equipment furnished will be paid for according to the unit price established for such work under the Contract Documents, wherever such unit price has been established; provided, that an adjustment in the contract Price may be made for changes which result in an increase or decrease in excess of 25 percent of the estimated quantity of any unit price bid item of work.

Figure 15–3   Changes in the Work Clause, General Conditions of the Contract, Unit-Price Contract

Change orders for design deficiencies, omission in the project documents, or errors in the specifications and drawings are fairly common. The process of visualizing, designing, and communicating all of the intricacies and details for a construction project is quite complicated. Architects and engineers, for the most part, produce complete and accurate construction documents. Some items, however, must be clarified or modified to meet project needs.

Occasionally during some projects, architects, engineers, and owners direct the contractor to alter the construction plan. This direction may be made to accelerate a certain portion of the project, delay the project, change a method of installation, or several other modifications of the contractor's plan or procedures. As these changes directly affect the cost of the construction bid by the contractor, compensation by change order may be necessary. The contractor's "means and methods" are considered to be under the contractor's control. **Means and methods** can be defined as the way in which the contractor constructs the designed product. Interference by the owner in these means and methods will result in extra costs. This type of change usually involves a dispute between the owner and contractor, resulting in difficulties in settlement by change order. The following example illustrates an owner-directed change concerning means and methods.

Example

In a building project, the contractor's excavation subcontractor decided on using a track-type hydraulic excavator for excavation of a sewer line trench. The excavation subcontractor's bid was based on the productivity of the hydraulic excavator, which was owned by the excavation contractor. There were no restrictions in the construction documents on the type of equipment, access, or protection of existing surrounding areas. The means and methods of the trench excavation were to be the contractor's responsibility. As construction proceeded, the owner requested that the contractor use a smaller piece of excavation equipment to minimize damage to the surrounding existing environment. Because the smaller piece of equipment was not owned by the excavation contractor, the rental rate exceeded the rate for the owned piece of equipment. The productivity of the smaller equipment was lower than the hydraulic excavator, requiring more time for the activity and resulting in higher labor costs. The excavation subcontractor requested a change order for an extra amount for a directed change in means and methods. Careful analysis and comparison were necessary to prove to the owner that the cost for the change was more than anticipated in the bid, as illustrated in Figure 15–4.

Item	Hydraulic Excavator	Rubber-tired Backhoe
Equipment	16 hrs @ $80/hr = $ 1280.	24 hrs @ $100/hr = $ 2400.
Labor	16 hrs @ $30/hr = $ 480.	24 hrs @ $ 30/hr = $ 720.
Equipment	16 hrs @ $20/hr = $ 320.	24 hrs @ $ 20/hr = $ 480.
Total Cost	$ 2080.	$ 3600.
Net Additional Cost		$ 1520.
Plus: 15% Allowable		$ 228.
Overhead & Profit		
Additional Cost Impact		$ 1748.

Figure 15–4   Cost Comparison, Excavation Change Order Example

A **change order** is an adjustment to the contract amount and/or to the contract duration, approved, accepted, and signed by the owner, architect, and contractor. An adjustment to the contract duration is needed if the contract's schedule is impacted by the additional work or delay caused in considering the change order. Some change orders will not affect the contract duration. Many contracts contain a liquidated damages clause, which stipulates a specific amount of reimbursement to the owner for completion of the contract beyond the contract completion date. A **liquidated damage** is an amount stipulated in the contract document that states that the owner receives compensation for impacted costs of late completion of a project. Liquidated damages are usually stated in a monetary amount per day, such as $1,000. Liquidated damages are not considered a penalty to the contractor for late completion of the project but rather compensation to the owner for impacted costs of not being able to use the facility when expected and contracted. If a change order affects the contractor's schedule, an extension of the appropriate number of days will be requested to ensure that liquidated damages are not imposed for the impacted period of time. Many contractors also will request payment for "impacted overhead," or jobsite overhead, for the extended contract period.

The General Conditions of the Contract clause, shown in Figure 15–5, is an example of a contract completion clause, including liquidated damages.

This example emphasizes that cost and time can be significant when related to liquidated damages. Considering the cost of jobsite overhead with liquidated damages, time is obviously an important factor in the construction project.

Article 2 - Contract times

The work shall be completed within 500 successive days from the commencement date stated in the Notice to Proceed

Article 3 - Liquidated Damages

Owner and the contractor recognize that time is of the essence of this agreement and that the owner will suffer financial loss if the work is not completed within the time specified in Article 2 herein, plus any extensions thereof allowed in accordance with Article 12 of the General Conditions. They also recognize the delays, expense, and difficulties involved in proving in a legal proceeding the actual loss suffered by the owner if the work is not completed on time. Accordingly, instead of requiring any such proof, the owner and the contractor agree that as liquidated damages for delay (but not as a penalty) the contractor shall pay the owner $ 6,000.00 for each day that expires after the time specified in Article 2 herein.

Figure 15–5   Contract Completion Clause, General Conditions of the Contract

The Change Order Process

The change order process is normally detailed in the construction contract. The term **change order** can be defined as the specific document signed by the contractor and owner that authorizes an addition, a deletion, or a revision in the scope of the work. The change order usually will adjust the contract amount and/or the contract completion date. A no-cost change order can be used to change the scope of work only to document changes from the contract documents. The sequence of events that follows is typical of the change order process, although some construction contracts will require specific time frames and slightly different sequences:

1. The contractor notices a difference between actual conditions and the conditions shown in the construction documents. The contractor notifies the architect via a request for information of the varying condition and requests direction.

2. The architect must respond to the contractor regarding what needs to be done. This is normally done in Contract Clarification.

3. The contractor must determine if this clarification is considered additional work. If it is, the contractor must price the work as quickly as possible. The architect may prepare a proposal request, followed by the official Change Order Proposal (COP), which is completed by the contractor with the pricing and request for time extension.

4. If the architect agrees that the price is appropriate for the work and if the owner agrees that a change order is necessary, the architect can prepare a change order. Work is not authorized to proceed until the change order is signed by both the owner and contractor. As the processing of a change order takes considerable time, the architect might issue a change directive or field order for the contractor to proceed with the work immediately. This change directive specifies a price for the work, or a method to determine the price, such as cost-plus-a-fee. The owner must sign the change directive. A change order may be a summary of several change directives.

The procedure described is a simplification and indicates accord by all parties. Construction contracts have a more involved procedure that considers all options. Figure 15–6 indicates the change order process under the AIA Document 201.

The process detailed in Figure 15–6 and in the General Conditions of the Contract, such as AIA Document A201, is critical to follow for successful change orders. The type of notification and conformance to the time frame are essential to a change order. Time is of the essence in this process. Authorization must be given for extra work to enable compensation for that work. It is important that all of the notifications, requests for proposals, pricing, and other change order paperwork be executed promptly and accurately. Multiple changes occurring simultaneously impact field personnel with considerable project pressures in both managing the work and documenting the changes. Despite the pressures, proper notification and authorization must be made for each change. Managing the project during these periods of pressure is still necessary. Pursuit of compensation for changes occasionally takes precedence over normal project management, resulting in lower productivity and profits for the contractor. A balance must be maintained during these periods, possibly with the addition of field personnel during these critical periods.

The change order process can be initiated by any of the parties involved, but must be made in writing. These notifications must be made within a certain time period and in a specified format. As the process continues, the owner and architect have opportunities to agree or disagree with the proposal from the contractor. If the owner and architect agree with the proposal by the contractor, the change order is processed. If the owner and architect disagree with the contractor's proposal, the contractor has three options: to revise the proposal, to withdraw the proposal, or to pursue the proposal as submitted. As this process continues, the change proposal becomes a claim. A **claim** is an unresolved change request. A claim, as defined by AIA Document A201, Section 4.3—Claims and Disputes, is a "demand or assertion by one of the parties seeking, as a matter of right, adjustment or interpretation of

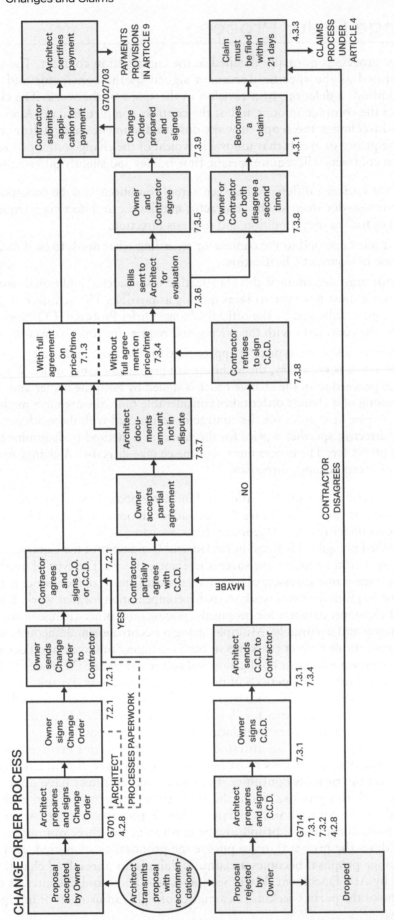

Figure 15–6   Change Order Process

Contract terms, payment of money, extension of time, or other relief with respect to the terms of the Contract." During the process, the claim can be settled, resulting in a change order, without further processing. Figure 15-7 is an example of the written notification required by the contract to start the process.

This written claim must be made in a timely manner. The exact time period will be specified in the General Conditions to the Contract. AIA Document A201 requires that the claim be made within 21 days after recognizing the change. Most contractors have formal letters of notification

FGH construction company

Change Order Proposal

To: _____   Date:_____

_____   Job No.:_____

_____

Subject: *Notification of Change or Claim for:* _____

Attn.: _____

Gentlemen:

The following *Request for Information. No. 45* has been determined by FGH Construction Company to be beyond the scope of our contract. You are hereby notified that this problem may create a suspension /delay of the work, increase scheduled time to complete the project, and/or cause additional cost to our work. We reserve the right to request additional time and costs for this work. This work could potentially have an adverse effect on other work being performed or that will be performed.

Description of Occurrence or Request for Information:

_____
_____
_____
_____
_____

Date of Occurrence   On: _____

From: _____   To: _____

You are hereby notified of our intention to seek recovery of all extra costs, including but not limited to General Condition Expenses if this delay affects scheduled completion. It is our intent to minimize the effect of this change.

Please issue the appropriate paperwork to complete this change. Thank you.
Sincerely,
Bill Jones
Project Engineer
cc: *Frank Canteen*
         Project Manager
         File CP - _____
Enclosures: _____

5390 Walnut Avenue, San Francisco,
California, 93422-0027
Phone: (415)555-2346, Fax: (415)555-2300

Figure 15–7   Change or Claim Notification

containing specific language, so the contractor is not waiving any contractual rights but rather fulfilling the notification time period as noted by the general conditions. Typical language in the body of the letter could read as follows:

> You are hereby notified that the contractor has uncovered a change of scope which directly changes the contract work. This change potentially will have costs and time impact on our contract. Please acknowledge this change of scope by issuing a formal Change Order per contract documents.

The change order or claims process will not stop the work from continuing unless it greatly impacts the proceeding work. Under section 4.3.4, Continuing Contract Performance, of AIA Document A201, General Conditions of the Contract, the contractor is contractually obligated to proceed with the completion of the contract, and the owner is obligated to continue making payments to the contracts. This area is often used to put pressure on both parties, the contractor threatening to stop work and the owner threatening to stop all payment. Contractually, neither party can refuse to uphold their part of the contract. Occasionally, both parties to the contract slow their obligations and use many tactics to influence the other.

A **Construction Change Directive (CCD)** can be used by the architect to keep work going and initiate a change order. The CCD is defined as a written notice directing a change in the work. This document can be used before a written change order has been fully agreed to by all parties. Many times a written COP from the contractor is sent to the architect following the notice of claim and used to write the CCD or the initial proposal to the owner. The CCD could look like the example shown in Figure 15–8.

It should clearly describe the additional work. It also should specify a method of determining payment by one of the following methods: a stipulated price; by unit price, including a method of measuring the units attributed to the change; or cost-plus-a-fee, when the method of measuring the cost and the fee are stipulated. Each of these price alternatives relates to the extent of the work known at the time of writing the CCD.

The information required for the COP is specifically defined by the General Conditions and often modified by the Supplementary Conditions. AIA Document A201 Section 7.3.6 generally defines the information requirement needed in the COP. A more complete specification or the modification found in the Supplementary Conditions could read as shown in Figure 15–9.

The fee for overhead and profit allowed in change orders is usually stated in the Contract Documents. The fee allowable may vary for different cost segments, as per the following example.

Example

Actual overhead and profit percentages to be added to the following direct cost categories.

Labor	20 percent
Materials	15 percent
Equipment	15 percent
Subcontractor	10 percent

The type of costs for the change order is usually stipulated in the Contract Documents, excluding off-site overhead, which is to be covered by the fee.

The COP will vary from one construction company to another but the specific form will contain most of the same information. Figure 15–10 is an example of a COP that could be adopted as a company standard.

CONSTRUCTION CHANGE DIRECTIVE
CONSTRUCTION MANAGER-ADVISER EDITION
AIA DOCUMENT G714/CMa

(Instructions on reverse side)

OWNER	☐
CONSTRUCTION MANAGER	☐
ARCHITECT	☐
CONTRACTOR	☐
FIELD	☐
OTHER	☐

PROJECT:
(Name and address)

DIRECTIVE NO.:

DATE:

TO CONTRACTOR:
(Name and address)

PROJECT NOS.:

CONTRACT FOR:

CONTRACT DATE:

You are hereby directed to make the following change(s) in this Contract:

PROPOSED ADJUSTMENTS

1. The proposed basis of adjustment to the Contract Sum or Guaranteed Maximum Price is:

   ☐ Lump Sum (increase) (decrease) of $_____

   ☐ Unit Price of $_____ per _____

   ☐ as provided in Subparagraph 7.3.6 of AIA Document A201/CMa, 1992 edition.

   ☐ as follows:

2. The Contract Time is proposed to (be adjusted) (remain unchanged). The proposed adjustment, if any, is (an increase of _____ days) (a decrease of _____ days).

Signature by the Contractor indicates the Contractor's agreement with the proposed adjustments in Contract Sum and Contract Time set forth in this Construction Change Directive.

CONTRACTOR _____

Address _____

BY _____

DATE _____

When signed by the Owner, Construction Manager and Architect and received by the Contractor, this document becomes effective IMMEDIATELY as a Construction Change Directive (CCD), and the Contractor shall proceed with the change(s) described above.

OWNER	CONSTRUCTION MANAGER	ARCHITECT
Address	Address	Address
BY	BY	BY
DATE	DATE	DATE

AIA CAUTION: You should use an original AIA document which has this caution printed in red. An original assures that changes will not be obscured as may occur when documents are reproduced.

Figure 15–8   Construction Change Directive

All necessary subcontract work is included in the COP. The contractor must solicit the necessary pricing from each subcontractor and coordinate the proper pricing. The contractor must determine which subcontracts are impacted by the change and request pricing for that work. As many changes affect virtually all of the work on the project, careful examination of the impact of each change is necessary. Determination of the work required by the contract and the additional work is usually required as well. A letter must be sent to each affected subcontractor, including an accurate description of the scope of the change; an accurate

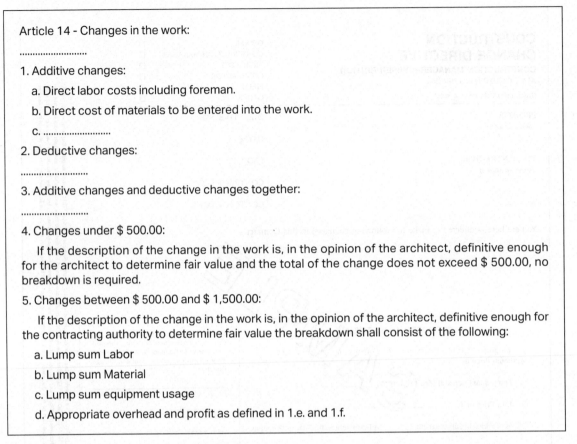

Article 14 - Changes in the work:

....

1. Additive changes:

   a. Direct labor costs including foreman.

   b. Direct cost of materials to be entered into the work.

   c. ....

2. Deductive changes:

....

3. Additive changes and deductive changes together:

....

4. Changes under $ 500.00:

   If the description of the change in the work is, in the opinion of the architect, definitive enough for the architect to determine fair value and the total of the change does not exceed $ 500.00, no breakdown is required.

5. Changes between $ 500.00 and $ 1,500.00:

   If the description of the change in the work is, in the opinion of the architect, definitive enough for the contracting authority to determine fair value the breakdown shall consist of the following:

   a. Lump sum Labor

   b. Lump sum Material

   c. Lump sum equipment usage

   d. Appropriate overhead and profit as defined in 1.e. and 1.f.

Figure 15–9   Change Order Proposal Requirements, Supplementary Conditions to the Contract

description of the scope of change to the particular subcontract; the form of proposal required; the allowable markup specified in the contract documents and the subcontract agreement; and other factors affecting the change. A formal request for cost information must be worded carefully to avoid committing the general contractor to a change until approved by the owner. Figure 15–11 is a sample letter requesting a change proposal from a subcontractor.

When using unit-price or cost-plus determination of the change order price, measurement procedures are necessary. Unit-price determination may require verification of the units affected, such as a truck count verified by the owner's inspector. Daily work reports, listing labor hours and material received, may be required for cost-plus changes. The daily work reports will probably also require verification from the owner's inspector. The form shown in Figure 15–12 could be used for cost-plus or "force account" work.

Payment for additional work is not allowed until the official change order is processed. Work description and the firm price for the work must be determined, and the change order has to be signed by both the owner and the contractor. This firm price is then included in the contract amount in the progress payment request, with payments related to the completion of the change order work.

Time Extension

The time extension requested by the contractor depends on a variety of factors. Extra work usually requires extra time to the contract. Analysis of the project schedule is necessary to show the impact of this additional work. The project may be delayed in determining what change is necessary, which also should be included in the requested time extension. Most time

FGH construction company

Change Order Proposal

To: _____   No. _____

_____   Project: _____

_____   Date: _____

From: _____

_____

_____

FGH Construction Co., wishes to submit the following Change Order Proposal for the change in scope of the contract work as described:

_____

_____

_____

_____

Cost of the work:

Description:	Labor	Mat.	Equip.	Other	Sub	Total

Labor Burden _____ %
    Subtotal
Bond Premium   _____ %
Liability Insurance   _____ %
Subtotal
Overhead
Profit

Grand Total: _____

Schedule Extension:

    Calendar Days to be added to the contract time: _____

FGH Construction will proceed on this change when authorized by _____ in writing. This information is time sensitive and is valid for 10 days without review.

Signed: _____

Title: _____

5390 Walnut Avenue, San Francisco, California, 93422-0027
Phone: (415)555-2346, Fax: (415)555-2300

Figure 15–10   **Example Change Order Proposal**

extension requests are fairly subjective, as the true impact of the change is rarely clearly determined. Discussion and negotiation of the time extension is a frequent occurrence in the change order process.

Some time extensions are due to delays in the project caused by outside influences. Most contracts allow extension of contract time for delays due to "labor disputes, fire, unusual delay in deliveries, unavoidable casualties, or other causes beyond the contractor's control." Delay

FGH construction company

Date: ______________________

Job No.: ______________________

To: ____

____

____

Subject: CP - _

Change Order Proposal for: ______________________

Attn.: ____

Gentlemen:

Please submit to the above address your firm change cost proposal encompassing your itemized Labor/Material/Jobsite Overhead/Markup as required by the specification. This cost proposal should include all additions and deletions.

For your portions of the work according to the following:

____

____

____

____

____

In the interest of saving time, submit this proposal first by fax no later than ______________
with your written confirmation to follow by mail.
This change cost proposal request is not authorization to proceed at this time so it is imperative that we have your proposal for review and approval by the above date. Proposals are subject to review and approval by ______________ (owner/architect) when it is incorporated into FGH Construction Company's proposal on the above mentioned project for this proposed change.

Please refer to Number CP - ______________ on all future correspondence related to this proposed cost change proposal.
Sincerely,

Bill Jones
Project Engineer
cc: ***Frank Canteen***
Project Manager
File CP - ____________
Enclosures: ____________

5390 Walnut Avenue, San Francisco,
California, 93422-0027
Phone: (415)555-2346, Fax: (415)555-2300

Figure 15–11 Sample Letter to Subcontractor Requesting Change Proposal Information

to the project due to unusual weather often is compensated by a time extension. Comparison of the average weather conditions to the actual weather conditions is made to determine the appropriate time extension. The severity of the weather also is examined. As mentioned in Chapter 4, daily documentation of weather and construction activity is essential in determining appropriate time extension. Delays in the project from unexpected sources also will extend the contractor's jobsite overhead, resulting in a request for compensation for this extended overhead cost.

Daily Time and Material Work Form

Subcontractor: _____   Date: _____

_____   Job No.: _____

_____   CP No.: _____

Description of Work: _____

_____

_____

Work in Progress: _____

Work Completed: _____

Payment for the above described work will be based upon actual cost for labor, materials, equipment, and jobsite overhead (described in specifications and subcontract).

Labor:

Name :	Craft	Journeyman Apprentice Foreman	Man-Hours

Materials Used:

Equipment Used:

FGH Const. - Superintendent _____

Subcontractor _____

5390 Walnut Avenue, San Francisco,
California, 93422-0027
Phone: (415)555-2346, Fax: (415)555-2300

Figure 15–12   Force Account Work Form

Documentation of Changes

A file should be established for each possible change, as defined by the change order proposal. This file should include all relevant documentation to the change, including photographs, daily reports, cost records, subcontractor correspondence, excerpts from meeting minutes, correspondence with the architect or owner, drawings details, applicable excerpts from the specification and contract, and other applicable information. Some computerized project documentation systems have a search function for all items related to a particular issue. This information should be assembled and kept for future reference.

Several change orders may be in processing at the same time during the project. As this involves many steps, it is extremely important to track all change proposals and change orders. A change order log records the dates of the steps in processing the change order. This log can be used to determine the current location of the change order. Clear knowledge of the responsibilities of the process helps speed up the system. Recording the dates of the processing also is necessary in claims procedures. Project meetings should involve updating the log, resulting in an updated version of the change order log being distributed with meeting minutes.

Each contractor will include different information in the change order log. Some typical information that might be included follows:

- COP number

- Change order number (after a formal change is issued)

- Description

- Original date of the COP

- Who initiated the change (individual and company)

- Price associated with the COP

- Number of calendar days for extension of contract requested

- Subcontractors that are affected and dates associated with pricing

- Date that formal change order was issued for signatures

- Status (approved or rejected) and date status was determined

- Reprocessing dates, if required

- Actual amount of the change order

- Date change order approved

An example of a change order log is contained in Chapter 5. The contractor must be able to use this log as a tool to facilitate the processing of the change orders. The log also will serve as a record of the processing. The information contained in the log for use in processing may be a bit different than the information used as a record. Change order logs can be formatted and developed on a computer spreadsheet. By using a computerized version of the change order log, different types of information can be made, and completed information can be left off if not required. As part of the change order control process, the general contractor must have a formal system for subcontract change control. On large projects, separate logs are kept of each of the major subcontractors within each correspondence file. This log must track all correspondence that relates to the change.

The formal change order should contain a complete description of the change, including additional drawings, sketches, and specification descriptions, as necessary. A detailed description of the change order will be referenced during the project, defining the work to be accomplished. AIA Document G701 is used as the formal change order when using an AIA Contract. This form, when filled out, keeps a continual cost update of the contract. This same information will show up on the application for payment. A special emphasis should note the line for change of contract time. "The Contract Time will be (increased) (decreased) (unchanged) by (___) days. The Date of Substantial Completion as of the date of this Change Order therefore is ___." This document is also signed by all three team members—the architect, the contractor, and the owner. AIA Form G701, Change Order, is shown in Figure 15–13.

CHANGE ORDER
CONSTRUCTION MANAGER-ADVISER EDITION
AIA DOCUMENT G701/CMa

(Instructions on reverse side)

OWNER ☐
CONSTRUCTION MANAGER ☐
ARCHITECT ☐
CONTRACTOR ☑
FIELD ☐
OTHER ☐

PROJECT:
(Name and address)

TO CONTRACTOR:
(Name and address)

CHANGE ORDER NO.:

INITIATION DATE:

PROJECT NOS.:

CONTRACT FOR:

CONTRACT DATE:

The Contract is changed as follows:

Not valid until signed by the Owner, Construction Manager, Architect and Contractor.

The original (Contract Sum) (Guaranteed Maximum Price) was .... $
Net change by previously authorized Change Orders .... $
The (Contract Sum) (Guaranteed Maximum Price) prior to this Change Order was .... $
The (Contract Sum) (Guaranteed Maximum Price) will be (increased) (decreased) (unchanged) by
this Change Order .... $
The new (Contract Sum) (Guaranteed Maximum Price) including this Change Order will be .... $
The Contract Time will be (increased) (decreased) (unchanged) by .... ( ) days
The date of Substantial Completion as of the date of this Change Order therefore is ....

NOTE: This summary does not reflect changes in the Contract Sum, Contract Time or Guaranteed Maximum Price which have been authorized by Construction Change Directive.

CONSTRUCTION MANAGER	ARCHITECT
ADDRESS	ADDRESS
BY DATE	BY DATE
CONTRACTOR	OWNER
ADDRESS	ADDRESS
BY DATE	BY DATE

AIA CAUTION: You should use an original AIA document which has this caution printed in red. An original assures that changes will not be obscured as may occur when documents are reproduced.

AIA DOCUMENT G701/CMa • CHANGE ORDER • CONSTRUCTION MANAGER-ADVISER EDITION • 1992 EDITION • AIA®
©1992 • THE AMERICAN INSTITUTE OF ARCHITECTS, 1735 NEW YORK AVENUE, N.W., WASHINGTON, D.C. 20006-5292
WARNING: Unlicensed photocopying violates U.S. copyright laws and will subject the violator to legal prosecution.   G701/CMa-1992

Figure 15–13   Change Order, Construction Manager—Adviser Edition

Implementation of Change Orders

The contractor's project team has not completed their work even after receiving a signed change order. Issuance of change orders to the subcontracts affected must also be accomplished. Many times the actual subcontractor change order still must be finalized and negotiated. If the contractor has asked for cost and time input from the subcontractor at each negotiation stage, from the original change order proposal to the finalized change order completion, then a finalized subcontract change order will not be hard to accomplish. This becomes a difficult process if the contractor has negotiated different terms with the owner than proposed by the subcontractor.

Summary

Changes to the contract require careful processing by the contractor. Prompt recognition of the change and its impact is important in avoiding unnecessary costs and delays. Cooperation between the architect, owner, contractor, and subcontractor also is necessary to continue construction without impact by changes.

Specific procedures are contained in each contract relating to the process flow of change requests, change orders, and claims. It is essential that these procedures are followed, complying with the requirements and time frame. In-depth knowledge of the process is necessary for all contractor's personnel involved with the project.

A variety of forms and correspondence is necessary in the change order process. Some contract document forms, such as the AIA documents, provide a complete set of forms for the process, including proposals, directives, and change orders. Proper use of these documents provides a uniform and systematic way of dealing with changes to the project. Documentation of each change order enables the contractor to deal completely with each change. This documentation also is necessary if the change order is not accepted and if a claim is pursued.

The contractor must manage the subcontractors' proposals and changes to subcontract amounts as well as the changes to the contract with the owner. Careful record keeping is necessary to keep track of all of these changes.

Changes can be managed without producing claims, which are unresolved change orders. Pursuit of claims can be expensive, involving arbitration or litigation. Honest, prompt, efficient, and cooperative processing of change orders will bring the project to a successful close, without further disagreement on contract claims.

Review Questions

1. Do all changes cost money or add time to a project? Explain.

2. Define a change order and state one reason it often carries a cost penalty.

3. Discuss in general the reasons that changes can occur.

4. What are liquidated damages, and are they a penalty to the contractor?

5. Draw a flowchart for the change order process.

6. When would a claim occur?

7. When can the contractor expect to receive payment for additional work, and why?

8. Do all cost change orders require additional time? Explain your answer.

Chapter 16

Progress Payments

Objectives

This chapter discusses progress payments and the various documents necessary for the payment process. The objectives of this chapter are to:

- Describe the variety of payment processes available and the owner's goals in progress payments
- Explain schedule of values, its contents, and its preparation
- Give examples of the uses of cash flow projections
- Summarize progress payment procedure and compilation of the progress payment

Proper management of payments for construction work is a very important responsibility of project administration for a contractor. An understanding of the process is necessary to efficiently manage the payment process. Prompt, accurate, and efficient processing of the payment request can literally save the contractor thousands of dollars on each project. A brief payment processing period will reduce interim financing costs incurred by the contractor.

Several methods of payment are available for construction work, depending on the project delivery method, the owner's financial situations, and the arrangements made for payment and payment frequency. The most common method of payment in commercial building construction, in the traditional owner–contractor contract, is monthly **progress payments**, which are partial payments for work completed during a portion, usually a month, of the construction period. By agreement, this payment frequency can be modified.

Payment for the project at the completion of the project is also done in some arrangements. This arrangement can be termed **turnkey**, as the project is delivered to the owner and payment is made for the project. In this type of arrangement, interim financing costs are included in the project cost. Speculative construction also normally requires payment after the project is completed. Although these arrangements require payment after the construction, accounting for the percentage complete at periodic periods is still necessary, usually to justify financing payments.

As the monthly progress payment is the most common method of payment in commercial building construction, this chapter will primarily deal with procedures concerning these periodic payments.

Progress payments reflect payment for the work in place and material delivered during the applicable period. Under the progress payment method, an estimate of the work completed is made and payment is made for that amount. Most contracts deduct an amount for **retainage** from the amount earned during the period. Retainage is an amount held by the owner until the final completion of the contract. It can be held for a number of reasons, depending on the owner and the owner's contracting rules. In some cases, retainage is held by the owner to complete the project, if necessary. Some owners, particularly public owners, retain an amount as a reserve fund to cover materialman and subcontractor liens on the project. Varying amounts of retainage are held by owners, usually 5 or 10 percent. This amount is expressed in the contract documents and is established in the agreement between the owner and contractor. Some contracts do not retain funds, as the contract's performance and payment bond is intended for the same purpose as retainage. When retainage is held, it is normally released in the final payment, when the contract requirements are completed.

Material delivered to the jobsite, even when not actually incorporated into the work, is usually included in the progress payment. Special care is normally taken to inventory the material stored at the jobsite. Some owners will also include material stored away from the jobsite in the progress payment, with special provisions. It is necessary to assure the owner that the material is insured and will be installed during the project. Some reluctance may occur on the owner's part in paying for material stored off-site that could be used for other projects, such as nonfabricated and generic material and lumber. The owner's primary concern with stored material is whether it will actually be incorporated into the project.

Varying methods of inspection and verification are done by the owner to determine accuracy of the payment request. This verification process can vary from a meticulous measurement of work in place and material stored to an approximation of the percentage completed for the activities. Owners and their agents, such as architects, engineers, and construction managers, are concerned that the proper amount be paid, without overpayment.

The actual payment period varies from contract to contract. The frequency of payment is generally on a 1-month, or 30-day, basis, but the actual cutoff dates can vary. Generally, the payment period extends from the first to the last day of the month. There are, however, many variations regarding the exact start and cutoff dates, depending on the owner's processing requirements. If the owner requires the verified payment on the first day of the month, the actual cutoff date may be the twentieth day of the month to facilitate compilation and review the progress payment request. This type of payment period is relatively easy to incorporate into the project procedures; however, each supplier and subcontractor must be made aware of the cutoff dates used for the project.

The Schedule of Values

The **schedule of values** is a written list in tabular form of the value amounts relating to the activities of work, associated with appropriate monetary amounts for each activity. The schedule of values is not time related but merely a list of the value of the construction activities upon which progress payments are based.

The items for the schedule of values are often prescribed in the project manual and are selected to accurately monitor the progress of the project. The activities listed should be adequately detailed to facilitate estimation of the percentage of completion of the item. Too many items in the schedule of values unnecessarily complicate the payment process. Some projects use the activities in the construction progress schedule as the schedule of values. This method creates a large number of payment activities. It is the authors' opinion that use of the construction schedule activities as the schedule of values for payment requests emphasizes the payment schedule rather than using it as a planning tool during construction. A separate schedule of values separates the management of payment request processing and construction scheduling.

The schedule of values normally will list construction activities that are identifiable as a system or installation. The list in Figure 16–1 shows two fairly typical schedules of values, with varying detail.

Example 1 is a broad-scope example of detail in the schedule of values. Example 2 takes the broad-scope of items in Example 1 and divides them into further detail, matching actual work activities. Example 2 provides a more accurate activity breakdown for estimating the

Example 1		Example 2	
Sitework	$ 50,000.00	Mass Excavation	$15,000.00
		Structural Excavation	$20,000.00
		Landscaping	$ 5,000.00
		Asphalt Paving	$ 7,000.00
		Concrete Walks	$ 3,000.00
Concrete	$125,000.00	Concrete Walls	$75,000.00
		Concrete Slabs	$35,000.00
		Precast Concrete	$15,000.00
Masonry	$ 80,000.00	Masonry	$80,000.00

Figure 16–1 Comparison of Detail in a Schedule of Values

amount completed in a given period. Estimates of actual progress will be more accurate using the detailed breakdown in Example 2.

The values for these construction activities normally include all material, labor, equipment, subcontracts, and distributed overhead and profit for each item.

Several items are optional for inclusion in the schedule of values, depending on the customs of the owner and architect and engineer. Some owners prefer that all overhead items be distributed into the construction activities. Others realize that some direct overhead items should be included in the schedule of values, as they relate to specific expenses incurred by the contractor. Some of these items include the following:

- *Mobilization:* Several costs are incurred by the contractor at the very start of a project. Some relate to temporary facilities, including transportation and setup of office and storage facilities for the contractor and subcontractors; temporary security fencing; installation of temporary utilities, such as power, water, and telephone; and access routes for the jobsite. Some of these initial costs include immediate payments required for performance and payment bonds, builder's risk insurance, and building permits. Some contracts treat the building permit as a reimbursable cost, paid by the owner when incurred by the contractor. Some owners refuse to pay for the performance bond initially and feel that it should be distributed evenly throughout the contract.

- *General conditions:* General conditions costs normally relate to direct (jobsite) overhead. The following items could be included in the general conditions value: cost of supervisory personnel, such as superintendent and field engineers, which would not be included in the work activities; monthly costs for temporary facilities; cleaning costs, both in progress and final; jobsite trucks and equipment; and miscellaneous direct overhead. These costs would be paid in monthly progress payments, as the costs would be incurred.

- *Punch list:* Many owners and architects and engineers include an additional item for punch list items. The **punch list** is a list of items that must be completed or repaired prior to final completion. Without the punch list value, all of the money in the project is claimed without anything left to cover the cost of completing the punch list. The project retainage often is not available to finish the punch list items, as it may be reserved for liens or reinvested in an interest-bearing escrow account. The punch list items are actually part of the work activities, and the amount to cover the list should be deducted from the work activity values. Many owners will assign a percentage of the contract amount to the punch list, usually from 1–5 percent.

The contractor's estimate is normally not arranged into the necessary items for a schedule of values. The estimate probably has more items than are required for the schedule of values. The contractor's estimate, which is confidential to the contractor, includes explicit items for indirect overhead and profit, included in the line items in the schedule of values. It is not customary for the contractor to reveal the amount of profit or indirect overhead in the project. As the estimate detail is different than the detail in the schedule of values, computation of the schedule of values is necessary. This computation involves the combination of estimate items relating to the schedule of values items; the separation of some lump-sum items, particularly subcontractor bids, into two or more schedule of value items; and the distribution of overhead and profit into the schedule of value items. Figures 16–2 through 16–7 illustrate the translation of the estimate into the schedule of values.

Figure 16–2: Example Estimate Summary Sheet

This is a typical contractor's estimate summary sheet, following the CSI MasterFormat and showing the costs for labor, material, equipment, and subcontracts for each item. It is more detailed than required for a schedule of values. The overhead and profit are shown as line items. The information from this summary sheet should be reorganized into a schedule of values.

Example Estimate Summary Sheet

Section	Description	Labor	Material	Equipment	Sub-Contract	TOTAL
00600	Bonds					$15,600
00650	All-Risk Insurance					$1,600
01050	Field Engineering	$2,000				$2,000
01450	Superintendent	$52,200				$52,200
01500	Temporary Facilities	$2,000	$2,000	$5,000	$1,000	$10,000
01710	Final Cleaning	$2,000	$300	$250		$2,550
02200	Earthwork				$45,000	$45,000
02510	Asphalt Paving				$27,600	$27,600
02900	Landscaping				$22,000	$22,000
03100	Concrete Formwork	$2,000	$1,300		$25,000	$28,300
03200	Concrete Reinforcing		$9,000		$10,500	$19,500
03300	Cast-In-Place Concrete	$4,000	$22,400	$2,500		$28,900
04000	Masonry				$65,000	$65,000
05100	Structural Steel	$4,500	$67,000		$45,000	$116,500
05200	Metal Joists		$34,000			$34,000
05300	Metal Deck		$23,000			$23,000
05520	Metal Handrails	$3,500	$4,000			$7,500
06100	Rough Carpentry	$1,200	$1,300			$2,500
06200	Finish Carpentry	$23,000	$65,000			$88,000
07150	Dampproofing	$600	$1,000			$1,600
07200	Insulation				$22,000	$22,000
07250	Fireproofing				$16,500	$16,500
07500	Roofing & Flashing				$65,000	$65,000
07900	Joint Sealants				$9,600	$9,600
08100	Metal Doors & Frames	$7,500	$34,000			$41,500
08350	Folding Doors	$2,500	$4,300			$6,800
08500	Metal Windows				$25,600	$25,600
08700	Finish Hardware		$23,000			$23,000
08800	Glazing				$9,340	$9,340
09250	Metal Studs/Gyp.Bd.				$102,000	$102,000
09310	Ceramic Tile				$16,500	$16,500
09510	Acoustical Ceilings				$35,000	$35,000
09600	Floor Covering				$43,000	$43,000
09900	Painting				$56,000	$56,000
10100	Tackboards	$1,000	$3,000			$4,000
10150	Toilet Compartments	$2,000	$4,000			$6,000
10400	Signage	$2,000	$5,600			$7,600
10520	Fire Extinguishers	$500	$4,500			$5,000
10800	Toilet Accessories	$2,400	$4,350			$6,750
15000	Mechanical				$123,000	$123,000
16000	Electrical				$104,000	$104,000
	Subtotal					$1,321,540
	3% Indirect Overhead					$39,646
						$1,361,186
	5% Profit					$68,059
	Total Bid					$1,429,246

Figure 16–2   Example Estimate Summary Sheet

Figure 16–3: Example Schedule of Values, Computations

This figure shows the combination of items from the estimate summary sheet (Figure 16–2) into items for the schedule of values. The requirements for the schedule of values on this particular project requires a punch list item of one percent of the contract amount. One percent of each schedule of value item has been deducted and combined into a punch list line item. The total for this worksheet indicates the project costs, without markup added at this point.

Example Project, Schedule of Values Computations

SOV Item	Estimate Item	Amount		Less 1%
Mobilization	Bonds	$15,600		
	All-Risk Insurance	$1,600		
	Temporary Facilities	$10,000		
			$27,200	$26,928
General Conditions	Field Engineering	$2,000		
	Superintendent	$52,200		
	Final Cleaning	$2,550		
			$56,750	$56,183
Earthwork	Earthwork	$45,000	$45,000	$44,550
Site Improvements	Asphalt Paving	$27,600		
	Landscaping	$22,000		
			$49,600	$49,104
Concrete	Concrete Formwork	$28,300		
	Concrete Reinforcing	$19,500		
	Cast-in-place Concrete	$28,900		
			$76,700	$75,933
Masonry	Masonry	$65,000	$65,000	$64,350
Structural Steel	Structural Steel	$116,500		
	Metal Joists	$34,000		
	Metal Deck	$23,000		
	Metal Handrails	$7,500		
			$181,000	$179,190
Carpentry	Rough Carpentry	$2,500		
	Finish Carpentry	$88,000		
			$90,500	$89,595
Dampproofing	Dampproofing	$1,600	$1,600	$1,584
Insulation	Insulation	$22,000		
	Fireproofing	$16,500		
			$38,500	$38,115
Roofing/Flashing	Roofing/Flashing	$65,000	$65,000	$64,350
Sealants	Sealants	$9,600	$9,600	$9,504
Doors, Hardware	Metal Doors & Frames	$41,500		
	Folding Doors	$6,800		
	Finish Hardware	$23,000		
			$71,300	$70,587
Windows, Glazing	Metal Windows	$25,600		
	Glazing	$9,340		
			$34,940	$34,591
Interior Partitions	Metal studs/Gyp.Bd.	$102,000	$102,000	$100,980
Acoustical Ceilings	Acoustical Ceilings	$35,000	$35,000	$34,650
Ceramic Tile	Ceramic Tile	$16,500	$16,500	$16,335
Resilient Flooring	Floor Covering (50%)	$21,500	$21,500	$21,285
Carpet	Floor Covering (50%)	$21,500	$21,500	$21,285
Painting	Painting (85%)	$47,600	$47,600	$47,124
Wallcovering	Painting (15%)	$8,400	$8,400	$8,316
Specialties	Tackboards	$4,000		
	Toilet Compartments	$6,000		
	Signage	$7,600		
	Fire Extinguishers	$5,000		
	Toilet Accessories	$6,750		
			$29,350	$29,057
Plumbing	Mechanical (40%)	$49,200	$49,200	$48,708
HVAC	Mechanical (45%)	$55,350	$55,350	$54,797
Fire Protection	Mechanical (15%)	$18,450	$18,450	$18,266
Electrical Power	Electrical (25%)	$26,000	$26,000	$25,740
Electrical Circuits	Electrical (20%)	$20,800	$20,800	$20,592
Lighting Fixtures	Electrical (35%)	$36,400	$36,400	$36,036
Fire Alarm	Electrical (20%)	$20,800	$20,800	$20,592
Punch List				$13,215
				$1,321,540

Figure 16–3   Example Schedule of Values, Computations

Figure 16–4. Example Schedule of Values, Computations, Evenly Distributed Markup

This figure is a progression from Figure 16–3, adding distribution of the overhead and profit evenly and proportionately to each schedule of values item. The right column, labeled "Value," will be the value shown on the schedule of values. The total of this column is the contract amount.

Example Project, Schedule of Values Computations				Evenly Distributed Overhead		
SOV Item	Estimate Item	Amount	Less 1%	% of Total OH	Distributed	Value
Mobilization	Bonds	$15,600				
	All-Risk Insurance	$1,600				
	Temporary Facilities	$10,000				
		$27,200	$26,928	2.04%	$2,195	$29,123
General Conditions	Field Engineering	$2,000				
	Superintendent	$52,200				
	Final Cleaning	$2,550				
		$56,750	$56,183	4.25%	$4,579	$60,761
Earthwork	Earthwork	$45,000	$45,000	$44,550	3.37%	$3,631
Site Improvements	Asphalt Paving	$27,600				$48,181
	Landscaping	$22,000				
		$49,600	$49,104	3.72%	$4,002	$53,106
Concrete	Concrete Formwork	$28,300				
	Concrete Reinforcing	$19,500				
	Cast-in-place Concrete	$28,900				
		$76,700	$75,933	5.75%	$6,189	$82,122
Masonry	Masonry	$65,000	$65,000	$64,350	4.87%	$5,245	$69,595
Structural Steel	Structural Steel	$116,500				
	Metal Joists	$34,000				
	Metal Deck	$23,000				
	Metal Handrails	$7,500				
		$181,000	$179,190	13.56%	$14,604	$193,794
Carpentry	Rough Carpentry	$2,500				
	Finish Carpentry	$88,000				
		$90,500	$89,595	6.78%	$7,302	$96,897
Dampproofing	Dampproofing	$1,600	$1,600	$1,584	0.12%	$129	$1,713
Insulation	Insulation	$22,000				
	Fireproofing	$16,500				
		$38,500	$38,115	2.88%	$3,106	$41,221
Roofing/Flashing	Roofing/Flashing	$65,000	$65,000	$64,350	4.87%	$5,245	$69,595
Sealants	Sealants	$9,600	$9,600	$9,504	0.72%	$775	$10,279
Doors, Hardware	Metal Doors & Frames	$41,500				
	Folding Doors	$6,800				
	Finish Hardware	$23,000				
		$71,300	$70,587	5.34%	$5,753	$76,340
Windows, Glazing	Metal Windows	$25,600				
	Glazing	$9,340				
		$34,940	$34,591	2.62%	$2,819	$37,410
Interior Partitions	Metal studs/Gyp.Bd.	$102,000	$102,000	$100,980	7.64%	$8,230	$109,210
Acoustical Ceilings	Acoustical Ceilings	$35,000	$35,000	$34,650	2.62%	$2,824	$37,474
Ceramic Tile	Ceramic Tile	$16,500	$16,500	$16,335	1.24%	$1,331	$17,666
Resilient Flooring	Floor Covering (50%)	$21,500	$21,500	$21,285	1.61%	$1,735	$23,020
Carpet	Floor Covering (50%)	$21,500	$21,500	$21,285	1.61%	$1,735	$23,020
Painting	Painting (85%)	$47,600	$47,600	$47,124	3.57%	$3,841	$50,965
Wallcovering	Painting (15%)	$8,400	$8,400	$8,316	0.63%	$678	$8,994
Specialties	Tackboards	$4,000				
	Toilet Compartments	$6,000				
	Signage	$7,600				
	Fire Extinguishers	$5,000				
	Toilet Accessories	$6,750				
		$29,350	$29,057	2.20%	$2,368	$31,425
Plumbing	Mechanical (40%)	$49,200	$49,200	$48,708	3.69%	$3,970	$52,678
HVAC	Mechanical (45%)	$55,350	$55,350	$54,797	4.15%	$4,466	$59,262
Fire Protection	Mechanical (15%)	$18,450	$18,450	$18,266	1.38%	$1,489	$19,754
Electrical Power	Electrical (25%)	$26,000	$26,000	$25,740	1.95%	$2,098	$27,838
Electrical Circuits	Electrical (20%)	$20,800	$20,800	$20,592	1.56%	$1,678	$22,270
Lighting Fixtures	Electrical (35%)	$36,400	$36,400	$36,036	2.73%	$2,937	$38,973
Fire Alarm	Electrical (20%)	$20,800	$20,800	$20,592	1.56%	$1,678	$22,270
Punch List			$13,215	1.00%	$1,075	$14,290
			$1,321,540	100%	$107,704	$1,429,246
Markup to Distribute	$107,708					

Figure 16–4   Example Schedule of Values, Computations, Evenly Distributed Markup

Figure 16–5: Schedule of Values, Evenly Distributed Overhead

This is the schedule of values that would be submitted to the owner for inclusion in the progress payment documentation. The architect and owner typically would not be aware of the computations accomplished to arrive at this schedule of values (see Figure 16–5).

Figure 16–6: Schedule of Values, Computations, Front-Loaded Distribution of Markup

Many contractors prefer to distribute their profit and overhead to activities that will be completed in the early phases of the project. In this computation, profit and overhead are distributed only to Mobilization, Earthwork, Concrete, and Masonry items (see Figure 16–6).

Example Project, Schedule of Values
Evenly Distributed Overhead

Item	Value
Mobilization	$29,123
General Conditions	$60,761
Earthwork	$48,181
Site Improvements	$53,106
Concrete	$82,122
Masonry	$69,595
Structural Steel	$193,794
Carpentry	$96,897
Dampproofing	$1,713
Insulation	$41,221
Roofing/Flashing	$69,595
Sealants	$10,279
Doors, Hardware	$76,340
Windows, Glazing	$37,410
Interior Partitions	$109,210
Acoustical Ceilings	$37,474
Ceramic Tile	$17,666
Resilient Flooring	$23,020
Carpet	$23,020
Painting	$50,965
Wallcovering	$8,994
Specialties	$31,425
Plumbing	$52,678
HVAC	$59,262
Fire Protection	$19,754
Electrical Power	$27,838
Electrical Circuits	$22,270
Lighting Fixtures	$38,973
Fire Alarm	$22,270
Punch List	$14,290
	$1,429,246

Figure 16–5 Schedule of Values,
Evenly Distributed Overhead

Example Project, Schedule of Values Computations   Front Load Overhead

SOV Item	Estimate Item	Amount	Less 1%		% of OH	Distribution	Value
Mobilization	Bonds	$15,600					
	All-Risk Insurance	$1,600					
	Temporary Facilities	$10,000					
		$27,200	$26,928		15%	$15,994	$42,922
General Conditions	Field Engineering	$2,000					
	Superintendent	$52,200					
	Final Cleaning	$2,550					
		$56,750	$56,183	$56,183			
Earthwork	Earthwork	$45,000	$45,000	$44,550	25%	$26,657	$71,207
Site Improvements	Asphalt Paving	$27,600					
	Landscaping	$22,000					
		$49,600	$49,104	$49,104			
Concrete	Concrete Formwork	$28,300					
	Concrete Reinforcing	$19,500					
	Cast-in-place Concrete	$28,900					
		$76,700	$75,933		40%	$42,652	$118,585
Masonry	Masonry	$65,000	$65,000	$64,350	20%	$21,326	$85,676
Structural Steel	Structural Steel	$116,500					
	Metal Joists	$34,000					
	Metal Deck	$23,000					
	Metal Handrails	$7,500					
		$181,000	$179,190	$179,190			
Carpentry	Rough Carpentry	$2,500					
	Finish Carpentry	$88,000					
		$90,500	$89,595	$89,595			
Dampproofing	Dampproofing	$1,600	$1,600	$1,584			$1,584
Insulation	Insulation	$22,000					
	Fireproofing	$16,500					
		$38,500	$38,115				$38,115
Roofing/Flashing	Roofing/Flashing	$65,000	$65,000	$64,350			$64,350
Sealants	Sealants	$9,600	$9,600	$9,504			$9,504
Doors, Hardware	Metal Doors & Frames	$41,500					
	Folding Doors	$6,800					
	Finish Hardware	$23,000					
		$71,300	$70,587				$70,587
Windows, Glazing	Metal Windows	$25,600					
	Glazing	$9,340					
		$34,940	$34,591				$34,591
Interior Partitions	Metal studs/Gyp.Bd.	$102,000	$102,000	$100,980			$100,980
Acoustical Ceilings	Acoustical Ceilings	$35,000	$35,000	$34,650			$34,650
Ceramic Tile	Ceramic Tile	$16,500	$16,500	$16,335			$16,335
Resilient Flooring	Floor Covering (50%)	$21,500	$21,500	$21,285			$21,285
Carpet	Floor Covering (50%)	$21,500	$21,500	$21,285			$21,285
Painting	Painting (85%)	$47,600	$47,600	$47,124			$47,124
Wallcovering	Painting (15%)	$8,400	$8,400	$8,316			$8,316
Specialties	Tackboards	$4,000					
	Toilet Compartments	$6,000					
	Signage	$7,600					
	Fire Extinguishers	$5,000					
	Toilet Accessories	$6,750					
		$29,350	$29,057				$29,057
Plumbing	Mechanical (40%)	$49,200	$49,200	$48,708			$48,708
HVAC	Mechanical (45%)	$55,350	$55,350	$54,797			$54,797
Fire Protection	Mechanical (15%)	$18,450	$18,450	$18,266			$18,266
Electrical Power	Electrical (25%)	$26,000	$26,000	$25,740			$25,740
Electrical Circuits	Electrical (20%)	$20,800	$20,800	$20,592			$20,592
Lighting Fixtures	Electrical (35%)	$36,400	$36,400	$36,036			$36,036
Fire Alarm	Electrical (20%)	$20,800	$20,800	$20,592			$20,592
Punch List				$13,215		$1,077	$14,292
				$1,321,640			$1,429,246

Markup | $107,706
Less markup to Punch List | $1,077
Markup to Distribute | **$108,629**

Figure 16–6   Schedule of Values, Computation, Front-Loaded Distribution of Markup

Figure 16–7: Schedule of Values, Front-Loaded Distribution of Profit and Overhead

This would be the schedule of values submitted to the owner (see Figure 16–7). In comparison with the schedule of values shown in Figure 16–5, the following conclusions can be made:

The total amount is the same for either schedule of values. Mobilization, Earthwork, Concrete, and Masonry activities are higher on the front-loaded schedule of values. All other items are slightly higher on the even distribution than in the front-loaded version.

Preparation of the schedule of values from the estimate can include the following steps:

1. *Combination of items:* The schedule of values may consolidate several line items from the estimate for clarity in the schedule of values. For example, the schedule of values

Schedule of Values, Front-Loaded

Item	Value
Mobilization	$42,920
General Conditions	$56,183
Earthwork	$71,207
Site Improvements	$49,104
Concrete	$118,585
Masonry	$85,676
Structural Steel	$179,190
Carpentry	$89,595
Dampproofing	$1,584
Insulation	$38,115
Roofing/Flashing	$64,350
Sealants	$9,504
Doors, Hardware	$70,587
Windows, Glazing	$34,591
Interior Partitions	$100,980
Acoustical Ceilings	$34,650
Ceramic Tile	$16,335
Resilient Flooring	$21,285
Carpet	$21,285
Painting	$47,124
Wallcovering	$8,316
Specialties	$29,057
Plumbing	$48,708
HVAC	$54,797
Fire Protection	$18,266
Electrical Power	$25,740
Electrical Circuits	$20,592
Lighting Fixtures	$36,036
Fire Alarm	$20,592
Punch List	$14,292
Total	$1,429,246

Figure 16–7   Schedule of Values, Front-Loaded Distribution of Profit and Overhead

may list "Concrete" as a single item. In the contractor's estimate, several items relate to concrete. In the estimate summary shown in Figure 16-2, three line items relate to "Concrete":

Section 03100 Concrete Formwork	$28,300.00
Section 03200 Concrete Reinforcing	$19,500.00
Section 03300 Cast-in-Place Concrete	$28,900.00

These three line items from the estimate total $76,700 for "Concrete."

2. *Separation of lump-sum items:* Some items, particularly subcontractor bids, combine several items into a lump sum in the estimate. The schedule of values may require further breakdown of these items. For example, the schedule of values requires an item for Resilient Flooring and another item for Carpet. The estimate has one item, a subcontractor bid for "floor covering," including both resilient flooring and carpet. This lump-sum item must be divided into proportionate amounts for each item. The subcontractor would be asked to divide the bid into the two items. Contractors often will estimate the percentage of each item, based on unit price and quantity, to determine this division.

3. *Distribution of overhead:* Several different methods exist for distribution of overhead and nonallocated items to the items on the schedule of values. The method used may be determined by the contractor, regulations, or local custom. Equal distribution of the overhead to the items, based on a percentage, is a method of allocating overhead. Figure 16-4 illustrates a proportionate allocation of overhead, with each item receiving an overhead allocation proportionate to its relative value.

4. *Front-loading:* Another method of allocating overhead is commonly referred to as **front-loading**. Front-loading is the allocation of overhead to items that will be completed early in the project. There are different degrees of front-loading, depending on the contractor and contract conditions. This method is commonly used by contractors. As the owner is very reluctant to pay for anything that is not earned, considerable caution is used by owners, architects and engineers, and construction managers to avoid front-loading. Regulations on public work may prohibit front-loading.

Many contractors feel the anticipated profit and indirect overhead should be available for sufficient funds to manage the project. Contractors normally use a single markup for all costs, including their work and the subcontract. This markup is fairly low, considering that the majority of costs in a project are subcontracts. Obviously, less overhead and cost is required for the subcontracts than work with the contractor's own forces. The majority of the contractor's work is completed early in the project, such as concrete work and the structure of the building. It is logical, then, that the profit and overhead be allocated early in the project.

Because front-loading is a common method of allocating overhead and profit in the schedule of values, it has been included in this discussion. The authors do not advocate front-loading or proportionate allocation. Local customs, regulations, and owners' attitudes vary on this subject, and contractors must determine their own course of action within context. A spread of overhead and profit into several progress payments is normally acceptable. Allocation of all overhead and profit into the first one or two progress payments is normally not acceptable.

The owner and architect review the schedule of values prior to its use in progress payments. The owner may reject the schedule of values submitted and request a revision by the contractor. Common reasons for rejection of the schedule of values include excessive front-loading, insufficient detail of construction activities, and noncompliance with contract requirements.

The total of the schedule of values is the contract amount. As change orders are added to the contract, they are added to the schedule of values, usually as lump sums.

Guaranteed Maximum Price, or GMP

This type of contract is a form of cost-plus contract and will have a different form of payment procedure than a lump-sum contract. Guaranteed maximum price contracts are "open book" agreements, meaning the customer can audit the contractor's project financials. Contractors are obliged to keep meticulous records, which can be time consuming. This openness can also feel like an infringement on the contractor's privacy.

- Cost-plus contracts reduce a contractor's risk by separating profit from a project's direct and indirect expenses. But customers lack certainty on the final bill.

- Contract variations may factor in incentives for work completed ahead of schedule or exceeding original specifications, or stipulate fee increases if project costs increase.

- Cost-plus contracts require careful accounting and tracking, and customers may insist on a cost-cap clause.

Cost-plus contracts, where a contractor bills for a project's direct and indirect expenses plus an additional fee, allow for considerable flexibility and ensure a profit. However, they're not blank checks. The contractor must produce a detailed estimate of expected costs upfront, and the buyer must agree to a set of recognized expense increases that may be incurred.

Typical price fluctuations covered in such contracts include the cost of commodities, such as lumber and copper, that may experience spikes in demand. Expenses may also include overhead, such as research and development costs necessary to meet contractual goals.

However, estimating errors, mistakes, and costs incurred due to negligence are not covered in most cost-plus contracts. In some cases, the customer may request a cap on total chargeable expenses. Finally, when a cost-plus contract is expected to last for many months or years, it usually provides for interim payments to reimburse the contractor's expenses along the way.

What is included in the cost-plus contract? No matter the specifics of a project, a cost-plus contract typically breaks down costs into three categories.

Direct Costs

These are the more obvious costs that relate to the specific job in the contract. Known as the cost of goods sold (COGS) in other contexts, examples of direct costs include labor for the project, raw materials required to complete the project, equipment purchased or rented for the job, subcontractors and fees for outside specialists such as engineers or consultants.

Indirect Costs/Overhead Costs

Also known as overhead costs, indirect costs are the countless expense categories associated with running a business. Such costs include administrative expenses, such as office leases, insurance fees, licensing, transportation expenses, and utilities. A percentage of the contractor's overall overhead is usually included in a cost-plus contract, with the amount depending on the size and timespan of the project.

Profit

The amount your company will earn for completing the project. This can be a fixed fee or vary depending on overall costs or incentives—for example, a bonus for finishing on time or early.

Progress billings are generally included in the contract, and this allows contractors to bill their clients incrementally while the project is in progress. For progress billings to work, the client and contractor must agree to a payment schedule when invoices will be submitted for payment.

Having a schedule of values included in the progress billings process helps contractors and owners develop a transparent process where all the financial details are known upfront. It also protects construction companies legally and financially by having the estimates in writing so that there are no surprises at the completion of the project.

The schedule of values for a GMP or cost-plus contract is different from one used for a lump-sum contract. As stated earlier in this chapter, the schedule of values for a lump-sum project reflects the total cost to the owner for the project, whereas a schedule of values on a GMP contract is an estimate and a grouping of cost items that is used to track the budget. This schedule of values will total the maximum cost to the owner, but the final cost can be less than that amount. The cost items are not the amount that will be paid to the contractor since, in a cost-plus contract, owner agrees to reimburse the contracting party for expenses plus pay a specified profit. This can often become a source of problems when the budgeted items do not reflect the actual cost that is later included in the progress bill or final bill. Many owners mistakenly think that the line items in the schedule of values may not be altered without owner approval, thus creating a guaranteed maximum price for each line item. Construction contracts should, but usually do not, clearly provide that the guaranteed maximum price applies only to the aggregate of all qualified costs of the work and that, by extension, the contractor may freely move values within the schedule of values, including the contingency.

It is important that the guaranteed maximum price contract define and clarify what costs will be reimbursed and what costs are not included and will not be reimbursed.

A shortened example of contract language from A.I.A. contract **AIA Document A111™ -1997, Article 7 and 8,** follows and it defines both Costs to be Reimbursed and Cost of the Work as:

Article 7 Costs to Be Reimbursed

§ 7.1 Cost of the Work

The term Cost of the Work shall mean all costs chargeable to Owner and actually and necessarily incurred by the Contractor in the proper performance of the Work by Contractor, without markup or add on of any kind by or at the request of Contractor, and less all discounts, rebates, and salvages. Such costs shall be at rates not higher than the standard paid at the place of the Project except with prior consent of the Owner. The Cost of the Work shall include only the items set forth in this Article 7. All amounts paid or payable as Cost of the Work shall be subject to verification and audit by Owner.

In the following contract articles, this contract specifically details and define these costs.

Also following is a further example of contract language from that same contract regarding non-reimbursements.

Article 8 Costs Not to Be Reimbursed

§ 8.1 The Cost of the Work shall not include:

§ **8.1.1** Salaries and other compensation of the Contractor's personnel stationed at the Contractor's principal office or offices other than the site office, except as specifically provided in Sections 7.2.2 and 7.2.3 or as may be provided in Article 14.

§ **8.1.2** Expenses of the Contractor's principal office and offices other than the site office.

§ **8.1.3** Overhead and general expenses, except as approved by the Owner.

§ **8.1.4** The Contractor's capital expenses, including interest on the Contractor's capital employed for the Work.

§ **8.1.5** Rental costs of machinery and equipment, except as specifically provided in Section 7.5.2.

§ **8.1.6** Except as provided in Section 7.7.3 or paragraph 2.2 of the Addendum to AIA 111 of this Agreement, costs due to the negligence or failure to fulfill a specific responsibility of the Contractor, Subcontractors and suppliers or anyone directly or indirectly employed by any of them or for whose acts any of them may be liable.

§ **8.1.7** Any cost not specifically and expressly described in Article 7.

§ **8.1.8** Costs, other than costs included in Change Orders approved by the Owner, that would cause the Guaranteed Maximum Price to be exceeded.

§ **8.1.9** All costs incurred by Contractor for bonuses, stock options, profit sharing arrangements and similar incentive programs, except as included within the Rates listed on Exhibit 1.

§ **8.1.10** All direct and indirect costs of any nature resulting from or attributable to either delays, disruptions or interferences to the extent caused by Contractor or its subcontractors of any tier, excepting only those costs which are expressly identified and permitted in accordance with the Contract, and subject to the Contingency in paragraph 2.2 of the Addendum to AIA Document A111-1997.

§ **8.1.11** All costs for state or local business licenses for Contractor, not related to this project in particular.

§ **8.1.12** Costs incurred by Contractor in satisfying its indemnification obligations pursuant to the Contract Documents, but subject to the Contingency in paragraph 2.2 of the Addendum to AIA Document A111-1997.

§ **8.1.13** Any Costs of the Work reimbursed by insurance to Contractor or any Subcontractor or Vendor, subject to the recovery of such insurance proceeds pursuant to paragraph 2.2 of the Addendum to the AIA111.

The request should include documentation of the work completed, as well as any supporting documentation, such as invoices for materials or subcontractors. On a large project the documents to support the costs that the contractor has incurred can be a very large number.

Unit-Price Contracts

Some contracts require that the bid be presented in unit prices for particular items of work. These types of contracts usually are in engineering construction and are found frequently in public works contracts. In these contracts, the unit-price breakdown is used as the schedule of values. Each unit price includes labor, material, equipment, subcontracts, direct overhead, indirect overhead, and distributed profit. A finite quantity is usually furnished in the bid forms, and the contractor supplies the unit price. A variety of strategies is used in allocating overhead and profit to the unit prices, including front-loading.

Figure 16–8 is an example of a typical unit-price breakdown contained in the bid form. The contractor normally would furnish the unit price and extension. These unit prices would be

Item #	Item	Quantity	Unit	Unit Price	Extension
1	Mobilization	1	L.S.	$ 20,000.00	$ 20,000.00
2	Trench Excavation	2,340	Cu. Yd.	$ 5.40	$ 12,636.00
3	Clear & Grub	15,555	Sq. Yd.	$ 1.36	$ 21,154.80
4	Mass Excavation	5,670	Cu. Yd.	$ 1.75	$ 9,922.50
5	Structural Excavation	12,965	Cu. Yd.	$ 2.90	$ 37,598.50
6	Structural Backfill	2,570	Cu. Yd.	$ .75	$ 1,927.50
7	3/8" Gravel	488	Tons	$ 7.67	$ 3,742.96
Total					$ 106,982.26

Figure 16–8   Example of Unit-Price Breakdown

used as the schedule of values. Quantities of each item complete are measured and tabulated, then multiplied by the unit price to determine the amount due for each work activity.

Project Cash Flow Projections

Project cash flow projections relate the schedule of values to the construction schedule, projecting the progress payments through the duration of the project. The cash flow projection approximates the progress payments for each payment period during the construction contract. This projection is used by the owner to make financial arrangements, which creates available funds for the payments and optimizes investment opportunities. The contractor also can use the cash flow projection for anticipating revenue for future periods.

Because the cash flow projection is based on the construction schedule, the projections are estimates only, as many fluctuations exist in the construction schedule. Several factors can affect the actual amount of progress payments at each period, producing a variance from the projection: late or early delivery of materials, late or early completion of work activities, revision in sequencing of work activities, and the disproportionate completion of work activities in their scheduled time period.

An approximate range can be established for the cash flow curve, using early start–early finish and late start–late finish dates defining the limits of the range. Some contractors prefer to present a range to the owner, because the cash flow projection is approximate. Other cash flow projections use a single curve, with a disclaimer that the amounts are approximate. Updating the cash flow projection is necessary as the project progresses to provide current and more accurate projections.

Because the cash flow projection relates to the amounts that will be requested for each progress payment, some factors differ from those relating to the construction schedule. The actual payments may not be equally distributed in the work activity period.

Example

Structural steel erection for the example project has a duration of 3 months, starting on June 1. During this 3-month period, there are three payment requests: July 1, August 1, and September 1. Labor and equipment are consistent throughout the period, but material is not evenly distributed. A summary of estimated costs for this work follows:

Item	Material	Labor	Equipment	Total
Structural Steel	$103,400.00	$28,300.00	$24,000.00	$165,700.00
Metal Joists	$ 32,400.00			$ 32,400.00
Metal Deck	$ 13,650.00			$ 13,650.00
Total Cost	$149,450.00	$28,300.00	$24,000.00	$201,750.00

Some cash flow projections will take the total, $201,750, and divide it evenly into each of the three payment periods, or $67,250.

Realistically, the material will not be received at the jobsite evenly throughout the period. The chart that follows reflects a realistic projection of structural steel costs.

(continued)

Item	July 1%	July 1 Amount	Aug. 1%	Aug. 1 Amount	Sept. 1%	Sept. 1 Amount
Str. Steel material	50%	$ 51,700	40%	$ 41,360	10%	$10,340
Metal Joists		100%	$ 32,400			
Metal Deck		100%	$ 13,650			
Labor	34%	$ 9,622	33%	$ 9,339	33%	$ 9,339
Equip.	33.33%	$ 8,000	33.33%	$ 8,000	33.33%	$ 8,000
Totals	57%	$116,372	29%	$ 58,699	14%	$27,679

Quite a difference exists between the evenly distributed projection and the realistic delivery projection. Figure 16–9 compares these two methods, which illustrate that by anticipating material delivery, the cash flow projection for that activity will be a larger payment request earlier in the process.

Cash Flow, Structural Steel

Method	Amount July 1	Accum. July 1	Amount Aug. 1	Accum. Aug. 1	Amount Sept. 1	Accum. Sept. 1
Even Distribution	$ 67,250	$ 67,250	$67,250	$134,500	$67,250	$201,750
Material Delivery	$115,372	$115,372	$58,699	$174,071	$27,679	$201,750

Month	Even Distribution	Material Delivery
1-Jun	$0	$0
1-Jul	$67,250	$115,372
1-Aug	$134,500	$174,071
1-Sep	$201,750	$201,750

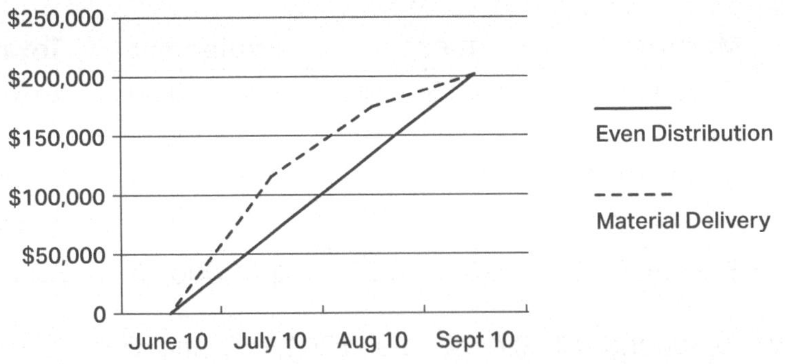

Figure 16–9   Cash Flow Projection, Method Comparison

Because cash flow projections are used by the owner and contractor for financial arrangements, the projected payments should reflect material delivery and other factors that would influence the payment amount.

Figure 16–10 is a tabular computation of the cash flow for each month of the example project, from July 1 through May 1, with the actual project starting on June 5 and ending on April 12. The schedule of values, on the left side of the spreadsheet, is from that shown in Figure 16–7. The Gantt chart for the construction schedule is shown in Figure 16–11. The percentage complete for each payment period is the cumulative total. What follows are examples of how the percentages in each period are determined, relating to the construction schedule in Figure 16–11.

Example

1. Mobilization is completed between the start of the project and July 1. The percent complete then for July 1 and all subsequent periods is 100 percent; 100 percent of the value of $42,922 is entered in the amount column for July 1.

2. General conditions are spread evenly in 10 periods, with 10 percent earned during the first period. Most items in the general conditions value, such as superintendent, temporary office rent, telephone charges, and so on, are fairly constant for each period. The value of $56,183 is multiplied by 10 percent, with the resulting amount of $5,618 for July 1. For August 1, the total percentage earned is 20 percent: 10 percent for the first period and 10 percent for the second period.

3. The construction schedule shows the Earthwork item spread between the June and July period. Because about half of the work will be done in June, 50 percent is entered in the percentage column. The August 1 period, then, shows 100 percent completion of the activity.

4. Site plumbing is shown on the construction schedule as being completed during June. The schedule of values, in this case, has only one item for plumbing, while four activities for plumbing are shown on the construction schedule. From conversations with the plumbing subcontractor, the following percentage of the plumbing value has been determined for the four activities:

Site plumbing:	10%
Plumbing rough-in, under slab:	10%
Plumbing rough-in, above grade:	40%
Plumbing fixtures:	40%

Site plumbing is scheduled for completion during June. Because much of the rough-in material will be delivered with the initial delivery, a total of 20 percent is estimated for work in place and delivered material during the June period.

Item	Value	1-Jul %	1-Jul Amount	1-Aug %	1-Aug Amount	1-Sep %	1-Sep Amount	1-Oct %	1-Oct Amount	1-Nov %
Mobilization	$42,920	100%	$42,920	100%	$42,920	100%	$42,920	100%	$42,920	100%
General Conditions	$56,183	10%	$5,618	20%	$11,237	30%	$16,855	40%	$22,473	50%
Earthwork	$71,207	50%	$35,604	100%	$71,207	100%	$71,207	100%	$71,207	100%
Site Improvements	$49,104									
Concrete	$118,585			60%	$71,151	100%	$118,585	100%	$118,585	100%
Masonry	$85,676					100%	$85,676	100%	$85,676	100%
Structural Steel	$179,190					60%	$107,514	100%	$179,190	100%
Carpentry	$89,595									10%
Dampproofing	$1,584					100%	$1,584	100%	$1,584	100%
Insulation	$38,115									
Roofing/Flashing	$64,350							70%	$45,045	100%
Sealants	$9,504									
Doors, Hardware	$70,587					25%	$17,647	25%	$17,647	50%
Windows, Glazing	$34,591									50%
Interior Partitions	$100,980									
Acoustical Ceilings	$34,650							20%	$6,930	20%
Ceramic Tile	$16,335									
Resilient Flooring	$21,285									
Carpet	$21,285									
Painting	$47,124									
Wallcovering	$8,316									
Specialties	$29,057									
Plumbing	$48,708	20%	$9,742	40%	$19,483	50%	$24,354	60%	$29,225	65%
HVAC	$54,797							30%	$16,439	40%
Fire Protection	$18,266									
Electrical Power	$25,740									
Electrical Circuits	$20,592			20%	$4,118	50%	$10,296	70%	$14,414	90%
Lighting Fixtures	$36,036									
Fire Alarm	$20,592									
Punch List	$14,292									
Total	$1,429,246	7%	$93,883	15%	$220,116	35%	$496,638	46%	$651,335	54%
		1-Jul		1-Aug		1-Sep		1-Oct		1-Nov

Figure 16–10   Tabular Cash Flow Projection

1-Nov Amount	1-Dec %	1-Dec Amount	1-Jan %	1-Jan Amount	1-Feb %	1-Feb Amount	1-Mar %	1-Mar Amount	1-Apr %	1-Apr Amount	1-May %	1-May Amount
$42,920	100%	$42,920	100%	$42,920	100%	$42,920	100%	$42,920	100%	$42,920	100%	$42,920
$28,092	60%	$33,710	70%	$39,328	80%	$44,946	90%	$50,565	100%	$56,183	100%	$56,183
$71,207	100%	$71,207	100%	$71,207	100%	$71,207	100%	$71,207	100%	$71,207	100%	$71,207
									100%	$49,104	100%	$49,104
$118,585	100%	$118,585	100%	$118,585	100%	$118,585	100%	$118,585	100%	$118,585	100%	$118,585
$85,676	100%	$85,676	100%	$85,676	100%	$85,676	100%	$85,676	100%	$85,676	100%	$85,676
$179,190	100%	$179,190	100%	$179,190	100%	$179,190	100%	$179,190	100%	$179,190	100%	$179,190
$8,960	10%	$8,960	90%	$80,636	100%	$89,595	100%	$89,595	100%	$89,595	100%	$89,595
$1,584	100%	$1,584	100%	$1,584	100%	$1,584	100%	$1,584	100%	$1,584	100%	$1,584
$38,115	100%	$38,115	100%	$38,115	100%	$38,115	100%	$38,115	100%	$38,115	100%	$38,115
$64,350	100%	$64,350	100%	$64,350	100%	$64,350	100%	$64,350	100%	$64,350	100%	$64,350
	100%	$9,504	100%	$9,504	100%	$9,504	100%	$9,504	100%	$9,504	100%	$9,504
$35,294	70%	$49,411	100%	$70,587	100%	$70,587	100%	$70,587	100%	$70,587	100%	$70,587
	100%	$34,591	100%	$34,591	100%	$34,591	100%	$34,591	100%	$34,591	100%	$34,591
$50,490	70%	$70,686	100%	$100,980	100%	$100,980	100%	$100,980	100%	$100,980	100%	$100,980
$6,930	20%	$6,930	20%	$6,930	100%	$34,650	100%	$34,650	100%	$34,650	100%	$34,650
			100%	$16,335	100%	$16,335	100%	$16,335	100%	$16,335	100%	$16,335
			50%	$10,643	100%	$21,285	100%	$21,285	100%	$21,285	100%	$21,285
			50%	$10,643	100%	$21,285	100%	$21,285	100%	$21,285	100%	$21,285
			40%	$18,850	100%	$47,124	100%	$47,124	100%	$47,124	100%	$47,124
					100%	$8,316	100%	$8,316	100%	$8,316	100%	$8,316
					90%	$26,151	100%	$29,057	100%	$29,057	100%	$29,057
$31,660	65%	$31,660	65%	$31,660	100%	$48,708	100%	$48,708	100%	$48,708	100%	$48,708
$21,919	60%	$32,878	70%	$38,358	80%	$43,838	90%	$49,317	100%	$54,797	100%	$54,797
	80%	$14,613	80%	$14,613	100%	$18,266	100%	$18,266	100%	$18,266	100%	$18,266
	80%	$20,592	100%	$25,740	100%	$25,740	100%	$25,740	100%	$25,740	100%	$25,740
$18,533	90%	$18,533	90%	$18,533	90%	$18,533	100%	$20,592	100%	$20,592	100%	$20,592
					70%	$25,225	100%	$36,036	100%	$36,036	100%	$36,036
							60%	$12,355	100%	$20,592	100%	$20,592
									25%	$3,573	100%	$14,292
$765,388	**65%**	**$933,694**	**79%**	**$1,129,556**	**91%**	**$1,307,286**	**94%**	**$1,346,515**	**99%**	**$1,418,527**	**100%**	**$1,429,246**
1-Nov		1-Dec		1-Jan		1-Feb		1-Mar		1-Apr		1-May

Figure 16–10 Tabular Cash Flow Projection (*Continued*)

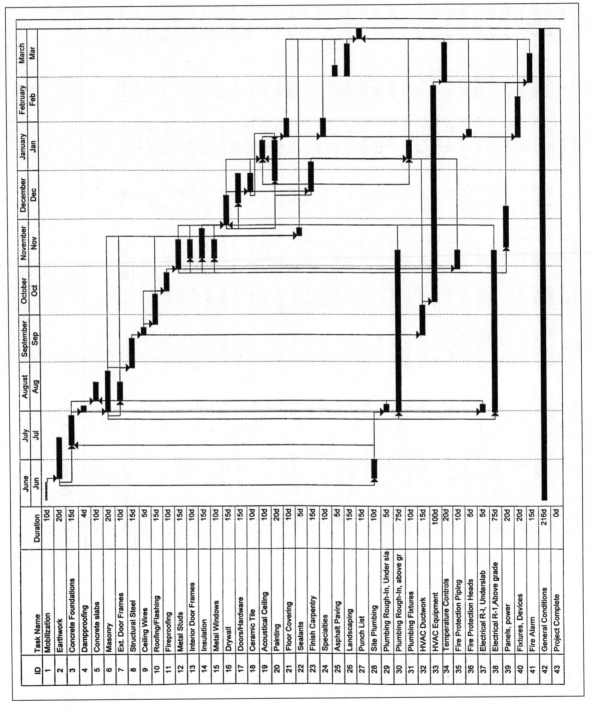

The following data appears in the chart table (ID, Task Name, Duration):

ID	Task Name	Duration
1	Mobilization	10d
2	Earthwork	20d
3	Concrete Foundations	15d
4	Dampproofing	4d
5	Concrete slabs	10d
6	Masonry	20d
7	Ext. Door Frames	10d
8	Structural Steel	15d
9	Ceiling Wires	5d
10	Roofing/Flashing	15d
11	Fireproofing	10d
12	Metal Studs	15d
13	Interior Door Frames	10d
14	Insulation	15d
15	Metal Windows	10d
16	Drywall	15d
17	Doors/Hardware	15d
18	Ceramic Tile	10d
19	Acoustical Ceiling	10d
20	Painting	20d
21	Floor Covering	10d
22	Sealants	5d
23	Finish Carpentry	15d
24	Specialties	10d
25	Asphalt Paving	5d
26	Landscaping	15d
27	Punch List	15d
28	Site Plumbing	10d
29	Plumbing Rough-In, Under sla	5d
30	Plumbing Rough-In, above gr	75d
31	Plumbing Fixtures	10d
32	HVAC Ductwork	15d
33	HVAC Equipment	100d
34	Temperature Controls	20d
35	Fire Protection Piping	10d
36	Fire Protection Heads	5d
37	Electrical R-I, Underslab	5d
38	Electrical R-1, Above grade	75d
39	Panels, power	20d
40	Fixtures, Devices	20d
41	Fire Alarm	15d
42	General Conditions	216d
43	Project Complete	0d

Figure 16–11   Example Project Schedule, Gantt Chart

The monthly accumulated total is then plotted in a line graph, as shown in Figure 16-12. The cash flow curve is initially a "lazy-S" curve. Since this curve is related to specific amounts at the payment dates, the curve is not a smooth line but rather is segmented at the payment dates.

A front loaded schedule of values will have a steeper initial section on the cash flow curve than a schedule of values with an evenly distributed overhead. Figure 16-13 shows a comparison of cash flow charts for the two different schedule of values methods described in this chapter. This comparison shows a slightly accelerated payment schedule for the front-loaded schedule of values, with similar amounts in the latter periods.

Some of the "bumps" in the cash flow curve, for example, for the September 1 and October 1 periods, indicate additional payment activity, such as payment for material delivered and not installed. This is a standard practice since contractors prefer to have material delivered as soon as possible, when feasible, rather than delaying the work by waiting for material delivery.

Some computerized scheduling programs generate a cash flow chart from the construction schedule and loaded costs. Careful examination of the cash flow charts in the scheduling software is necessary to ensure that pertinent information is generated. Most programs evenly distribute cost when the activity extends into two or more periods. If an uneven distribution of the costs is anticipated, splitting the work activity into segments might be advisable. Using material delivery items and anticipated delivery dates also will help make the cash flow curve more accurate.

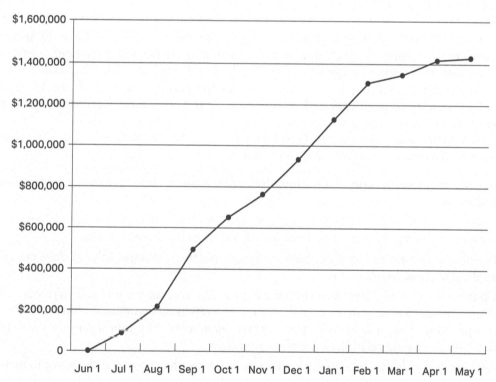

Figure 16-12   **Example Project Cash Flow Projection, Line Graph**

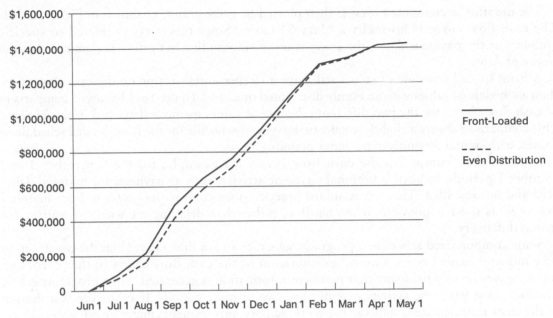

Figure 16–13 Cash Flow Projection, Comparison of Evenly Distributed Markup and Front-Loaded Distribution of Markup

Project Payment Procedures

Each owner will have specific progress payment requirements. Many will use the forms and procedures recommended by AIA documents or other standardized document forms. Most public agencies have specific procedures required by law for the municipality, state, or federal agency. Most owners will require a detail sheet for the period and a certificate of payment, which is a summary of payments and certification by the contractor, architect/engineer, and representative of the owner.

The AIA forms for payment are G702 and G703. AIA Form G702, "Application and Certificate for Payment," has five major sections:

1. General information, contract information, contractor, architect, owner, payment number, and so on.
2. Contract status: original contract amount, approved change orders to date, change orders performed during the period and net contract change by change orders.
3. Payment computation: total contract, progress to date, retainage, sales tax/use tax (if applicable), and payment due.
4. Contractor's certifications: Several certifications are necessary with each payment. The contractor must certify that the payment request represents work completed and the work completed is in accordance with the contract documents. The contractor must also certify that bills were paid relating to previous payments.
5. Architect's certification: certification that the architect has reviewed the work in progress and the payment request.

The Application for Payment form is shown in Figure 16–14. It shows the amounts necessary to compute the progress payment:

1. Initial Contract Amount between owner and contractor.
2. Additive or deductive amounts of approved change orders. This is the total amount of change orders formally approved by the owner. It does not include the amounts for Construction Change Directives which authorize the work, but still needs to be formally approved.

Project:
Date:
Application #

APPLICATION FOR PAYMENT

Contract Amount	______
Approved Change Orders	______
Adjusted Contract Amount	______
Total Value Work Completed and Materials Stored Onsite	______
Amount Retained %	______
Total Amount Earned	______
Total Amount Received to Date	______
Current Payment Due	______
Balance to Finish(including retainage)	______

Figure 16–14 Application for Payment, blank

Application for Payment Detail Sheet

Application Number:
Application Date:
Period:
Owner Project Number

Item #	Work Description	Value	Work Completed		Materials Stored	Total Completed & Stored to date	% Complete	Balance to Finish	Retainage
			Prev. App.	This Period					

Figure 16–15 Detail Sheet, Application for Payment, blank

3. Adjusted Contract Amount: Current contract including original amount and approved change orders.
4. Total value of work completed and materials stored on site: This is the sum of completed work and materials stored on site from the detail sheet (Figure 16-15).
5. Amount retained: The percentage stipulated in the contract for retainage multiple by the total amount earned. This amount is typically 5% or 10% or another percentage according to the owner's practices.
6. Total Amount earned: Value of completed work and materials stored onsite less retainage.
7. Total Amount Received to Date: Sum of all previous payments for this contract.
8. Current Payment Due: The amount that the owner will pay the contractor for this payment.
9. Balance to Finish (Including retainage: Total Contract amount less payments plus retainage withheld.

The contractor will also add legal clauses relating to the progress payment. These clauses could be standard clauses or custom clauses composed by the company attorney in accordance with federal, state and local regulations. Some of these clauses and information could include:

1. Project Information: Project title/description, identification numbers, owner, architect/engineer, contractor, payment number and date submitted.

2. Contractor statement: certified to the best of current knowledge, in accordance with contract documents and supplements, amounts in payment request have been paid within agreements.

3. Contractor's signature: authorized representative of contractor signature and date.

4. Architect's Certificate for Payment: Work claimed in accordance with contract documents, and the work is in progress as claimed by contractor. Certification that the contractor's request is correct.

5. Owners have different procedures for payment for materials stored on site or in a certified location. In some cases, the owner will require a specific listing of material, quantity, location, and realistic value. This statement is attached to the request for payment.

The Continuation Sheet, shown in Figure 16–15 details the progress of each item in the schedule of values, including previous progress, current completed work, current materials stored at the jobsite, total work completed and stored to date, balance to finish, and current retainage. The totals from this sheet are used in the Application and Certification for Payment.

Figures 16–16 and 16–17 illustrate the process of completion of Payment 1:

1. Figure 16–16 is the detail sheet for payment 1. The data used in this payment request were derived from the cash flow projection, Figure 16–10. The amounts in the cash flow projection and the payment request rarely coincide exactly; however, these data are appropriate for examples. As mobilization was completed during the month, it is 100 percent complete, with no balance to finish. Retainage of 5 percent, $2,146, will be held for that item. Item 23, Plumbing, is divided into work completed and with material stored, combined in column G. It is important to separate work completed from material stored for verification of payment. Some owners calculate only work in place as work progress treating material stored separately. Some owners use different rates of retainage for material stored as well. The retainage amounts for the project will be found in the General Conditions to the Contract/Supplementary Conditions to the contract, and the Agreement between the owner and the contractor.

2. The total generated on the detail sheet is used to complete the application for payment form. Since this is the first payment request, no change orders have been processed, and the original contract amount is still current. Figure 16–17 is the computation for the progress payment. "Contract sum to date" is the contract amount and the same total amount shown on Figure 16–16. The retainage breakdown can retainage separately on complete work and material stored or use one calculation for retainage. The retainage is then deducted from the amount earned to determine the total amount due the contractor to date. Progress payments, then, are deducted from the amount due the contractor to determine the amount due for the current payment period. In this case, no previous payments have been made because this is the first payment request. The amount remaining to be paid, plus retainage, is also computed.

Figures 16–18, 16–19 and 16–20 illustrate a later progress payment, Progress Payment Application Number 4, October 1:

1. More items are active in Figure 17–18. Three change orders have been added, because three change orders have been formally approved. The total of the scheduled value reflects the current amended contract price.

Application for Payment Detail Sheet

Application Number: 1
Application Date:
Period:
Owner Project Number

Item #	Work Description	Value	Work Completed		Materials Stored	Total Completed & Stored to date	% Complete	Balance to Finish	Retainage
			Prev. App.	This Period					
1	Mobilization	$ 42,922		$ 42,922		$ 42,922	100%	$ –	$ 2,146
2	General Conditions	$ 56,183		$ 5,618		$ 5,618	10%	$ 50,565.00	$ 281
3	Earthwork	$ 71,207		$ 35,604		$ 35,604	50%	$ 35,603.00	$ 1,780
4	Site Improvements	$ 49,104							
5	Concrete	$ 1,18,585							
6	Masonry	$ 85,676							
7	Structural Steel	$ 1,79,190							
8	Carpentry	$ 89,595							
9	Dampproofing	$ 1,584							
10	Insulation	$ 38,115							
11	Roofing/flashing	$ 64,350							
12	Sealants	$ 9,504							
13	Doors, hardware	$ 70,587							
14	Windows, Glazing	$ 34,591							
15	Interior Partitions	$ 1,00,980							
16	Acoustical Ceilings	$ 34,650							
17	Ceramic Tile	$ 16,335							
18	Resilient Flooring	$ 21,285							
19	Carpet	$ 21,285							
20	Painting	$ 47,124							
21	Wallcovering	$ 8,316							
22	Specialties	$ 29,057							
23	Plumbing	$ 48,708		$ 4,871	$ 4,871	$ 9,742	20%	$ 38,966	$ 487
24	HVAC	$ 54,796							
25	Fire Protection	$ 18,265							
26	Electrical Power	$ 25,740							
27	Electrical circuits	$ 20,592							
28	Lighting fixtures	$ 36,036							
29	Fire Alarm	$ 20,592							
30	Punch List (1%)	$ 14,292							
	Total	$ 14,29,246	$ –	$ 89,015	$ 4,871	$ 93,886	6.57%	$ 1,25,134	$ 4,694

Figure 16–16   Example Computation, Payment 1, Detail Sheet, Application for Payment

Project:
Date:
Application #   1

APPLICATION FOR PAYMENT

Contract Amount	$ 14,29,246
Approved Change Orders	$ -
Adjusted Contract Amount	$ 14,29,246
Total Value Work Completed and Materials Stored Onsite	$ 93,886
Amount Retained %	$ 4,694
Total Amount Earned	$ 89,192
Total Amount Received to Date	$ -
Current Payment Due	$ 89,192
Balance to Finish(including retainage)	$ 13,40,054

Figure 16–17   Example Computation, Payment 1, Application for Payment

Application for Payment Detail Sheet									

Application Number: 4
Application Date:
Period:
Owner Project Number

Item #	Work Description	Value	Work Completed		Materials Stored	Total Completed & Stored to date	% Complete	Balance to Finish	Retainage
			Prev. App.	This Period					
1	Mobilization	$ 42,922	$ 42,922			$ 42,922	100%	$ -	$ 2,146
2	General Conditions	$ 56,183	$ 16,855	$ 5,618		$ 22,473	40%	$ 33,710.00	$ 1,124
3	Earthwork	$ 71,207	$ 71,207			$ 71,207	100%	$ -	$ 3,560
4	Site Improvements	$ 49,104				$ -	0%	$ 49,104.00	$ -
5	Concrete	$ 1,18,585	$ 1,18,585			$ 1,18,585	100%	$ -	$ 5,929
6	Masonry	$ 85,676	$ 85,676			$ 85,676	100%	$ -	$ 4,284
7	Structural Steel	$ 1,79,190	$ 1,07,514	$ 71,676		$ 1,79,190	100%	$ -	$ 8,960
8	Carpentry	$ 89,595				$ -	0%	$ 89,595.00	$ -
9	Dampproofing	$ 1,584	$ 1,584			$ 1,584	100%	$ -	$ 79
10	Insulation	$ 38,115				$ -	0%	$ 38,115.00	$ -
11	Roofing/flashing	$ 64,350		$ 19,305	$ 25,740	$ 45,045	70%	$ 19,305.00	$ 2,252
12	Sealants	$ 9,504				$ -	0%	$ 9,504.00	$ -
13	Doors, hardware	$ 70,587	$ 10,588		$ 7,059	$ 17,647	25%	$ 52,940.00	$ 882
14	Windows, Glazing	$ 34,591				$ -	0%	$ 34,591.00	$ -
15	Interior Partitions	$ 1,00,980				$ -	0%	$ 1,00,980.00	$ -
16	Acoustical Ceilings	$ 34,650		$ 6,930		$ 6,930	20%	$ 27,720.00	$ 347
17	Ceramic Tile	$ 16,335				$ -	0%	$ 16,335.00	$ -
18	Resilient Flooring	$ 21,285				$ -	0%	$ 21,285.00	$ -
19	Carpet	$ 21,285				$ -	0%	$ 21,285.00	$ -
20	Painting	$ 47,124				$ -	0%	$ 47,124.00	$ -
21	Wallcovering	$ 8,316				$ -	0%	$ 8,316.00	$ -
22	Specialties	$ 29,057				$ -	0%	$ 29,057.00	$ -
23	Plumbing	$ 48,708	$ 24,354	$ 4,871		$ 29,225	60%	$ 19,483.00	$ 1,461
24	HVAC	$ 54,796		$ 10,959	$ 5,480	$ 16,439	30%	$ 38,357.00	$ 822
25	Fire Protection	$ 18,265				$ -	0%	$ 18,265.00	$ -
26	Electrical Power	$ 25,740				$ -	0%	$ 25,740.00	$ -
27	Electrical circuits	$ 20,592	$ 10,296	$ 4,118		$ 14,414	70%	$ 6,178.00	$ 721
28	Lighting fixtures	$ 36,036				$ -	0%	$ 36,036.00	$ -
29	Fire Alarm	$ 20,592				$ -	0%	$ 20,592.00	$ -
30	Punch List (1%)	$ 14,292				$ -	0%	$ 14,292.00	$ -
	Change Order 1	$ 15,300	$ 15,300.00			$ 15,300	100%	$ -	$ 765
	Change Order 2	$ 22,450		$ 22,450.00		$ 22,450	100%	$ -	$ 1,123
	Change Order 3	$ 5,600				$ -	0%	$ 5,600.00	$ -
	Total	$ 14,72,596	$ 5,04,881	$ 1,45,927	$ 38,279	$ 6,89,087	46.79%	$ 7,83,509	$ 34,455
						$ 6,89,087		$ 14,72,596	$ 34,455

Figure 16–18   Example Computation, Payment 4, Detail Sheet, Application for Payment

Change Order Summary

Change Order	Amount
Change Order 1, 5/6/26	$ 15,300.00
Change Order 2, 6/8/26	$ 22,450.00
Change Order 3, 7/7/26	$ 5,600.00
Total Change Orders to date	$ 43,350.00

Figure 16–19   Example Computation, Payment 4, Change Order Summary

APPLICATION FOR PAYMENT

Date, Application #		4

APPLICATION FOR PAYMENT

Contract Amount		$ 14,29,246
Approved Change Orders	$ 7,83,509	$ 43,350
Adjusted Contract Amount		$ 14,72,596
Total Value Work Completed and Materials Stored Onsite		$ 6,89,087
Amount Retained %		$ 34,455
Total Amount Earned		$ 6,54,632
Total Amount Received to Date		$ 4,79,637
Current Payment Due		$ 1,74,995
Balance to Finish(including retainage)		$ 8,17,964

Figure 16–20   Example Computation, Payment 4, Application for Payment

2. Figure 16–19 illustrates the Change Form. Change orders previously approved (Change Order 1) amount to an additional $ 16,300. Change Orders 2 and 3 are added to the contract amount for this Application for Payment, as they were approved during the payment period.

3. The payment computation for Payment 4, Figure 16–20, is similar to Application for Payment 1. The "Contract Sum to Date" has been changed because of the three change orders. Previous certificates for payment have been deducted. The previous certificate for payment amount is the net amount received from previous payments and does not include retainage.

   Some states require payment of sales tax on construction projects. This sales tax computation modifies the computation for payment amount. As each state has different requirements concerning the tax and its collection, the reader is encouraged to contact the appropriate state agency to determine where sales tax applies and its common method of collection.

Payment Processing

After the contractor completes the application for payment, the architect and engineer review the application and certify the payment request if correct. Some architects and engineers request a rough payment to review, then the final application is prepared with the architect's comments. This procedure usually saves time, avoiding rejection of the application for payment. Most contracts specify how long the owner can take to process the progress payment after receipt of the certified application. This period usually is 30 days but can vary, depending on specific factors relating to the owner and project financing. Figure 16–21 illustrates the progress payment process. Many owners, even public owners, try to expedite progress payments to the contractor. A good relationship between the owner and contractor can facilitate prompt payment of applications.

THE PROGRESS PAYMENT PROCESS

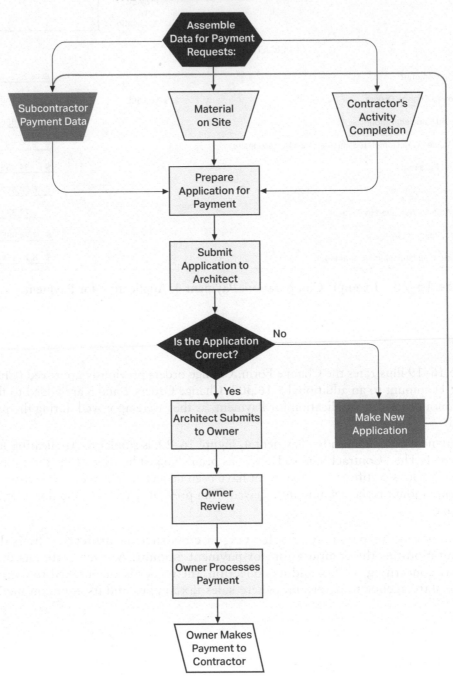

Figure 16–21 The Progress Payment Process

Summary

Progress payments are an important part of contract administration for the contractor. Proper preparation of the information necessary for payment processing can help the contractor financially complete the project.

At the start of the project, the contractor prepares the schedule of values and a cash flow projection. The schedule of values is a list of the amounts for work activities, which is the basis for progress payments. Preparation of the schedule of values from the estimate can include a combination of estimate items, a separation of estimate items, and distribution of markup (indirect overhead and profit).

The cash flow projection is an estimate of progress payments throughout the project, according to the construction schedule. Some construction scheduling software provide cash flow projections. Cash flow projections should accurately estimate progress payments since the owner and contractor make financial arrangements based on the cash flow projection.

Most contracts use a standard format for progress payments. These forms use a detail sheet to show the completion of each payment item, material stored, amount remaining, and proportionate amount of retainage held for each item. The Application and Certification for Payment includes certifications for both the contractor and the architect, a change order summary, and a computation of the current progress payment.

Review Questions

1. What is retainage?

2. What is the schedule of values?

3. What are some items that would be included in a "mobilization" item in the schedule of values?

4. What is front-loading?

5. What is a cash flow projection?

6. What are the two AIA forms for progress payments?

7. What is the process for progress payments?

Project Closeout

Objectives

This chapter discusses project closeout and the activities necessary to complete a construction project. The objectives of this chapter are:

- Explain the reasons for completing the closeout procedures and project completion as quickly as possible
- Discuss the methods to help subcontractors complete their project requirements
- Describe the punch list procedure and physical completion of the work
- Summarize the completion of paperwork requirements
- Review the financial resolution of the project

The contractor's primary goal is to complete a successful project. The **project closeout** is an important element in achieving this goal and is defined as the process of completing a construction project, including completion of contractual requirements, approvals, financial resolution, and required documentation. Completing a construction project can take a long time because of waiting for delivery of minor items, repair work, or completion of required paperwork. During this period, the contractor still has overhead costs, such as temporary jobsite facilities and field staff. Quick and efficient completion of closeout requirements minimizes the additional amount spent by the contractor on continuing overhead and enables personnel to pursue other projects. The owner is also usually anxious to complete the project as quickly as possible. The owner remembers the completion phase of the project, and the last impression of the contractor will affect the project's timeliness and ultimate success.

Project closeout consists of the activities that complete the project requirements. This phase of the project naturally includes the physical completion of the project, with the remaining items completed and the defective areas repaired. The project closeout phase also involves completion of paperwork and other contractual requirements, such as operation and maintenance manuals and instructions. Financial resolution of the project is necessary during the closeout phase as well.

This phase of the construction process is perhaps the most difficult to successfully coordinate. As the project approaches completion, the remaining items usually consist of:

1. Completion of seemingly minor details of work. Many of these remaining details are neglected by subcontractors when they leave the project.
2. Delivery of late material and equipment. Many of these items are not essential to the operation of the facility.
3. Replacement of defective materials, equipment, or parts of assemblies. Replacement materials normally are ordered prior to the closeout period, but they may not have arrived or been installed.
4. Repair of defective workmanship. Most defective workmanship relates primarily to finishes, as workmanship repairs to structural assemblies or the building envelope probably are completed prior to the project closeout phase.
5. Testing and approval of building systems, including code inspections, fire alarm and building safety, testing of HVAC systems, temperature control systems, and other specialized systems.

The aforementioned items require identification and usually a special follow-up with subcontractors and suppliers. As the majority of the subcontractor's work is complete and most of the payment has been received, the subcontractor usually is not highly motivated to return to the project to complete minor items and repair defective work. Suppliers, as well as subcontractors, have priorities other than pursuing replacement parts or equipment.

To accomplish this work, the contractor must ensure that subcontractors and suppliers complete contractual requirements. Some methods that help minimize the time required to complete these items include:

1. The contractor's field personnel should be aware of the quality of the subcontractors' work during its progress. A list of remaining items and defective installations should be presented to the subcontractor, emphasizing that the items must be completed prior to the subcontractor leaving the jobsite. Although this method alone does not ensure that the subcontractor will complete the work satisfactorily before leaving the jobsite, it does help.

2. All defective equipment delivered to the jobsite should be tracked for date delivered to jobsite; date rejected; description of defective parts or equipment needing replacement; responsible party, subcontractor, supplier, or the subcontractor's supplier; date ordered; date scheduled for delivery; follow-up checks by contractor; and date actually delivered to the jobsite. Documentation is necessary to manage the replacement of material or equipment. Written notification to the subcontractor and supplier serves as documentation and also encourages the subcontractor or supplier to order and pursue replacements.

3. At completion or near completion of the project, the contractor must make for each subcontractor and its crews a list of work that needs to be completed. Many contractors wait for the architect and engineer to make this list since subcontractors dislike making several trips back to the jobsite to complete work. The earlier the subcontractors receive the list of remaining items, the sooner the problems will be solved. The list of items to the subcontractor should be specific. Some contractors describe the remaining work to the subcontractor as "complete contract requirements" to avoid omitting items that must be completed. A specific list of items, such as "Complete ceramic tile base in restrooms 105 and 106," is much more effective in facilitating successful completion of the work.

4. Follow-up with subcontractors and suppliers usually is necessary. Both written reminders and telephone conversations are necessary to emphasize the importance of completion of the work and to update work and delivery schedules.

5. Many contractors are cautious about releasing all or most of the subcontractors' and suppliers' payments until all work is complete. If no amount is due the subcontractor other than retainage or a very small amount remains to be paid, subcontractors may have stronger priorities other than completing their work.

As indicated earlier, special care is required for the contractor's personnel to complete the closeout of the project. All of the contract requirements for closeout must be actively pursued, as nothing will automatically fall into place. Because all closeout items, both physical completion and paperwork requirements, require additional effort, they simply will not be completed unless they are pursued.

The Closeout Process

Figure 17–1 illustrates the steps for closing out a project. A distinct order of activities should be observed during this process, as dictated contractually and by custom. The relative amount of completion of work has a large influence on the progress of this sequence.

As the project nears completion, the contractor should compile a list of remaining work to be done, including repairs—this is normally called a punch list. This list is distributed to all appropriate parties and completed. Most contracts require that this preliminary or contractor's punch list be completed prior to notification of the architect and engineer. In actual practice, however, this preliminary punch list may not be actively pursued since most subcontractors wish to make only one trip back to the jobsite. It is important, however, that this punch list is addressed and completed, as it actually speeds up the closeout of the project.

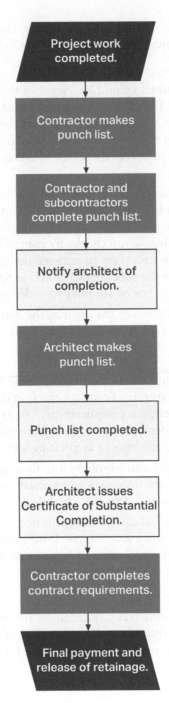

Figure 17–1   Steps in the Project Closeout Process

Most architects and engineers expect the project to be complete upon their arrival, requiring minimal punch list items. Because the architect's inspection is directly related to substantial completion, most architects will not conduct the punch list inspection if many and/or large items must still be completed. In this case, architects and engineers bill the contractor for extra inspections, particularly in situations where travel is required.

When the preliminary punch list is complete, the architect is notified and requested to perform a punch list on the project. Notification to the architect should always be in writing as it begins to establish the completion sequence. The architect and consulting engineers will then inspect the project or the requested portions of the project and compile the punch list. Punch lists exist in many forms, but they usually list the room number and the particular problem.

The architect probably will not separate items according to subcontract because of a lack of awareness about subcontractor division on the project. Consulting engineers, such as electrical and mechanical engineers, usually will prepare a separate punch list that relates only to their portion of the work.

Punch Lists

Punch lists come in every and any form, typed and handwritten. The owner's maintenance personnel often make a punch list, but this should be coordinated with and included in the architect's punch list. The contractor is responsible for the project and thus must provide specific punch lists to subcontractors and suppliers.

Common types of punch lists include the following:

- A sheet of paper posted on each door or in every room indicating the items that need to be completed in the room and a sign-off date for each item for both the contractor and the architect. This method is effective for having personnel complete items in every room. The sheets of paper, however, are occasionally removed or signed by unauthorized personnel. This punch list is hard to use as a record and requires separate permanent documentation. Items that apply to the entire project or entire systems do not usually fall into the room-by-room categories and must be tracked as a conventional punch list. Figure 17–2 illustrates a typical form for this type of punch list.

- Another form of punch list is a written list of items from the architect to the contractor. There also are several variations to this type of list. Usually, items are related to the specific room or area. Figure 17–3 illustrates this type of punch list.

This type of punch list does not include log information. The contractor probably will want to make a log form on a database for the punch list to enable tracking of activities. The use of a database on a computer permits sorting, for example, by room or by subcontractor. The punch list log in Figure 17–4 contains basic information, but other facts might be included, such as the date the subcontractor was notified, subcontractor identification number, scheduled dates for completion of the items, and punch list version.

Several "apps" for mobile devices are available for the contract punch list. These "apps" include description of the item, item responsibility, and a photograph of the condition. This information can be emailed to the responsible subcontractor and a complete log can be compiled.

ROOM 1065
OFFICE
POSTED 6/27/26

Item	Gen. Cont. Complete	Architect Approval	Remarks
Rubber base	6/29/26	7/5/26 HDA	
Replace defective faucet @ sink	6/30/26	7/6/26	
Install folding door			Delivery scheduled for 7/10/26
Replace cracked outlet plate	6/29/26	7/6/26 JLD	
Touch-up paint, west wall	6/29/26		*Not acceptable 7/5/26 HDF*

Figure 17–2   Punch List Example, Posted in Each Room

PUNCH LIST PROJECT: PROMINENT OFFICE BUILDING
JUNE 28, 2026
PUNCH LIST CONDUCTED BY A.L. SMITH
ARCHITECT: SMITH ASSOCIATES, P.S.
CONTRACTOR: XYZ, INC.

I. **General Items:**
  A. Final Cleaning of all surfaces is necessary, as per section 01710
  B. Install new filters in HVAC equipment
  C. Remove all waste and debris from site

II. **Exterior:**
  A. West Elevation:
    1. Install splash block at downspout
    2. Caulk around aluminum storefront
  B. North Elevation:
    1. Touch-up paint on coping
  C. East Elevation:
    1. Adjust operator on overhead door at room 1001
    2. Paint trim around overhead door
  D. South Elevation:
    1. Install sign at entrance

III. **Interior:**
  A. Room 1065
    1. Install rubber base
    2. Replace defective faucet at sink
    3. Install Folding Door
    4. Replace cracked outlet plate
    5. Touch-up paint, west wall

Figure 17–3 Punch List Example, Comprehensive List

Item #	Location	Item	Response	Completed Date	Init	Approval Date	By	Remarks
I A	General	Final clean	XYZ	7/5/26	RTZ	7/10/26	ALS	
I B	General	New filters	ABC Mech.	7/6/26	RTZ	7/10/26	ALS	
I C	General	Waste Rem.	XYZ	7/6/26	RTZ	7/10/26	ALS	
II A 1	West Ext.	Splash block	XYZ	7/6/26	RTZ	7/10/26	ALS	
II A 2	West Ext.	Caulking	A-1 Sealants	7/9/26	RTZ	7/10/26	ALS	
II B 1	North Ext.	Paint Coping	Steve's Painting	7/9/26	RTZ	7/10/26	ALS	
II C 1	East Ext.	Ovhd. door	Doors, Inc.					Scheduled: 7/13/26
II C 2	East Ext.	Paint trim at ovhd. door	Steve's Painting	7/9/26	RTZ	7/10/26	ALS	
II D 1	South Ext.	Sign	DG Specialities					Delivery: 7/15/26
III A 1	Rm 1065	Rub. base	Floors, Inc.	7/8/26	RTZ	7/10/26	ALS	
III A 2	Rm 1065	Repl. Faucet	ABC Mech.					Delivery: 7/15/26
III A 3	Rm 1065	Folding door	DG Specialities					Delivery: 7/20/26
III A 4	Rm 1065	Replace outlet plate	Sparks Electric	7/6/26	RTZ	7/10/26	ALS	
III A 5	Rm 1065	Touch up paint, W. wall	Steve's Painting	7/9/26	RTZ	7/10/26	ALS	

Figure 17–4 Punch List Log

Substantial Completion

After the architect has compiled the punch list and the items have been corrected, a "Certificate of Substantial Completion" will be issued. Substantial completion has several different meanings to the participants in the construction process, but basically it is defined as the point in the project when the architect has determined that the facility or a portion of the facility is acceptable for owner use and occupancy. The commonly used term for this stage of completion is **beneficial occupancy**, indicating when the facility can be used for its intended purpose. The punch list has been issued, items have been corrected, and corrections have been approved. Some items may still need to be completed, but these are considered minor. All remaining items are included in the Certificate of Substantial Completion. The date of the substantial completion is extremely important, as it stops the potential of liquidated damages and establishes the contract warranty period. Upon reaching substantial completion, liquidated damages usually cannot be imposed, and if they are in effect, substantial completion will stop the liquidated damages from being further imposed. Each project may have several substantial completions for portions of the work and may also have several warranty periods. The contractor must keep a record of multiple substantial completions when the project has phased completion, as shown in Figure 17–5.

Most contract document systems, such as the AIA and EJCDC documents, use a standard form for the Certificate of Substantial Completion. AIA Document G704, "Certificate of Substantial Completion," is commonly used in commercial building construction (Figure 17–6).

Essential elements of the "Certificate of Substantial Completion" include:

- *Project identification*: Official project name and address, architect's identification number, contract amount, contract date, and names of architect, owner, and contractor.

- *Date of issuance/date of substantial completion*: The date of issuance is not as important as the date established for substantial completion, which is in a separate location on Form AIA G704. The date of substantial completion establishes the completion date of the project relating to liquidated damages and also is the beginning of the warranty period.

- *Description of the project or portion of the project*: In cases of substantial completion for a portion of the project, the description must be made in adequate detail, including an explanation of the applicable environmental systems. When using a standardized form, an attachment may be necessary for the detailed description of the portion of the work.

- *Definition of "Substantial Completion"*: AIA Form G704 defines "Substantial Completion" on the actual form. Although it may not be essential to contain the definition in this certificate, it can be useful since many different opinions exist.

- *List of remaining responsibilities*: A list of remaining items to be "completed or corrected" must be attached to the certificate. Because most punch list items are completed or corrected prior to the certificate, the attached list should be minimal. Final payment usually will not be made until all items are complete.

- *List of warranty dates*: A list of warranty dates also should be attached to the certificate. Several different warranty dates are possible; however, the customary general warranty is 1 year. Other special warranties, such as roofing, equipment, and finish hardware, can be specified in the documents.

Area Complete (Description)	Substantial Completion Date	List Completion Date	Warranty Completion Date
Warehouse, Bldg. A	7/31/26	8/15/26	7/31/26
Office, Bldg. A	8/15/26	9/15/26	8/15/26
Building B	10/1/26	11/1/26	10/1/26
Building C	12/11/26	12/30/26	12/1/26

Figure 17–5 Substantial Completion Log

AIA® Document G704™ – 2000

Certificate of Substantial Completion

PROJECT: *(Name and address)*

PROJECT NUMBER:

CONTRACT FOR:

CONTRACT DATE:

TO OWNER: *(Name and address)*

TO CONTRACTOR: *(Name and address)*

OWNER ☐
ARCHITECT ☐
CONTRACTOR ☐
FIELD ☐
OTHER ☐

PROJECT OR PORTION OF THE PROJECT DESIGNATED FOR PARTIAL OCCUPANCY OR USE SHALL INCLUDE:

The Work performed under this Contract has been reviewed and found, to the Architect's best knowledge, information and belief, to be substantially complete. Substantial Completion is the stage in the progress of the Work when the Work or designated portion is sufficiently complete in accordance with the Contract Documents so that the Owner can occupy or utilize the Work for its intended use. The date of Substantial Completion of the Project or portion designated above is the date of issuance established by this Certificate, which is also the date of commencement of applicable warranties required by the Contract Documents, except as stated below:

ARCHITECT   BY   DATE OF ISSUANCE

A list of items to be completed or corrected is attached hereto. The failure to include any items on such list does not alter the responsibility of the Contractor to complete all Work in accordance with the Contract Documents. Unless otherwise agreed to in writing, the date of commencement of warranties for items on the attached list will be the date of issuance of the final Certificate of Payment or the date of final payment.

Cost estimate of Work that is incomplete or defective: $ _____

The Contractor will complete or correct the Work on the list of items attached hereto within
(   ) days from the above date of Substantial Completion.

CONTRACTOR   BY   DATE

The Owner accepts the Work or designated portion as substantially complete and will assume full possession at *(time)* on _____ *(date)*.

OWNER   BY   DATE

The responsibilities of the Owner and Contractor for security, maintenance, heat, utilities, damage to the Work and insurance shall be as follows: *(Note: Owner's and Contractor's legal and insurance counsel should determine and review insurance requirements and coverage.)*

Figure 17–6   Certificate of Substantial Completion, AIA Document G704, 2000

- *Signatures:* Signatures by the architect, contractor, and owner are necessary to validate this document. The certificate is an agreement by all three parties stating that the work is substantially complete.

- *List of agreements:* An agreed-upon list of responsibilities for heat, utilities, and other services should be attached. Property insurance must be established by the owner, particularly if immediate occupancy is desired. Any future damage to finishes is normally the owner's responsibility.

Following completion of the remaining items and financial resolution of the project, final payment and release of retainage are made to the contractor.

Paperwork Requirements

The old adage that "the job isn't done until the paperwork is done" applies to the construction project. Most contracts contain provisions for lien releases, written warranties, and contract receivables, such as operating and maintenance (O & M) manuals. Most public work requires further releases, certifications, and affidavits from public agencies.

Prompt pursuit of these finalizing documents is essential to releasing the final payment for the project. The majority of documents are completed by subcontractors and governmental agencies. The contractor must actively pursue all responsible parties to quickly process these documents.

Inspection Agency Releases

Most communities have local building code authorities that must inspect the project through construction at specific phases. Final inspection and a "Certificate of Occupancy" must be issued prior to the owner occupying the facility. Most communities require a final inspection on the entire project and special inspections/certifications in the following areas:

Plumbing	Electrical
HVAC Equipment	Fire Alarm
Elevator	Environmental/Storm Water Drainage
Public Works (roads etc.)	Health Department (sewage systems)
Planning Compliance	ADA Requirements (handicapped access)
Fire Protection Systems	

Requirements will vary from one community to another. The contractor should devise a checklist that relates to the inspection and certification requirements in the community. These supersede the contractual requirements and probably will not be delineated in the contract documents other than as a reference to comply with all local codes and regulations.

Documentation of the final inspections should be kept, with a copy of all certifications and final inspections given to the owner. Some inspection certificates, such as plumbing and electrical, are presented to the subcontractor by the inspector. Contractors should obtain copies of these certificates for their own as well as the owner's records.

System Testing and Documentation

During the punch list and closeout period, certain building systems are tested for compliance to specifications. Most tests are in the mechanical and electrical subcontract areas. Testing may be required in several different ways:

- Independent testing, contracted to the owner; this could be testing a specific system or the overall testing and adjustment of the entire building system, usually referred to as "commissioning"

- Independent testing, contracted to the subcontractor

- Testing and start-up by an authorized manufacturer's representative

- Testing by the mechanical and/or electrical sub-consultant

- Testing by the owner's personnel

Test	System	Date	Method	Results	Tested by	Witnessed
Fire Protect.	Fire Alarm, Fire Sprinkler	6/3/26	Alarm, Smoke	OK	John Smith Fire Marshall	*JLS*
Plumbing Vents, Drains	Plumbing	3/23/26	Hydrostatic Pressure	OK	Fred Johnson Plumbing Inspector	*FEJ*
Pumps	Plumbing, Fire Sprinkler	5/2/26	Pressure, Flow	OK	Ole Olsen Pump Rep.	*OO*
Fans	HVAC	5/10/26	Speed, Blade angle	OK	N.T. Jones Fan Rep.	*NTA*
Temperature Controls	HVAC	5/13/26	Calibration, computer chk	OK	R.T. Andrews Temp. Cont. Rep.	*RTA*
Elevator	Elevator	4/2/26 5/8/26	Complete	No OK	O. McCarthy State Elevator Inspector	*OJM*

Figure 17–7 Testing Log

Figure 17–7 illustrates a sample testing log.

These tests must be accomplished after the system is fully operational. Arrangements should be made with the owner and architect and engineer for their representatives to be present to witness the tests. Depending upon the nature of the test, code officials may wish to witness tests as well. Subcontractor or installer personnel also should be present at this time. Documentation of each test should be made, with the following information:

- Date and location of test

- System or equipment tested

- Method of testing

- Individual conducting the test

- Results of the test

- Witnesses to the test, signed by each

Standardized test forms provide uniform information and are easily referenced. All systems testing should be done prior to occupancy and use of the facility.

HVAC systems require testing and balancing of equipment. Both operations are often combined. Outside consultants may be used to provide this testing and balancing to verify that the system meets the requirements.

O & M Manuals and Instructions

Most contract documents require that the contractor furnish O & M manuals for all equipment on the project. Although these manuals normally include mechanical and electrical information, relevant facts about other operating systems installed by the contractor or other subcontractors should be included as well. Operating doors, finish hardware, folding partitions, and other equipment items could be listed.

The O & M manuals include manufacturer's instructions about the equipment, including diagrams and parts lists. Some of the data contains catalog information, and some is furnished with the equipment. Because installation and maintenance instructions often are destroyed in the uncrating process, special care must be taken to save all information that is sent with equipment. This information must be saved and contained in the appropriate volume of the O & M manuals.

For larger projects, the contract documents usually must be contained in hardcover, bound volumes of the O & M manuals, which are permanent references that should be kept at the facility by maintenance personnel for the life of the building. Documents are bound to prevent removal of information, as this information may not be available in later years. Separate volumes usually are made for the mechanical and electrical areas since they are compiled by separate subcontractors. The subcontractor can compile this information in-house or can ask a consultant to prepare it.

The O & M manuals should be organized as they relate to project specifications. If the CSI MasterFormat numbering system is used, manuals should be organized in that manner. Contract documents may list a specific organization for these manuals.

Delivery of manuals must be made through the proper channels, with documentation of their receipt. Because these manuals are unique, specifically assembled for the particular project, they are difficult to replace if they are lost or not directed to the proper individual. Follow-up often is necessary to ensure proper distribution.

Instruction sessions also are held for O & M instructions, normally conducted by the subcontractor and manufacturer's representatives for the facility's maintenance personnel. Instructions should be given after systems are complete and tested but prior to owner occupancy of the building. Maintenance personnel should be familiar with the operation of the equipment prior to occupancy, if possible. Instructional sessions can be held after testing when the manufacturer's representatives are on the site. Some projects may require several different instructional sessions to cover all of the equipment installed on the project. Documentation of instructional meetings is necessary to indicate who demonstrated the equipment and who received instruction.

Videotaping of instructional periods provides a record that shows that instructional sessions were indeed held and also provides the owner with a reference for use by maintenance personnel. Because maintenance personnel changes frequently, the owner can use the videotapes to train new maintenance workers.

Spare Parts and Extra Materials

Most contracts require delivery of extra material and spare parts to the owner at the conclusion of the project. The technical specification for each area of work will specify, if required, the necessary spare parts or material to leave on the project. Material and equipment installed during construction projects can be quickly dated from the manufacturer or supplier. Finish materials usually are in specific dye lots that cannot be easily matched. Technical specifications require extra material, such as carpet, floor tile, or paint, to patch changes or future damage. Some spare parts will be specified to enable the owner to quickly repair equipment items that are worn.

Most spare parts and extra material come from subcontractors. The contractor should prepare a checklist of spare parts and extra material early in the project and refer to it as subcontractors leave the project. Because this material is in order, it will be available as subcontractors finish their segments of the project. The material and spare parts should be collected from subcontractors prior to their leaving the jobsite and should be stored in a safe area. All keys to the equipment should be collected as well prior to the subcontractor leaving the jobsite. An example of a checklist for spare parts and extra material is shown in Figure 17–8.

Section	Subcontractor	Material Description	Date Received	Location Stored
08700, Fin. Hdwe	National Hdwe.	2 ea. locksets	8/24/26	Trailer
09300, Cer. Tile	United Floors	2 boxes tile	7/27/26	Trailer
09680, Carpet	United Floors	10 SY carpet	10/15/26	Rm. 1011
09900, Painting	City Painting	1 gal/color	10/2/26	Rm. B-0027
09950, Wallcvrg	City Painting	1 bolt/pattern	10/2/26	Rm. B-0027

Figure 17–8 Spare Parts Log

Keys, Permanent Cylinders, and Rekeying

Turnover of keys and changing door lock cylinders can be a cumbersome task. Many owners prefer, for security reasons, that the permanent keying of locks be done just prior to occupancy. Some keying systems have removable cores that can be replaced just prior to the owner's occupancy of the building. Under this system, the contractor is supplied "construction cores" by the hardware supplier, providing locking capabilities during construction. At the end of the construction period, the cores are changed by the supplier or the owner's maintenance personnel, providing the final keying and security for the locks.

During the construction period, preferably during the submittal period, the finish hardware supplier requests a keying schedule for the building. This can be a very complicated list, with master and submaster systems. Depending upon the type of lock furnished, locks may be keyed prior to delivery or furnished with construction cores. If permanent keying is provided with the locks, the contractor must organize all of the keys to ensure that they are given to the owner. Most security issues affect the keying of facilities, requiring the contractor to be extremely careful distributing and organizing keys. In some arrangements, the hardware supplier handles the keys and key cabinets with the owner. Regardless of who is responsible for key turnover, the contractor is required to facilitate the keying and key turnover prior to final acceptance of the facility. A signed receipt for any keys is necessary, similar to procedures for other receivables to the owner.

Record Drawings

Most contracts require the contractor to prepare record drawings or "as-built" drawings during the project. This process entails recording actual dimensions, location of utilities, and any changes in drawings. These changes and dimensions usually are written on clean sets of drawings during the entire project. Electrical and mechanical contractors normally record relevant information on their own drawings.

Since the as-built set of drawings is usually fairly worn by the end of the project, some contracts request that the contractor transfer changes onto sepia or velum sets of drawings. The contractor normally completes the record drawings and provides the necessary drawings to the owner. Some as-built drawings are recorded into CAD media on the jobsite. In this case, the contractor would provide the owner with the revised set on disk, furnishing the hard copy as well.

As with all of the other receivables during the closeout period, signed documentation of receipt of the necessary as-built drawings is necessary. It is important that the contractor keep this documentation safe in a retrievable location. Owners will occasionally misplace receivables and claim they never received the documents from the contractor; therefore, written records are essential.

Warranties and Guarantees

Most contracts require a 1-year warranty on all installations in the project. Some items may require 2- or 5-year warranties. The applicable information is found in the technical specification in each section. Warranties are provided during the closeout period. Most subcontractors furnish a warranty to the contractor for their work. All special warranties beyond the 1-year program should be copied and sent to the owner. Since the owner's contract is with the contractor only, the contractor is ultimately responsible for the warranty to the owner.

A checklist on warranties should be made from the information contained in the technical specification, similar to the table shown in Figure 17–9.

Prompt repair of warranty items is essential during the warranty period. Many items, particularly mechanical and electrical, can require emergency repair. The contractor, with the owner's maintenance personnel, should formulate a plan for warranty calls and repairs. Most contractors prefer that mechanical and electrical problems be reported directly to the appropriate subcontractor, with subsequent notice to the contractor that the subcontractor

WARRANTY CHECKLIST

Section	Subcontractor	Warranty Required	Date Received	Date to Owner
02850 Irrigation System	City Sprinkler Co.	2-season special warranty	10/10/26	12/1/26
02900 Landscaping	Trees-R-Us	2-season special warranty	10/01/26	12/1/26
03400 Precast Concrete	County Precast, Inc.	1 year standard warranty	9/08/26	
04000 Masonry	ABC Masonry	1 year standard warranty	9/01/26	
07500 Roofing	Anderson Roofing	5 year warranty; bond	10/15/26	12/1/26
08200 Metal Doors/ Frames	Doors-R-Us	1 year standard warranty	9/15/26	
08700 Finish Hardware	Acme Hardware	1 year standard warranty	9/15/26	

Figure 17–9 Warranty Checklist

has been contacted. All other calls should be made directly to the contractor. The contractor should discuss and agree with maintenance personnel on the parameters of warranty work. For instance, warranty will include repair to an air handler but will not include filters, belts, and other maintenance replacement items.

Affidavits of Payment, Lien Releases, and Consent of Surety

The owner usually will request an affidavit of payment, lien releases, and consent of surety prior to releasing final payment. An "affidavit of payment" certifies that payment of all debts and claims relating to the project has been made, with the noted specific exceptions, which usually is only retainage. If further items remain, the contractor can post a bond to cover payment of the associated debt or claim. The owner must be assured that the contractor has paid all material, labor, taxes, and subcontracts in relation to the project. The owner does not want to be held liable for these debts after releasing payment to the contractor. Retainage, in many cases, is reserved solely for payment of "labor and materialmen" (suppliers) and cannot be released until the owner has some assurance that these entities have been paid.

Lien releases may be requested from the contractor and all subcontractors. The lien release indicates that the potential lien holder has received payment for the work, with the exceptions noted, usually retainage. The owner must be assured that the project will be received free and clear, with no further obligation. The owner normally will require a waiver or release of lien from the contractor, as the legal contract is with the contractor. The owner can ask for lien releases from all subcontractors and suppliers as well to provide additional assurance that the project will not have further encumbrances.

An accompanying document to the affidavit of payment and lien releases is the "Consent of Surety," when bonding is used on the project. Consent of Surety is executed by the bonding company, indicating approval of the contractor's receiving final payment for the project. This requirement provides the bonding company with the opportunity to audit the contractor's records to ensure that a financial obligation does not exist. Consent of Surety also should be required by the contractor on subcontractors that have been bonded on the project.

AIA standard forms exist for the following documents:

AIA Document G706: Contractor's Affidavit of Payment of Debts and Claims

AIA Document G706 A: Contractor's Affidavit of Release of Liens

AIA Document G707: Consent of Surety Company to Final Payment

AIA Document G707 A: Consent of Surety to Reduction in or Partial Release of Retainage

These forms contain the standard language used in these documents. Custom documents often are used for releases as well. The contractor must use the proper wording and submit the correct forms, as these are important legal documents that establish a basis for final payment and termination of the contract.

Miscellaneous Certifications and Releases

Particularly in public work, the contractor may be required to supply additional certifications, affidavits, and releases from public agencies. These certifications vary, depending on the owner of the project, the type of work, size of contract, and the city, county, and state in which the project is located.

Prevailing wage certificates and affidavits are required on most public work where Davis-Bacon regulations or state prevailing wage laws apply. For federal projects, weekly payroll certificates are required for all labor on the project, both contractor and subcontractor. These certified payrolls should be submitted prior to the closeout period, but some may still need to be completed. Each state has different prevailing wage requirements for state-funded work. Some states require notarized affidavits from each contractor and subcontractor stating that wages were paid. All affidavits and certifications must be promptly submitted at the end of the project, as final payment will not be made until release by the monitoring agency.

In public work for states, the states may require release of state agencies prior to final payment. These agencies may include sales tax collection, workers' compensation, and unemployment insurance funds. Application for these releases must be made immediately at the close of the project to facilitate timely release of the final payment.

Closeout Software

Several closeout application software programs address procedures during the closeout process. A number of spreadsheet templates are available that organize the punch-list process. Several project management programs include closeout procedures integrated with construction progress documentation.

In addition to punch list organization software, there are software programs that help organize the entire closeout process. Included in this software are a plan for closeout; a checklist of closeout procedures; documentation of the successful closeout procedures; and agenda/minutes of the closeout meeting. Typically, the closeout meeting includes discussion about the construction process, with problems, successes, and lessons learned.

The closeout procedures are complex and involve many team members. The software application can organize all the activities together to enable quick and efficient closeout and completion of the project.

Financial Resolution of the Project

All financial issues must be completed, just as the physical attributes of the facility must be. The objective in financial resolution is to resolve all outstanding cost commitments, establish a final project cost, and determine profit or loss. This can be a large task even on a small project. Final payment cannot be issued until financial issues are settled between the contractor and subcontractors and between the contractor and owner.

Subcontractor Payment

At the end of the project or approaching the end of the project, the contractor should determine the following for each subcontract:

- The amount of work remaining and the value of such work

- The amount of payment, excluding retainage, due

- The amount of back-charges and disputed payment

- The amount of retainage due

- The approximate dates of completion of the remaining work

With this information, the contractor must proceed to make remaining payments to the subcontractor and establish what must be completed prior to final payment. Because the contractor must certify that payment has been made, the remaining amount should be established and resolved. Resolution of disputed issues needs to be negotiated and finalized. Some issues may remain in dispute and should be listed as exceptions to the payment. These disputed items should be pursued, however, to avoid confusing payment and settlement issues.

Resolution with the Owner

The final contract amount needs to be established. To accomplish this, all change orders must be completed and issued as well as the associated work done. Last-minute change orders, summary change orders, and delayed change orders frequently seem to accumulate at the end of the project. These change orders should be dealt with quickly, expediting the process.

Claims also need to be resolved. The contractor should examine each unresolved issue and determine what can be done to solve the dispute. A procedure for resolution, even if the resolution involves arbitration or litigation, must be established for each disputed item. After procedures have been created, the contractor should pursue each issue as quickly as possible. Issues may arise that cannot be immediately resolved; thus, third parties may have to resolve them.

For items that need to be completed or issues that need to be resolved, the contractor can post a **retainage bond** for the amount of retainage or amount being held. The retainage bond is issued by a surety company for the remaining value, allowing the contractor to be paid the retainage. The retainage bond assures the owner that the remainder of contract requirements will be completed. The surety company charges the contractor additional premium for this bond.

The contractor also may need to file a lien on the project for an unpaid balance or disputed items. Each state has finite lien periods after the completion of the work. All liens must be filed within this period, or the contractor loses the right to file a lien. This is a serious action and must be done within state regulations.

Cost Control Completion

The final accounting of the project must be done as the final resolutions close. The contractor must analyze the project accounting to determine whether a profit or loss was realized. Beyond the accounting for the project, each activity cost should be compared to the estimate. A variance of 10 percent over or under the estimate should be examined. As the actual costs are used to create historical cost data, large variances need to be examined, and a reason for the variance needs to be established. Any unusual condition should be noted, but this should not adversely affect the historical cost data.

Final reports for the project's financial condition should be in a standard format, comparable to other projects. It is important that management review the project and determine its success and failures and reasons for each. Conclusions can relate to personnel, locality, type of work, specific subcontracts used, and a variety of other reasons. Management must understand the successes and failures and apply that knowledge to future projects.

Archiving Records

Records of the project must be stored as a reference. This reference is used for dispute resolution, public agency audits, management reference, and financial (tax) accounting. Most of the records should be stored for at least the specified period of the statute of limitations in the state in which the project is located. Some companies store records for 10 years before destroying them.

Most project records today are kept on computer media for the duration of the project. At the project's conclusion, though, all documents must be converted to hard copy. Storing the documents on computer disks is acceptable for short-term use, but with the evolution of computer hardware and software, the computer data may not be accessible in the future. Records should be stored in an environment that will not cause deterioration of the documents.

All project records have some value, but it is impractical to store all documents. Project documents should be examined, anticipating future need. Two major sets of documents exist: project documents and financial documents.

Project documents include:

- Drawings, specifications, change orders, as-built drawings

- Precontract estimates, proposals

- Shop drawings, submittals

- Contracts, agreements, change orders, change directives (with owner)

- Subcontracts, subcontract change orders, purchase orders, delivery records

- Correspondence: owner, architect, subcontractors, suppliers, miscellaneous (with issue cross-index)

- Photographs, videotapes

- Daily reports, diaries, special reports on occurrences

- Minutes of meetings

- Logs: submittals and telephone

- Safety records: minutes, reports, injury reports, and inspections

- Permits and inspection records

- Financial documents include the following:

  - Payroll

  - Cost reports

  - Vendor invoices and payment records

  - Subcontractor bonds, releases, warranties

  - Billings and receipts from owner

For large projects, documents available for storage are mammoth. Microfilm storage may be desirable in this case to conserve space. All agreements, change orders, and other documents with original signatures should be saved in their original form.

Summary

The closeout phase of the construction project requires diligent and focused efforts by the contractor's personnel to complete contractual requirements, allowing final payment for the project. Careful coordination with subcontractors, the architect, building officials, and the owner is necessary to minimize the duration of the closeout phase.

A sequence of closeout activities, starting with the contractor's punch list and ending with the issuance of the certificate of substantial completion, is done to complete the physical work at the jobsite. Use of checklists and logs can help organize the complicated process of completing remaining work. Substantial completion occurs at the culmination of the punch list. Substantial completion starts the warranty period for the affected areas and stops the potential of liquidated damages or further liquidated damages.

In addition to completion of the physical project, several requirements must be met. Inspection and testing are essential prior to occupancy of the facility. The owner's maintenance personnel should be trained in the operation and maintenance of the facility. O & M manuals must be prepared and given to maintenance personnel. Spare parts, additional material, and keys need to be given to the owner. The record drawings must be completed by the contractor and subcontractors and delivered to the owner. Warranties and guarantees need to be prepared and given to the owner. A number of releases, such as affidavits of payments, lien releases, consent of surety, and miscellaneous agency releases, as required, should be requested, prepared, and delivered to the owner.

Financial resolution must be made for all subcontracts and contracts on the project prior to final payment. Resolution of change orders, claims, back-charges, and any outstanding financial relationships needs to be done to enable release of the final payment. The contractor should determine the project's profitability as well as analyze its positive and negative aspects. Each project creates data for estimating, controlling, and managing future projects.

When concluding the project, the contractor must store the necessary documents for reference. Organized archives permit efficient audits and document searches.

Efficient closeout procedures allow the contractor to promptly proceed to other work. The contractor should concentrate on this area prior to proceeding to the next undertaking. Closeout ultimately affects whether the project is viewed as successful or unsuccessful.

Review Questions

1. Describe what is meant by project closeout.

2. What is the punch list procedure for completing a project?

3. What is substantial completion?

4. What establishes the start of the warranty period?

5. What are some final inspections required by public agencies?

6. What type of information is contained in the O & M manuals?

7. What is another term for record drawings?

8. What is consent of surety?

9. What are the four major areas that a contractor must determine to ensure financial resolution?

Chapter 18

Lean Construction

Objectives

- Breakdown theses **5-S: Sort, Set-to-Order (Straighten), Shine, Standardize, Sustain**
- Define the terms used in the discussion of lean construction
- Illustrate the waste management part of lean construction
- Summarize the process that defines lean construction
- Give example of a how lean construction can improve the construction process
- Explain the ides and importance that lean construction brings to construction management

Many contractors are adopting "lean construction" methods in their operations to increase the efficiency of the construction process. The Lean Construction Institute defines lean construction as "a project delivery process that uses Lean methods of maximizing stakeholder value while reducing waste by emphasizing collaboration between teams on a project. The goal of Lean construction is to increase productivity, profits, and innovation in the industry."

Most contractors have always intended to increase productivity. The result of increased productivity is increased profitability. Typical construction operations, however, can result in as much as 50 percent waste. Waste can be wasted material, as described in Chapter 13, but is primarily wasted labor cost in inefficient construction practices. Wasted labor could be: waiting, inappropriate work activities, crew movement, material movement, overproduction, excess inventory, defects/repair, and several other activities. Part of lean construction involves analysis of tasks, determining their value to the project, eliminating waste, and maximizing value.

The Lean Construction Institute states that "Lean can be implemented into any project business plan through focusing on six tenets":

1. Respect for People
2. Removal of Waste
3. Focus on Process and Flow
4. Generation of Value
5. Continuous Improvement
6. Optimize the Whole

Many contractors have programs for some of these measures. Combining all of the tenets results in a cumulative effect forming a plan that is achieved by all of the stakeholders. "Lean Project Delivery" organizes the implementation of lean principles and methods to encourage the team collaboratively to enhance the project's flow. Lean concepts can be added to project delivery systems to create better outcomes for the stakeholders.

Lean practices are applicable to both the design phase and the construction phase. When the contractor is involved during the design phase, such as in GC Construction Management, the contractor needs to lead and implement lean methods. Several of the lean methods typically used in the construction process can be adapted to the design process. Some of these techniques, which will be discussed in the lean construction delivery process, are collaborative decision making, the Last Planner System®, and A3 thinking.

Lean Construction Delivery

Lean construction is a relatively new delivery system that is developing new and innovative approaches. The Lean Construction Institute is active in the innovative pursuit of new and effective procedures for lean construction. Several groups of procedures are used together to provide the optimum results of lean construction. Several participants in lean construction programs have implemented customized versions of the procedures to match their operations. A discussion of the typical lean construction methods used to optimize lean construction delivery follows.

Respect for People

Over the years, the construction project was a war zone. The architect/engineer and the contractor were in constant conflict over change orders and extra payment for the work. Contractors and subcontractors were also in battle over time, cost, and quality issues. The result of the strong conflicts between project participants results in unsuccessful projects for all involved. In these situations, there is little respect between the participants for the other participants in the project team.

Every participant in the construction is experienced and knowledgeable in construction. They all have knowledge that adds to innovative approaches in the construction process. Leaders in the process need to provide opportunities for positive input to construction problems and situations. The attitudes of all the participants need to be positive and project-oriented, rather than oriented toward their own situations. This is an obvious difficult change from past project behaviors but can be achieved by effective leadership and education/training for the participants. Contractors have found that respectful and cooperative sites provide profitability for all involved.

Collaboration

Respect among the participants in the construction process leads to an atmosphere conducive to collaboration. Traditionally, both in design and problem solving, results are obtained by individual effort rather than using input from other knowledgeable participants. Collaboration with other knowledgeable and multi-disciplinary participants provides a full view at the problem to provide optimum value to the project. Some value engineering teams have used a multi-disciplinary team of professionals to analyze design solutions successfully. The collaborative system is very effective with cooperative and respectful participants.

A technique used in lean construction delivery systems is the "Big Room." This technique is used in the design process but could be used in major construction decisions. A large room is used with tables around the perimeter, accommodating several participants. This technique can be used for brainstorming and problem solving. Controlled open discussion with professionals collaborating can be successful in optimizing value decisions.

5-S: Sort, Set-to-Order (Straighten), Shine, Standardize, Shine

This process is the optimization of value in the construction project. It is basically inventory and analysis of the construction processes leading to the successful revision and implementation of those processes. The purpose of these steps is to identify and eliminate waste and optimize value in the project for the owner. During the enhanced process, efficiency is increased resulting in the potential of increased profitability.

The first step is "Sort." The Sort phase involves identification of waste and the separation of waste and value. Waste can be defined as anything that does not add value to the final product or service. Value is a task or activity that the organization provides that the owner is willing to pay for. The types of waste encountered in construction are defects/corrections, overproduction, waiting, underutilization of worker skills, transportation/movement, inventory, motion, and excessive processing. Work tasks need to be examined for labor that is not necessary to the efficient installation of the activity. Careful examination of all work tasks will expose the labor and material currently wasted. Waste exists even in seemingly efficiently implemented tasks. The elimination of waste results in conserving time in the process, increasing profitability, and achieving quality in the project.

The second step is "Set-to-Order," which involves organizing the revised tasks after removal of waste in a logical and timely manner. The site needs to be set in order to logically flow in the intended sequence of work. This step is intended to achieve a smooth flow of the construction process. This involves proper sequencing of equipment and activities enhanced by appropriate ordering and delivery. The flow of projects often is choppy, waiting for material, equipment, or installation. Choppy delivery is not profitable for the contractor and subcontractors and is irritating for the owner. Without a steady flow, the project tends to not be completed within the intended time frame, which usually incurs extra cost for the owner.

The third step is "Shine." A construction site needs to be seen by the owner and observers as a place of business. It needs to be clean and orderly. Housekeeping on the construction site is essential for safety reasons as well as public relations. Equipment and material need to orderly stored. Trash needs to be contained in appropriate containers. Access roads need to be unencumbered and maintained to provide movement of equipment. A clean and orderly jobsite provides the opportunity for efficient work by contractors and subcontractors.

The fourth "S" step is "Standardize," establishing routines. In organizing the material and equipment, the appropriate workers are aware of the location of the necessary items to eliminate waste. Maintaining the organization of the jobsite eliminates wasted time with movement of materials and equipment. Chapter 6 describes material movement and location to reduce wasted effort supplying the work locations.

"Sustain" is the fifth phase of the 5-S group of activities establishing lean construction on the jobsite. Programs that implement change in work habits typically can revert to the original methods. Considerable effort is necessary by management and workers to sustain the changed program. The elimination of waste and optimization of value needs to be monitored with continued training to achieve the goals. A dedicated team to achieving lean construction can contribute to sustaining the goals of the program.

Last Planner System®

Most contractors are currently using computerized scheduling based on the critical path method. The use of these scheduling programs has greatly increased contractors' control of project durations. Although these schedules provide the path for the project, they don't adequately address the in-progress detail of all of the contractors and subcontractors on the project. The Last Planner System® was developed by the Lean Construction Institute to show closer detail as work progresses using input from those doing the work. It uses input from all foremen involved in the work, interchanging ideas of process constraints. In this interchange, reliable promises are made for work duration, sequence, and cooperation. This method identifies more logical sequence, optimizes duration, and builds a team atmosphere on the project.

The five elements of the Last Planner System® are:

1. A traditional start-to-completion master schedule indicating milestones, long-lead items, and major constraints. This serves as the schedule guide for the project.

2. Phase scheduling: using the "pull-planning" system, contractors and subcontractors collaborate, starting from milestone or completion point, pulling activities to the left. This is also called "backward" scheduling.

3. Work-ready planning: A major delay in project workflow relates to the work for subcontractors not being ready for the following work. The work-ready planning is a look-ahead activity coordinating subcontractor work to provide a steady flow of the work. This work-ready coordination is possible by the full collaboration of the subcontractors on the project.

4. Weekly work planning: Detailed work planning is necessary on a weekly basis. Adjustments in the schedule are usually required to keep the project on track. All applicable participants, contractor and subcontractors, interact with Post-its® on a large board (Figure 18-1),

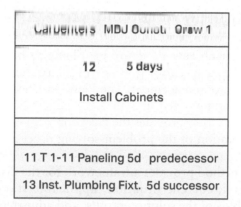

Figure 18–1   Example Activity Post

rearranging to a logical sequence. This process involves discussion, some conflict, and compromise between the represented trades. The goals in weekly planning are to maintain the milestones and completion dates, work efficiently, and provide quality work.

5. Learning: During this process, several mistakes and enhancements in the work occur. These changes need to be applied to the work as it progresses. Collaboration between the project participants tends to grow during the project. Application of the lessons learned will provide continuous improvement in the process.

The Last Planner System® is a fairly complex system, which requires education and training to fully implement the program. The Lean Construction Institute® (leanconstruction .org) posts resources on their website. *The Last Planner Production System® Workbook* is available for download on the website. Several other publications describe the Last Planner System®. Several consultants are available to introduce and train the Last Planner System®. After a construction firm uses the system, it will be easy to implement it on other projects. This system is spreading to many projects as it is effective in operating a smooth flowing construction project.

Value Stream Mapping/Process Mapping

Value stream mapping is a tool to identify value streams in the construction process. It maps the process of creating value, which the customer is willing to purchase as a product or service. It maps out the steps in the working process, enabling the team to identify the value stream and wasted effort. In identifying the value and the waste, the team is able to streamline the flow of the work.

The value stream map could be on a story board examining the raw material and information flows, decision points, hand-offs, and interactions with other systems. In the examination of the process flow, any of the eight waste types will become evident, and this provides an opportunity to eliminate them.

The value stream mapping technique can identify specific types of waste while examining the processes. Some of these waste areas are disconnected processes, insufficient information flow, uneven workloads, wasted time in activities, long delays in material delivery or by subcontractors, ineffective quality outcomes, cost overrun, and disappointing the customer.

Value stream mapping can be implemented in several different phases in the process. It could be accomplished early in the process or after the master schedule is produced. It can also be used with select short-term processes. The goal of the value stream mapping is to enhance the outcome of the processes.

A3 Problem Solving (Plan-Do-Check-Act)

The lean construction approach reveals many problems to be solved by optimizing lean principles. A3 Problem Solving is a tool that solves a problem, encourages collaborative work, and provides reporting to management. The Plan-Do-Check-Act (PDCA) framework of problem-solving thinking is summarized in a 11 × 17 paper sheet (A3 size). The A3 process doesn't present a solution, but rather provides the basis for team members to use lean tools. The A3 reports provide documentation of the problem-solving process that can be used for lessons learned in the project.

The Plan-Do-Check-Act method provides a framework for the discovery process. It examines the problem for background, current situation, applicable standards, possible solutions, application of solution, analysis of the solution results, and adjustment to optimize the solution.

In the Plan phase, the goal is to identify the issue in the problem that will lead to continuous improvement. In this phase, the problem is exposed, with its background and current state. Determination is then made of its future state or goal.

The recommendation for the process improvement and its implementation is made during the Do phase. The recommendation is based on the situation's characteristics and lean concepts. Positive results within the lean context are expected from these recommendations and implementations.

"Check" in quality management refers to informed inspections. The improvement implementation in the D3 context refers to assurance that the solution to the problem satisfies project requirements and lean recommendations. If the solution does not meet intended requirements, then the Act phase continues the process.

The Act phase is often referred to as "Adjust." When the solution doesn't fulfill the requirements, adjustment is made to the solution to make it compliant in the project's requirements. Documentation of the solution is made with the A3 report to be used again in the project and other projects. Examination of the A3 reports are done periodically for positive and negative lessons learned.

Continuous improvement follows the investigation of problems in the A3 process. The entire team needs to be in a continuous improvement mindset throughout the lean construction delivery. The continuous improvement process is often called "kaizen," from the Japanese Lean Production System. In active lean construction systems, periodic meetings of the entire team (kaizen events) examine the process systems for improvement. Continuous improvement improves the product that is delivered to the customer and improves the flow of the construction process.

The A3 process is a method of thinking collaboratively to solve problems in implementing lean construction principles. The Lean Construction Institute and lean consultants can provide more information on A3 Problem Solving.

Just-in-Time Delivery

Lean Production, developed initially in Japan for manufacturing organizations, uses just-in-time delivery to reduce inventory cost and the cost of storing and handling the extraneous inventory. Site storage is very limited on construction sites and contractors have used just-in-time delivery of material in most construction projects. Constructed facilities are structures which require unique materials that are mostly supplied direct to the project, rather than from inventory. The most efficient material delivery method is from truck to the installation location. Just-in-time delivery reduces inventory cost, storage space on the jobsite, movement cost on the jobsite, and jobsite clutter. Although just-in-time delivery is already common in construction jobsite operations, it is worthwhile to keep it in lean construction delivery to be able to maintain an efficient jobsite.

Summary

Lean construction is a method to increase the efficiency of the construction process. It involves a positive atmosphere for collaboration, reduction of waste, optimization of value for the customer, smooth flow of construction, continuous improvement, and the optimum completion of the project. Several other techniques not included herein are also used to enhance the lean concept in the project. It is a complex process involving many new and innovative techniques. Education and training is essential to prepare and perform full lean construction delivery.

Several good publications are available on lean construction. As previously mentioned, the Lean Construction Institute (leanconstruction.org) is the definitive resource for the subject. The text *Transforming Design and Construction*, William R. Seed, executive editor, is available from the Lean Construction Institute. *Lean Project Delivery* by David Umstot and Dan Fauchier is an excellent text on the entire process. A contractor's perspective on implementing and using a lean construction system is *Lean Construction, One Company's Journey to Success* by Ted J. Angelo.

Review Questions

1. Describe what makes lean construction unique in its overall philosophy.

2. What are the six tenets of lean construction?

3. What are the 5 S's in lean construction?

4. What makes pull–push scheduling different from normal scheduling techniques?

5. How are respect and collaboration defined under lean construction?

6. Define the process that is used to optimize the value in the construction project with lean construction.

Index